MANHOOD *of* HUMANITY

THE TIME-BINDER

A portrait of Alfred Korzybski by Mira Edgerly Korzybska presented to the Chicago Art Institute by John G. Shedd in 1922

MANHOOD *of* HUMANITY

BY

ALFRED KORZYBSKI

AUTHOR OF *SCIENCE AND SANITY*
An Introduction to Non-aristotelian Systems and
General Semantics

SECOND EDITION
WITH ADDITIONAL MATERIALS

THE INTERNATIONAL NON-ARISTOTELIAN
LIBRARY PUBLISHING COMPANY

INSTITUTE OF GENERAL SEMANTICS,
DISTRIBUTORS

LAKEVILLE, CONNECTICUT

Printed in the United States of America by
COUNTRY LIFE PRESS CORPORATION
GARDEN CITY, NEW YORK

TO
THE QUICK AND THE DEAD
I DEDICATE THIS WORK
A. K.

EDITOR'S NOTE

'Tis time new hopes should animate mankind,
New light should dawn . . .

Robert Browning

This quotation from Browning was chosen by Korzybski to begin the new introduction he was preparing for the second edition of this book. In the spring of 1949 when I was working with him on that introduction as his editorial assistant, he started one day in a facetious (or prophetic?) moment to dictate to me, 'This new introduction by Korzybski has been edited by me, as it was not finished . . .' Now, indeed, this must be so. For due to the pressure of other work since that date, the introduction as he had planned it was never completed by him, and on March 1, 1950 he suddenly died. The manuscripts on which he had worked will be edited and incorporated into later editions of this book. The new material will also be available separately, for those who have copies of this present edition.

He had planned to write of some of the experiences in his life which were influential in the formulation of his work. 'This book was an immediate result of the First World War,' he said. 'My military experiences gave me a very serious insight into the character of those endless historical disasters which have beset mankind from time immemorial, and sharpened my awareness of the hopelessness of the old evaluations. I began to search for the origin of such recurring catastrophes, and finally it dawned upon me that humanity so far had never had a "just conception" of the "nature of man". The question had bothered me practically since childhood of how to talk intelligently about different manifestations of life as found in animals and in humans, without confusing the two.'

His childhood experiences on the family estate of Korzybie near Warsaw, Poland, and his early supervision of the farming activities, his training in scientific and mathematical orientations by his father, his education as an engineer, etc., were other factors which shaped his outlooks.

It seemed to Korzybski that the new functional definition of 'man' as a time-binding class of life, given originally in the first edition of this book, is more important today than ever. The fertility of this 'germinal idea' has been amply shown in his own development of his work, and its potentialities for the future work of others have begun to be felt. 'All human achievements, constructive or destructive, are man-made, and so to properly evaluate them, we have to understand the mechanism of how this fundamental characteristic activity of humans [time-binding] works,' he wrote. 'A beginning of such understanding has been made, indicating the workability of the new methods. The extent of the revision in our orientations which this new notion of man as a time-binder requires, however, is not generally realized. The functional definition cannot be denied; yet once accepted, not only verbally but as a life orientation, it leads automatically to the foundation of a science of man based on the application of up-to-date scientific (physico-mathematical) methods.'

It led him to the formulation of the first non-aristotelian system and general semantics, and the first theory of sanity, as given in 1933 in his *Science and Sanity; An Introduction to Non-aristotelian Systems and General Semantics.*

In his new introduction he was also dealing with the electro-colloidal character of our nervous systems, suggesting investigations of the effect of the continuous cosmic ray bombardments on our own life processes, which we may assume involve a slow liberation of nuclear energy from the radio-active carbon of which all life consists.

He was particularly concerned with international problems today, with the Soviet dictatorship, etc. 'It is useless to argue in terms of "capitalism" or "communism", etc.,' he said. 'Both involve some economic theory, the working of which can be judged only by the empirical results, and on the theoretical side, by our understanding of "human nature". Obviously no system which disregards or violates "human nature" can possibly survive in time, no matter how many more wars and revolutions we may have. What we have to analyze intelligently is the problem of *dictatorship*, be it the dictatorship of "Wall Street" or the "Proletarians", both of which are against our time-binding potentialities, and so in the long run will not cover human needs. In a future sane society individuals must have the freedom to revise their premises, which under the absolutism and rigidity of dictators is impossible.'

He was also writing about symbolism considered as a form of human behavior. 'Here I may mention the well-known manifestations called "intellectual honesty" and "linguistic conscience". We humans are not born with a consciousness of symbolism as such, nor with an understanding of its importance and mechanisms, involving *responsibilities*. Those issues have to be clarified and taught through the accumulation of past experiences and theoretical research.'

Appendices I, II, and III were published in the first edition of this book; the other two appendices have been added in this second edition, in accordance with Korzybski's plans.

In Appendix IV, 'Some Non-aristotelian Data for Efficiency in Human Adjustment,' he deals with examples in our daily living which involve exponential functions. He explains that life complexities are non-additive, and grow in exponential function. Researches in the essentials of management in industry, business, and military organization are cited which show through the work of Graicunas and Urwick that strict limits are placed on the number of separate factors which the human nervous system can handle simultaneously without breaking down.

In Appendix V, the Author's Note from *Selections from Science and Sanity,* Korzybski gives a brief history of the term 'general semantics', which should not be confused with 'semantics'. Although General Semantics originated with this book in 1921, when he wrote this book he intended, as the reader will see, to call his work 'human engineering'. His reasons for changing the name, and how he happened to introduce the term 'general semantics', are given in the appendix.

The following is quoted from the manuscript he was preparing for this book: 'In reading what I wrote in this book in 1921 I find that I have nothing to retract, and that the problems dealt with here have become more urgent than ever. Only some typographical corrections have been made. The reader will find that different kinds of punctuation have been used in my earlier writings than in more recent writings, such as the last two appendices and *What I*

Believe, which are in conformity with the style of the Non-aristotelian Library publications. Also, here and there the terminologies differ. For the sake of expediency, these minor deviations have not been changed, as they do not interfere with the more fundamental issues.

'I have also deliberately kept in those issues which deal specifically with the problems and scientific knowledge current in 1921, which now have a more historical aspect. The thoughtful reader will be amazed at this example of the exponential character of our time-binding process, revealing the extent to which our knowledge of the world and ourselves has grown in only twenty-nine years.

'Our human progress is an exponential function of time, and I can do no better than refer the reader to Chapter XX reprinted here from *Mathematical Philosophy* by the late Professor Cassius Jackson Keyser. It is an exceptionally deep and beautifully written contemplation. Only Keyser, a mathematician, a profound student of humanity, a philosopher, and, we might say, a poet, could have written such an inspiring chapter. It deals with the exponential function of time as applied to a self-perpetuating and living organism called "mankind", and pictures the potentialities of a time-binding class of life with the "forward-leaping" exponential function of time.

'I must express here, at long last, an indebtedness

which Professor Keyser did not wish expressed at the time this book first appeared. My dear friend and mentor, feeling that this new theory of time-binding was very important, gave most freely of his time in helping me with the original manuscript, which I wrote in a language at that time new to me. He not only helped me greatly by his editing, but in some instances practically rewrote my original rather clumsy expressions.

'I am also grateful for the encouragement which the late Jacques Loeb gave to me. It was because of his urging me to stay in this country and develop my work here, that I did not return to Poland as I had intended after the First World War.'

The outstanding mathematician, Professor Edward Kasner, who was a warm friend of both Korzybski and Keyser, has set a keynote for the reappearance of Korzybski's basic work in his Foreword to this new edition.

In 'A Memoir: Alfred Korzybski & His Work' Miss M. Kendig has given us a picture of Korzybski as a human being, and contributed toward a deeper understanding of his work as a whole. Miss Kendig has been the Educational Director of the Institute of General Semantics since it was founded by Korzybski in 1938 as the center for training in his work. She has been the Associate Director since 1942, and its program is now being carried forward under her direction.

There could perhaps be no more eloquent summary of Korzybski's life work than his own 'credo', *What I Believe*, originally written in 1948 as a contribution to a symposium entitled 'The Faith I Live By.' It is included now in this volume.

Charlotte Schuchardt

Lakeville, Connecticut
April 1950

CONTENTS

FOREWORD

I am happy to write a brief foreword to this new edition of Korzybski's *Manhood of Humanity*.

With the engineering of world peace more imperative each day, a new presentation of Korzybski's ideas together with Keyser's exposition and clarification is particularly urgent.

The fundamental thesis of the book is that man, while as 'natural' as animal, is different in dimensionality. Just as the sphere and circle, though both are round objects, differ in essence; so man is unlike animal, being a time-binder as well as a space-binder. Indoctrinated from childhood with a zoological view of his own nature, man tends to accept as inevitable human greed, selfishness and competitiveness.

From the convictions of these two gifted thinkers, Korzybski and Keyser, both men of keen intellect, good-will and broad humanitarian interest, we can gain much-needed insight into a basic cause of war. They inspire and direct our continued efforts to find solutions for the very real and perplexing problems of human welfare everywhere. Indeed they do us an inestimable service.

Edward Kasner

Columbia University
New York City

A MEMOIR:
ALFRED KORZYBSKI & HIS WORK

*Every scientific discovery is in a sense the
autobiography of the man who made it.*

Alfred Korzybski came to America in December
1915. He wrote this book in 1920 when he was 41
years old. It is, so far as I know, his first written
work published or unpublished in any language. To
me this has always seemed a very significant thing,
related to the creativeness, the relentless vigor, the
simplicity of the man, the integrity, the depth, the
practicality of his work and methods. Over the years
as I observed him and his method of work—visualiz-
ing, concretizing, slowly slowly bringing the most
complex problems down to their structural essentials
in terms of simple earthy examples—I could well
believe his report: 'From babyhood I was silent. I
had nothing to say.'—that is, before he came to
America, made English *his* language, formulated his
functional definition of man in this book. All his life
he looked wide-eyed at the world, he contemplated
what he saw, he questioned, why, how. He seemed
possessed by a passion for comprehension. He lived
and studied men on the soil of Poland, in the cities
of Europe, on the battlefields of the eastern front.

He studied the history of men, in books and at the universities—the successes and the tragedies of man-made civilizations. He questioned why so?—how could we do better in our time? He was a lover of life, of music, of the poetry of feeling. He loved mathematics, engineering. They fitted the life facts. When men used them they escaped from animal trial and error, they could predict outcomes, pass on their findings, progress in their control of non-human things. Why was this not so in human affairs?

The impact of his experience in World War I, of coming to live in this new country and this open society, of finding a new language which suited him for the formulation of his non-verbal 'thinking'— these among others were precipitants. His lifetime studies and questions fell into new focus. He saw the significance of the obvious and the implications of the obvious. He verbalized the obvious in his *functional definition of man as a time-binding class of life:* Not what man *is.* What men *do,* as an exponential function of time. He developed the implications of the obvious characteristic of man and of man's unique environments of symbolism and valuations, in *Time-Binding: The General Theory* (1924–1926), in his *Science and Sanity* (1933), and on through to the end of his life in his later writings, in his seminars, and in his working with students.

This book has been out of print for eleven years. In these years Korzybski did his major teaching at the Institute of General Semantics, and *Science and Sanity* has been increasingly read, viz. 12 *hundred* copies bought from 1933 to 1938; 17 *thousand* since. Very many who have read *Science and Sanity* and who have studied general semantics with him at the Institute have, I suspect, never held a copy of *Manhood of Humanity* in their hands. *Science and Sanity,* or someone else's writings about general semantics has been their first introduction to Korzybski, and many have little notion what the term *time-binding* and its implications represent. Some of these persons have expressed in diverse ways vague discontent, an uneasiness as if they were missing something methodologically in the socio-cultural import which they felt but could not find made explicit in *Science and Sanity*. Korzybski was himself so full of the significance of time-binding, of the social feelings engendered by this new 'image of man', I do not believe that he saw this need until quite recent years. Meantime, requests for re-publication of his first book have been mounting steadily. He was meditating on a new introduction for over three years, and he was still working on it when he died. As the 'Editor's Note' indicates, plans for publication had been completed and this Second Edition must appear without his introduction. Fortunately, Korzybski's own recent paper, 'What I Be-

lieve' (1948), summarizes his life's work, emphasizing the central rôle of his time-binding definition of
man. This paper and Professor Keyser's chapter on
'Korzybski's Concept of Man' (1922) were already
planned for inclusion. They serve now as introductions, retrospective and contemporary, to this
book. The editor, my friend and colleague Charlotte
Schuchardt, has asked me to add some prefatory
words before the volume goes to press.

I knew and worked with Alfred Korzybski for
fifteen years, first at a school where I was principal
and then at the Institute he founded and which I am
now privileged to carry on. I studied with him inten-
sively and used his methodology at the school. He
re-educated me as an educator, and I gained insights
into multiple aspects of his life, his feelings and his
methods. I also observed most of the 1800 who
studied general semantics with him at the Institute
seminars. Over the years, I came to feel that Alfred
Korzybski, his life, his writings, the work he did,
were singularly indivisible. In this brief memoir, I
feel impelled to communicate something of that
unique human-being-life-work complex, and to record
an approach I have found clarifying in 'seeing' his
work as a whole. In writing it, I have a picture of
the potential readers of this book and tend to see
them mostly as people who have read *Science and
Sanity* and other writings dealing with general se-

mantics per se. To convey briefly something of what I would like to convey to these readers, I must use Korzybskian formulations and terminology without explanation. For this I ask indulgence from other readers of the book.

This seems to me important: Korzybski's time-binding definition makes a sharp distinction between men and animals. But he emphasized the *differences* without dismissing the similarities (not either-or) — without, that is, breaking the continuity of a dimensional hierarchy of life. Viewed on a scale of increasing orders of complexity, amoeba$_1$ ...... Smith$_1$-in-western-civilization[today] represent natural phenomena; differ not in kind but in degree of complexity, the number of factors to be taken account of. With the time-binding theory, he made man and the accomplishments of men, the successes and the tragedies of human histories and cultures comprehensible. He reduced human phenomena to something already known, evident. He satisfied the creative scientist's striving for unification and simplification of premises (i.e. Mach's principle of economy). He formulated a basic theory for the foundations of a *natural* science of man, encompassing not only man's biological but his psycho-symbolic nature, and his accomplishments (e.g. mathematics, the exact sciences, the arts, ethics, etc.). As a new theory must, time-binding covered all the old assumptions, included and explained new or neglected factors, led to the discovery of new factors, and their incorporation into that theory. The skeptic will question this. He may say this 'is not science', but a 'miracle creed'. Admittedly so—perhaps. The values of a scientific theory, it seems, can only be assayed by what comes out of it by the process of 'methodo-logic' development, and by empiric demonstration of workability of principles and methods derived from it.

The theory of time-binding led Korzybski, inevitably, to the formulation of a first non-aristotelian system on premises of great simplicity, and to the formulation of a *modus operandi* for that system. This body of coordinated assumptions, doctrines, principles, etc., and methodological procedures and techniques for changing the structure of our neuro-symbolic reactions to fit an assumptive world of dynamic processes, he called *General Semantics*. He described this whole discipline as an empirical natural science and the extensional method as a generalization of the physico-mathematical 'way of thinking' applicable in all human evaluations.

For the rest of his life Korzybski was concerned with testing out the human values of his formulations, his hypotheses. Would the practice of general semantics liberate human time-binding energies, lead to more adequate evaluations, greater predictability and so sanity—in the lives of individuals, in their conduct of human affairs, and so eventually in the effects of science on society, narrowing the gap between these rates of progress?

Twelve years of study went into the formulations before he was ready to publish *Science and Sanity*. He studied human evaluations in science and mathematics and in psychiatry, 'at their best and at their worst' as he put it, from the standpoint of predictability and human survival. He wrote the first draft of *Science and Sanity* in 1927–28. Published it in 1933 after tirelessly checking the data necessary for his methodological synthesis of modern sciences and testing the structural implications of the terminology in which he cast his formulations. As Poincaré said, 'All the scientist creates in a fact is the language in which he enunciates it.' The changes Korzybski made in the verbalization of his formulations from his first book to *Science and Sanity* make a fascinating study in development of linguistic rigor. He called this testing of the structural implications of terms (and formulations) his 'linguistic conscience'. Few know that Korzybski originally intended to call his major work *Time-Binding*. He changed the title to *Science and Sanity* practically on the eve of publication, because he felt he should emphasize that interrelation. The verbal continuity between *Manhood* and *Science and Sanity* he preserved in the title of Part VII, 'On the Mechanisms of Time-Binding.' In those pages,

369–561, he expounds his non-aristotelian system and general semantics. Many readers have apparently missed this continuity.

In this book, and in his early papers outlining the general theory of time-binding, the reader familiar with *Science and Sanity* can see and trace back the process of methodo-logic development from 1921 to 1933. He can see how the non-aristotelian system and general semantics followed from the theory of time-binding as inevitably as theorems from geometric postulates.[1] He will see how the Structural Differential, the principle of consciousness of abstracting, the extensional method and devices, etc., came out of the theory and the related investigations of the mechanisms of time-binding. He will see, among others, the beginnings of Korzybski's formulation of neuro-linguistic and neuro-semantic environments as the unique inescapable environment conditioning the reactions of the human-organism-as-a-whole, in any culture at any time—an invariant relation. This formulation of the neuro-linguistic and neuro-semantic environments (and the neurological mechanisms involved) seems to me one of the great

[1] For more on this development, see two papers by Professor Oliver L. Reiser, 'Historical-Cultural Significance of Non-Aristotelian Movement and the Methodological Contributions of Korzybski' (pp. 3–10), and 'From Classical Physical to Modern Scientific Assumptions' (pp. 69–78) in *Papers From the Second American Congress on General Semantics,* M. Kendig, Editor (Chicago: Institute of General Semantics, 1943).

and most useful of Korzybski's higher order generalizations directly derived from time-binding theory.
It generalizes to a higher order the 'psycho-cultural
approach' (Lawrence K. Frank, et al). It has made
the mechanisms of cultural conditioning and cultural
continuity comprehensible to me and many other
students. It will, I believe, eventually unify and
simplify the premises of cultural anthropology, psychiatry, Pavlovian and Lewinian psychology, empiric
social sciences, etc.

The reader who has studied *Science and Sanity,*
trained his nervous system with the techniques of the
non-aristotelian discipline of general semantics, applied it in his life and work, has made his own non-
verbal demonstration of empiric workability. He can
assay the values great or small to him of what came
out of Korzybski's time-binding theory and compare
his evaluations with the reports of others who, with
various degrees of competence, have applied it in
many fields.[2] The reader who has merely read *Science
and Sanity,* who 'knows' it verbally, even if he can
repeat verbatim all the principles and terminology,
has slight criteria for his evaluations. He may or
may not get insights from the reports of others, i.e.

[2] See for example *Papers From the Second American Congress on
General Semantics,* op. cit.; papers on the publication list of the
Institute of General Semantics; other papers distributed to 'Mem-
bers of the Institute' and the recently inaugurated *General Semantics
Bulletin* published for Members by the Institute.

accept their evaluations as shown in practice. If he enjoys skepticism he can argue as endlessly about the validity of the reports as he can about Korzybski's theories, in the abstract. The aristotelian tradition has trained him to do that: words and experience are equated in the tacit assumption that if he knows the words he knows 'all'; any proposition can be proved or disproved by talking, etc., etc. If he is trained in some scientific specialty, where he can, or thinks he can, narrow his problems down so that he has only two variables to control, he may balk at 'accepting' the empiric value of anything that deals with the multiple variables of human life and cannot be fitted into his formula.

Some have dismissed Korzybski's work as 'nothing new'. Others consider it 'too radical' (or too 'unscientific') for serious 'scientific consideration'. Such receptions of the new and different are not rare in the history of science. For 'philosophic' or 'scientific' skeptics who wished to argue *a priori* about his work, Korzybski had a favorite expression, 'Don't talk. Do it.' ('It is strictly empirical.') This epitomizes the non-verbal character of the working mechanisms of the discipline, its strength—and the difficulties he faced in his pioneering efforts.

'I don't know, let's see!' was another pet saying of his, when faced with something new. This was the attitude he, the engineer, took toward his formulations. That is, he was his own best skeptic—he knew, for example, the pitfalls of 'logical' consistency versus life reactions. He remained 'the skeptic' for many years until he *saw* (had empiric evidence which satisfied him*) that the formulations, the verbal and non-verbal techniques of the extensional method he expounded and demonstrated in his seminars on general semantics were teachable and workable—were, in fact, an appropriate scientific methodology for the time-binding theory and for general education toward realizing human time-binding potentialities.

Korzybski founded the Institute in June 1938. In September Chamberlain went to Munich. The *words* were 'peace in our time' by 'democratic appeasement', and the *facts* were war and more dictatorships —as Korzybski sadly predicted in his seminar that autumn of '38. His papers written during the next seven years record the impact on him, his reactions to World War II, in terms of his formulations and the direction his work was taking. Only those who knew and worked with him intimately know the depth of his social feelings, how he suffered in his whole person about the war. The daily chaos of today blunts our memories of what he—all of us have —lived through then.[3]

* In most matters of uniquely human significance, we have to be content with observing phenomena that cannot be quantitatively measured as of 1950.

[3] Some famous *words* of the fighting-war years bring them sharply

He was 59 years old the summer he founded the Institute. The work he set himself to do there radically changed his life pattern. Behind him was a tremendous feat of physiological endurance, 'mental' power and vigor, the vast methodologic synthesis he had encompassed in *Science and Sanity*. The elegant simplicity of his formulations can be misleading in counting what they cost him as an organism. More feats of endurance were ahead of him. The new conditions were ill-suited to his make-up. Among others they deprived him of long periods of silence and isolation which were the *sine qua non* of his creative work, which he needed, craved as most of us do physical comforts. For the next eleven years he was surrounded by people and pressures. In the beginning he directed the Institute down to minutest details. He taught seminar courses and worked with individual students interminably. He carried on a mountainous correspondence. The number of papers he was able to write under the circumstances is remarkable to us who know the care he lavished on everything he wrote for publication. For many years he still hoped to write another book, incorporating

back to me. I refer to the recording, 'I Can Hear It Now.' In a half hour's listening, the sensitive reader may re-live the background Korzybski did his work against in the first six years of the Institute. 'I Can Hear It Now,' Volume 1, edited by Edward R. Murrow and Fred Friendly. Narrated by Edward R. Murrow (Columbia Masterworks ML4095, Long Playing; also on standard records).

the deductive presentation of the non-aristotelian system and general semantics which he made in his seminar courses. He was constantly harassed by our lack of money and security in carrying on the Institute and by the anomalies of a situation in which he could not approve or accept some well-intentioned suggestions and efforts made to help us gain acceptance and support. For example: Some wanted him to popularize his work, i.e. rewrite *Science and Sanity* for 'the man in the street', etc. Others wanted him to be less forthright in his presentations, to modify his theoretical position and so compromise with current academic and scientific orthodoxies to woo acceptance at the universities and support by the foundations. The price was too high for him to pay if it meant compromising the integrity of the discipline, and so eliminating the possibilities of demonstrating the human, scientific values of the general semantics methodology in clear-cut applications, and their eventual comparison with what was accomplished by prevailing methods. He had to continue to work beyond the institutional 'safety zone', although he was well aware of the disadvantages of doing so. Persons who themselves seemed unconcerned about the scientific integrity of the discipline, took easier paths and did not understand his position; labelled it 'monomania', 'cultism', 'jealousy', etc. This fretted and saddened him. To him, his position seemed as simple as saying, 'Let's stick to our premises. If we set out to solve a problem by non-euclidean geometry, we don't switch to euclidean postulates. We would just make a mess. We have to have some honesty, stick to the method we start out with and then compare results. Which fits the facts best, which gives the most predictability in doing what we set out to do?'

The Institute was for Korzybski a training school and his research laboratory. He both taught and studied the students in his seminar courses. He was just as passionately absorbed in testing his work as he had been in formulating it. Each seminar meant 30 to 50 hours of vigorous lecturing, in some intensive courses eight hours a day. It meant hours of private work with each of the 40 to 50 students. He gave seminar after seminar, year after year. His endurance seemed endless. The results he saw in the lives and work of hundreds of these students and their reports to him over the years were not only his empiric evidence that his formulations did work. They were his chief source of happiness in the arduous Institute years.

He had his own peculiar style of lecturing, a non-linear method of developing his exposition of non-aristotelian orientations by going round and round in widening circles, turning back to some example given at the beginning to illustrate a mechanism in his later lectures. He used shocking examples from his study in mental hospitals, from psychiatry, from his own experience with deeply maladjusted people, criminals, etc., to (as he called it) 'get under the skins' of the class, to 'shake them up'. He used examples from daily life, from the history of science, from mathematics. At times he was elegant, crisp, suave—at others, humorous and discursive. Often his face, his hands, conveyed as much as his words and diagrams. One educator said he was the 'most powerful and effective teacher' he knew, 'a master of pedagogy'. Another said he was 'the worst, should study pedagogy'. People were seldom neutral about him, what he did, or how he did it. The more he shook their complacency, irritated them by 'rubbing in' the method, the more they learned. He insisted that anyone who wished to, could enroll for a seminar. 'Because a general method of evaluation,' he said, 'has to work with anybody in any human activity or it's no good.' Professors, doctors, psychiatrists, artists, researchers, young college students, businessmen, social workers, laborers, etc., all sat in the same classes. This may all sound chaotic; it was effective.

In private interviews he showed individuals how to apply the methodology in analyzing and re-evaluating their personal lives and problems; he taught them to question their rationalizations, etc., constantly. These personal applications, he contended, must come first. The student must rigorously and continuously apply the extensional method in his personal living. Only then would he have a sure basis for successful application in handling 'impersonal' problems—the human relations, the methodological problems in his work in any field, whether science, art, medicine, education, business, etc. A psychiatrist said, 'Korzybski deals with, uncovers "the cultural unconscious", makes it "conscious".* In psychotherapy we do the "same" with the personal unconscious which is only a special case of the cultural.' Some like to call the seminars a 'school of wisdom'. 'Maybe,' said Korzybski, 'but wisdom is not enough. There's been plenty of wisdom in this world for millenniums and what? Wisdom, alone, doesn't work. You have to have a method for applying it continuously.'

A significantly large number of those who studied with Korzybski in some 56 seminars benefited, continue to benefit, from the training in various degrees. He had his failures. 'Ten percent of every class,' he claimed, 'got nothing out of it.' 'Some became,' he said, 'my enemies for life.' (When you touch the

---

* That is to say, changes unconscious assumptions about the world, about man, carried in the structure of language; attitudes, value judgments, 'modes of thought' learned from our neuro-linguistic and neuro-semantic environments.

fundamental verbalisms around which an individual has organized his life pattern, it may be too disturbing for him to face.) Some 'got it' quickly and as easily fell back into old habits of thinking-feeling. They use the words but not the method. 'They "refused" to work at themselves,' he said. Some learned general semantics 'intellectually' (i.e. verbally, 'cortically'), knew all the principles and terminology and techniques, but simply could not apply them, change their evaluations, their living reactions. Some 'got it' very slowly, over the years. It apparently had no effect on their lives, their work, and then—something happened. Because to me it shows many things, I want to quote a letter written to Korzybski in April 1950 by a research psychiatrist who had not heard of his death:

Dear Count Alfred:

I think I owe you a little apology, a vote of thanks, and an explanation. As you recall it was in the summer of 1939 that I first became aware of General Semantics. At that time your and my good friend Dr. _____ [deceased] . . . took me with him to your Seminar. I could 'get' the cortical aspect [verbal] but for some reason the thalamic portion [change in living, feeling] seemed to elude me. However in this last month something apparently has happened. I begin now for the first time to 'feel' that General Semantics

has something I need and which can help. What
the explanation is I do not know—all I can give
you is the answer my small son (thirty-four
months) gives me—when I ask him why he does
this or that, he simply says, 'Well I did it' . . .
Just to let you know that sometimes it takes a
little while for things to sink in, I remain,

Semantically yours

Korzybski held his last seminar December 27–
January 4, 1950. That vast physiological endurance
was running out. He no longer tramped up and down
the platform waving his stick. His lecturing was as
vigorous, his 'thinking' as creative as ever. In January and February he wrote his last scientific paper
for the Clinical Psychology Symposium on Perception at the University of Texas.[4]

The circumstances of his death, it so happened,
were symbolic of his life and work. In working with
students, he exhibited a tremendous power of caring
about any individual bit of humanity before him. He
was continuously aware that some infantile evaluation he might be struggling to change in an individual

[4] Clinical Psychology Symposium 1949–50 on *Perception: An Ap-
proach to Personality.* Presented by The Department of Psychology,
University of Texas, under the direction of Dr. Robert R. Blake and
Dr. Glenn V. Ramsey. To be published by Ronald Press, New York.
Title of paper by Alfred Korzybski: 'Functional Determinants of
Perceptual Processes: Language; a) The Effect on Perceptual
Processes of the Language System, b) Aristotelian and Non-aris-
totelian Language Systems.'

mirrored a symptom from the social syndrome. He spent the last few hours of his life at his desk working on such a problem. In his non-elementalistic orientation, the individual *and* society were split verbally only for convenience. Empirically, they could no more be split in the world of facts than space *and* time, psyche *and* soma, heredity *and* environment, etc. To him, no human problems were 'insignificant' problems. Thus the intensity, the warmth of his social feelings, the lavish extravagant ways he spent himself. He died March first at three o'clock in the morning. He had lived for 70 years, 7 months and 29 days.

In one way, we can say his work was 'finished.' In another hardly begun. For him it was finished in the sense that he had fulfilled the criteria he must have set himself after he had completed this book in 1921 from the point of view of theory, inductive and deductive methods, and empirical verification to a considerable degree (page xliv).

For us the work of the future calls for more cooperative endeavors. A methodological synthesis needed for progress of our knowledge of man-as-a-whole-in-his-environments, for its application in science and education, research and practice, has been elaborated in a single brain. Its use values have been demonstrated by Korzybski himself and by a substantial number of individuals trained in the

non-aristotelian discipline. Together these persons
represent a cross section of human activities and
problems—theory and practice in the sciences and
arts, education, industry, community life, etc. To
date their efforts have a common characteristic.
They have been undertaken by courageous individuals as individuals, developed in ways to meet individual situations. These individuals have been
isolated from each other by geography and more
intangible factors. Pioneering the discipline has, of
necessity, been carried on in an amorphous atmosphere. To go forward we shall need to coalesce. We
need not less spontaneity but more consensus on
essentials, on directions. We need inter-discipline
cooperation and some mechanism for working in
groups. Fostering such development now becomes a
function and aim of the Institute as the center for
non-aristotelian training and work. Thus Korzybski's
time-binding efforts will live and grow.

In his life he wrote two books and 22 papers.[5]
Stood together they measure exactly 4 and ½ inches,
in extra-neural space. At this date, I doubt that anyone would care to take the measure of Korzybski's
work, his influence and the extent of it in our time.

---

[5] A complete bibliography of Korzybski's published writings
which also includes brief introductions and comments, is available
on request from the Institute of General Semantics. Books and reprints of papers may be ordered from the Institute. Address: Lakeville, Connecticut, U. S. A.

Those who know these works might join me in saying:
Seldom if ever in human history has so little represented so much for human understanding and progress.

The re-publication of this book with the inclusion
of Professor Keyser's early appreciation of the significance of time-binding and with three of Korzybski's more recent papers may be the first step towards
disentangling the values of his work as a scientific
discipline from a web of narrow conceptions and
mis-conceptions—fabricated from certain methodo-
logic necessities, emphases, historic accidents in its
development. Among others these have resulted in
linking his name with language and communication
to the exclusion of other aspects of his work in
scientific and educational circles, and with the word
'semantics' as now popularly used. Such are some of
the artificial obstructions. Added to the inherent
difficulty of changing to new premises, non-aristotelian orientations, etc., they have retarded 'seeing'
his work as-a-whole in proper perspective. As I sense
it, the 'climate of opinion' in cultural anthropology,
psycho-somatic medicine, the psychologies, the arts,
etc., has changed slowly in the non-aristotelian direction towards non-elementalistic 'concepts' of man in
society. By now it may be that some in these disciplines are ready to review Korzybski's works as a
whole, and accept his bold hypotheses and method-

ology for further verification. All his writings are now available, and students can trace the development of his thinking in historic sequence. The slender bulk of his works may encourage study or re-study —especially, I hope, by social scientists and educators.

In the paper which follows this memoir and which he wrote during 1947 and 1948, Korzybski has summarized his life's work, his conclusions, his hopes, in a quite remarkable way. In these twelve pages we have what we may consider Korzybski's 'testament' —a bequest to workers concerned with human welfare in all the sciences and arts. I look upon it as a challenge and a program for future workers endowed with creative imagination who will take the foundations Korzybski has left us in time-binding, the non-aristotelian system and general semantics, re-formulate the theories and practices of their specialties, generalize them to a higher-order 'science of science'—or, if you prefer, an inter-discipline discipline—to cover the whole of human life and the potentialities of time-binding. That is looking far far ahead—twenty-five, fifty years perhaps.

Reading this book for the first time seems to me an experience very much like getting a first clear look at human beings and human history after wearing glasses with distorting lenses all one's life. One feels a release from unsuspected tensions. One has

some hope. The audacity and simplicity of Korzybski's approach that cut through ages-old problems to
a fresh, new way of looking at 'man' seem more, not
less, remarkable with the passage of time. We have
learned so much about 'man' and 'society'—and done
so little with it—since he wrote. Ignore the allusions
which date this book historically to the socio-eco-
nomic-scientific contexts of the post-war world of
1920, and it might have been written last year. It
is a trite and easy thing to say a man lived before
his time. I believe, however, that only now after
thirty years are we ready to take in the significance
of his first book.

                                        M. Kendig

Institute of General Semantics
Lakeville, Connecticut
11 May 1950

WHAT I BELIEVE

I AM deeply honored to participate in the Symposium, *The Faith I Live By,* compiled and edited by Krishna M. Talgeri, and to contribute this paper particularly written for the contemplative audience of Indian readers.* This is the first opportunity I have had to write a 'credo', where I do not need to go into theoretical explanations.

It happens that I come from an old family of agriculturists, mathematicians, soldiers, jurists, and engineers, etc. When I was five years old my father, an engineer, gave me the feel of the world's most important scientific discoveries of the nineteenth century, which prepared the groundwork for the scientific achievements of the twentieth century and remain fundamentally valid today. The *feel* of the differential calculus, as well as non-euclidean and four-dimensional geometries, which he conveyed to me at that

* This was originally written in 1948 in response to an invitation from Mr. Krishna Mangesh Talgeri, M.A. of 26, Atul Grove, New Delhi, India, to contribute to a symposium entitled, *The Faith I Live By.* It is to be published soon, and includes such international contributors as Gandhi, Nehru, Montessori, John H. Holmes, Radhakrishnan and others. I admit that without Mr. Talgeri's invitation, and the most valuable assistance of Miss Charlotte Schuchardt, which I wish to gratefully acknowledge, I would never have undertaken the difficult task of formulating such a condensed summary of life studies and experiences which any 'credo' would require.

time shaped the future interests and orientations of my life, and became the foundation of my whole work.

My observations and theoretical studies of life and mathematics, mathematical foundations, many branches of sciences, also history, history of cultures, anthropology, 'philosophy', 'psychology', 'logic', comparative religions, etc., convinced me that:

1) Human evaluations with reference to themselves were mythological or zoological, or a combination of both; but,

2) Neither of these approaches could give us a workable base for understanding the living, uniquely human, extremely complex (deeply inter-related) reactions of $Smith_1$, $Smith_2$, etc., generalized in such high-order abstractions as 'mind', or 'intellect'; and,

3) A functional analysis, free from the old mythological and zoological assumptions, showed that humans, with the most highly developed nervous system, are uniquely characterized by the capacity of an individual or a generation to begin where the former left off. I called this essential capacity 'time-binding'. This can be accomplished only by a class of life which uses symbols as means for time-binding. Such a capacity depends on and necessitates 'intelligence', means of communication, etc. On this inherently human level of interdependence time-binding leads inevitably to feelings of responsibility, duty toward others and

the future, and therefore to some type of ethics, morals, and similar social and/or socio-cultural reactions.

In the time-binding orientation I took those characteristics for granted as the empirical end-products of the functioning of the healthy human nervous system.

It was a fundamental error of the old evaluations to postulate 'human nature' as 'evil'. 'Human nature' depends to a large extent on the character of our creeds or rationalizations, etc., for these ultimately build up our socio-cultural and other environments.

I believe that our approaches to the problems of humans have been vitiated by primitive methods of evaluation which still often dominate our attitudes and outlooks. With a time-binding consciousness, our criteria of values, and so behaviour, are based on the study of human potentialities, not on statistical averages on the level of *homo homini lupus* drawn from primitive and/or un-sane semantic (evaluational) reactions which are on record. Instead of studying elementalistic 'thinking', 'feeling', 'intellect', 'emotion', etc., a misguiding approach implying the inherited archaic, *artificial,* divisions or schizophrenic splits of human characteristics which actually cannot be split, I *investigated functionally and therefore non-elementalistically the psycho-biological mechanisms of time-binding*—how they work.

By induction we pass from particulars to the general. However, this method is not reliable enough. We have to build a deductive system and verify empirically whether the general applies to the eventual random particular, which then would become the foundation for predictability. This, after all, is the main aim of all science. So far what we 'knew' about 'man' were statistical averages gathered inductively, and so our human world picture was rather sad, distorted, if not hopeless. The human understanding of time-binding as explained here establishes the deductive grounds for a full-fledged 'science of man', where both inductive and deductive methods are utilized. I believe that this very point of inductive and deductive scientific methods with regard to humans tangibly marks a sharp difference between the childhood and the manhood of humanity. In other words, we try to learn from the study of the individual the main characteristics of the *phylum* (the human race). Now with the time-binding theory, for the first time to my knowledge, having accumulated data by induction (statistical averages), we can start with what we have learned about the *phylum* and analyze the individual from the point of view of human potentialities *as a phylum*. I may be wrong, but perhaps this may become the turning of a page of human history.

I could not use, in my further studies, the older 'organism-as-a-whole' approaches, but had to base my analysis on the much more complex 'organism-as-a-whole-in-an-environment'. I had to include neuro-linguistic and neuro-semantic (evaluational) environments as environments, and also had to consider geographic, physico-chemical, economic, political, ecological, socio-cultural, etc., conditions as factors which mould human personalities, and so even group behaviour. This statement is entirely general, and applies to highly civilized people as well as the most primitive.

Common sense and ordinary observations convinced me that the average, so-called 'normal person' is so extremely complex as to practically evade an over-all analysis. So I had to concentrate on the study of two extremes of human psycho-logical reactions: a) reactions at their best, because of their exceptional predictability, as in mathematics, the foundations of mathematics, mathematical physics, exact sciences, etc., which exhibit the deepest kind of strictly human psycho-logical reactions, and b) reactions at their worst, as exemplified by psychiatric cases. In these investigations I discovered that physico-mathematical methods have application to our daily life on all levels, linking science with problems of sanity, in the sense of adjustment to 'facts' and 'reality'.

I found that human reactions within these two limits do not differ in some objectified 'kind', but only in psycho-biological 'degrees', and that the 'normal' person hovers somewhere in between the two ex-

tremes. Nobody is as 'insane' as the composite picture
a textbook of psychiatry would give us, and nobody is
as sane as that which a textbook of sanity would give,
the author included. The mechanisms of time-binding
are exhibited in most humans except those with se-
vere psycho-biological illnesses. However, some *inac-
cessible* dogmatists in power, particularly dictators of
every kind, have blocked this capacity considerably.
Clearly police states of secrecy, withholding from
the people knowledge of, and from, the world,
or twisting that knowledge to suit their purposes,
'iron curtains', etc., must be classified as saboteurs
among time-binders, and certainly not a socio-cultural
asset to the evolution of humanity.

Linguistic and grammatical structures also have
prevented our understanding of human reactions.
For instance, we used and still use a terminology of
'objective' and 'subjective', both extremely confusing,
as the so-called 'objective' must be considered a construct made by our nervous system, and what we call
'subjective' may also be considered 'objective' for the
same reasons.

My analysis showed that happenings in the world
outside our skins, and also such organismal psychological reactions inside our skins as those we label
'feelings', 'thinking', 'emotions', 'love', 'hate', 'happiness', 'unhappiness', 'anger', 'fear', 'resentment',
'pain', 'pleasure', etc., occur only on the *non-verbal,* or

what I call *silent levels*. Our speaking occurs on the verbal levels, and we can speak *about,* but not *on,* the silent or un-speakable levels. This sharp, and inherently natural, yet thoroughly unorthodox differentiation between verbal and non-verbal levels automatically eliminates the useless metaphysical verbal bickerings of millenniums about 'the nature of things', 'human nature', etc. For many metaphysical verbal futile arguments, such as solipsism, or 'the unknowable', have been the result of the identifications of verbal levels with the silent levels of happenings, 'feelings', etc., that the words are merely supposed to represent, never being the 'reality' behind them.

words represent the silent levels — not to reality behind them

Such psycho-logical manifestations as those mentioned above can be dealt with in a unified terminology of *evaluation,* with the result that an empirical general theory of values, or general semantics, becomes possible, and, with its roots in the methods of exact sciences, this can become the foundation of a *science of man.* For through the study of exact sciences we can discover factors of sanity. Different philosophical trends as found in disciplines such as Nominalism, Realism, Phenomenalism, Significs, Semiotic, Logical Positivism, etc., also become unified by a methodology, with internationally applicable techniques, which I call 'non-aristotelian', as it includes, yet goes beyond and brings *up to date,* the aims and formulations of Aristotle.

Whatever we may *say* something is, obviously *is not* the 'something' on the silent levels. Indeed, as Wittgenstein wrote, 'What *can* be shown, *cannot* be said.' In my experience I found that it is practically impossible to convey the differentiation of silent (unspeakable) levels from the verbal without having the reader or the hearer pinch with one hand the finger of the other hand. He would then realize organismally that the first-order psycho-logical direct experiences are not verbal. The simplicity of this statement is misleading, unless we become aware of its implications, as in our living reactions most of us identify in value the two entirely *different* levels, with often disastrous consequences. Note the sadness of the beautiful passage of Eddington on page lv. He seems to be unhappy that the silent levels can never be the verbal levels. Is this not an example of unjustified 'maximum expectation'?

I firmly believe that the *consciousness of the differences between these levels of abstractions;* i.e., the silent and the verbal levels, is the key and perhaps the first step for the solution of human problems. This belief is based on my own observations, and studies of the endless observations of other investigators.

There is a tremendous difference between 'thinking' in verbal terms, and 'contemplating', inwardly silent, on non-verbal levels, and then searching for the proper structure of language to fit the supposedly

discovered structure of the silent processes that mod- *thinking*
ern science tries to find. If we 'think' *verbally,* we act *Bias*
as biased observers and project onto the silent levels
the structure of the language we use, and so remain in
our rut of old orientations, making keen, unbiased,
observations and creative work well-nigh impossible.
In contrast, when we 'think' without words, or in pictures (which involve structure and therefore relations), we may discover new aspects and relations on
silent levels, and so may produce important theoretical results in the general search for a similarity of
structure between the two levels, silent and verbal.
Practically all important advances are made that
way.

So far the only possible link between the two levels
is found in terms of relations, which apply equally to
both non-verbal and verbal levels, such as 'order'
(serial, linear, cyclic, spiral, etc.), 'between-ness',
'space-time', 'equality' or 'inequality', 'before',
'after', 'more than', 'less than', etc. *Relations, as fac-*
tors of structure, give the sole content of all human *Relations*
knowledge. *reveal the*
content of
Human Know

It has been said that 'to know anything we have to
know everything.' Unfortunately it is true, but expressed *in the above form* 'knowledge' would be impossible. Mathematicians solved this impasse simply
and effectively. They introduced postulational meth-

ods, thus *limiting* the 'everything', out of which the *limited* 'anything' follows.

The identification (confusion) of verbal with silent levels leads automatically to the asking of indefinitely long arrays of verbal 'why's', *as if* the verbal levels could ever possibly cover all the factors and chains of antecedents of the silent levels, or ever '*be*' the silent levels. This is why in science we limit our 'why' to the data at hand, thus avoiding the unlimited metaphysical questioning without data, to which there cannot be an answer. Mathematicians solved these inherent dilemmas by stating explicitly their undefined terms in their postulational systems, terms which label nothing but occurrences on the silent levels. Metaphysicians of many kinds or many creeds since time immemorial tried to solve the same perplexities by postulating different 'prime movers' or 'final causes', beyond which the further 'why' is ruled out as leading to the logically 'verboten' 'infinite regress'. Originally religions were polytheistic. Later, in the attempt for unification, perhaps to strengthen the power of the priesthood, and also because of the increasing ability of humans to make generalizations, monotheisms were invented, which have led to the most cruel religious wars. Different rulers, dictators, 'fuehrers', etc., have followed similar psycho-logical patterns with historically known

destructive or constructive results. The above statements are limited by the historical contexts.

In our human evolutionary development the structures of religions and sciences, because all man-made,
do not differ psycho-logically. They all depend on
fundamental assumptions, hypotheses, etc., from
which we try to build some understanding of, and/or
rapport with, this world, ourselves included. Some of
these involve archaic and false-to-fact assumptions,
etc., others, such as sciences, involve modern, poten-
tially verifiable, assumptions and hypotheses. In
brief, any religion may be considered 'primitive
science' to satisfy human *unconscious* organismal
longings; and modern science may be considered 'up-
to-date religion', to satisfy *consciously* the same
human feelings. If we are supposed not to separate
elementalistically 'emotion' and 'intellect', we have to
take into consideration organismal longings spread
over continents for millenniums, which find their
proper expression according to the date of the specific
human developments, at a date. Religions and sciences are both expressions of our human search for
security, and so predictability, for solace, guidance,
feelings of 'belonging', etc., culminating in self-real-
ization through a general 'consciousness of abstracting', the main aim of my work.

The progress of modern science, *including the new
science of man as a time-binder,* has been due uniquely

to the freedom of scientists to revise their *fundamental assumptions,* terminologies, undefined terms, which involve hidden assumptions, etc., underlying our reflections, a freedom prohibited in 'primitive sciences' and also in dictatorships, past and present.

As to the space-time problem of the 'beginning and the end of the world', I have 'solved' it for myself effectively by the conviction that we are not yet evolved enough and so mature enough as humans to be able to understand such problems *at this date.* In scientific practice, however, I would go on, in search for structure, asking 'why' under consciously *limited* conditions. Probably in the future this problem will be shown to be no problem, and the solution will be found in the disappearance of the problem. By now science has already solved many dilemmas which at first seemed insoluble, as exemplified, for instance, in the new quantum mechanics.

Another important point which clarifies the problem of the 'unknowable', religions, etc., is that we humans have a capacity for *inferential knowledge,* which is not based on sense data, but on inferences from observed happenings. All modern sciences on the submicroscopic, electro-colloidal, etc., levels are of this 'as if' character. In fact, inferential knowledge today leads to testing in unexpected fields, and so is very creative. Epistemologically the fundamental theories must develop in converging lines of investi-

gation, and if they do not converge it is an indication
that there are flaws in the theories, and they are revised. Inferential knowledge today in science is much
more reliable than sense data, which often deceive us.
In religions we also translate the *still unknown* into
inferentially 'known', which become creeds, but based
on primitive or prescientific assumptions. The most
primitive religion in which the savage believes, or the
more generalized and more organized religions in
which the 'man in the street' believes, represent non-
elementalistically his *inferential* 'knowledge', which
involves his 'feelings', wishes, desires, needs, fears,
and what not, as combined inseparably in living reactions with his 'intellect'.

I firmly believe that the still prevailing archaic,
split, schizophrenic orientations about ourselves,
which without a modern science of man are practically impossible to avoid, are an extremely hampering
influence to any understanding of the potentialities of
'human nature'. These outlooks, inherited from the
'childhood of humanity' and perpetuated linguisti-
cally, keep our human reactions and so our cultures
on unnecessarily low levels, from which we try to ex-
tricate ourselves through violence, murder, rioting,
and in larger expressions of mass sufferings, through
revolutions and wars. This is in sharp contrast to the
peaceful progress we have in science, where we are

free to analyze our basic assumptions, and where we use a language of appropriate structure.

I firmly believe that an adequate structure of language is fundamental for human adjustment to the silent levels of happenings, 'feelings', etc. Thus, the non-elementalistic Einstein-Minkowski *space-time,* instead of the split, elementalistic newtonian 'space' *and* 'time', revolutionized physics. The non-elementalistic *psycho-biology* of Adolf Meyer, instead of 'psychology' *and* 'biology', marks the sharp difference between humans and animals. Non-elementalistic *psycho-somatic* considerations, instead of the older 'psyche' *and* 'soma', revolutionized the whole of medicine and rescued it from being merely glorified veterinary science. Etc., etc. I give these specific examples to indicate the general practical value of structural linguistic innovations which express and convey to others our new structural outlooks.

I am deeply convinced by theoretical considerations and empirical data that the new (historically the first to my knowledge) formulation of time-binding throws enormous light on our understanding of 'human nature', and will help to formulate new perspectives for the future of time-binders. This new functional definition of humans as time-binders, not mere 'space-binders', carries very far-reaching scientific, psycho-logical, moral and ethical beneficial consequences, which often remain lasting, today verified

in many thousands of instances. It explains also how
we humans, and humans alone, were able to produce
sciences and civilizations, making us by necessity
*inter*dependent, and the builders of our own destinies.

All through history man has been groping to find
his place in the hierarchy of life, to discover, so to
say, his rôle in the 'nature of things'. To this end he
must first discover himself and his 'essential nature',
before he can fully realize himself—then perhaps our
civilizations will pass by peaceful evolutions from
their childhood to the manhood of humanity.

It is a source of deep satisfaction to me that similar notions about the circularity and self-reflexiveness
of human knowledge are taking root in our orientations as expressed by other writers. In 1942 in Mono-
graph III published by the Institute of General
Semantics, in my foreword with M. Kendig, we
wrote:

'It should be noticed that in human life self-reflexiveness
has even "material" implications, which introduce serious
difficulties. Professor Cassius J. Keyser expresses this very
aptly: "It is obvious, once the fact is pointed out, that the
character of human history, the character of human conduct,
and the character of all our human institutions depend both
upon what man *is* and in equal or greater measure upon
what we humans *think* man is." This is profoundly true.

'Professor Arthur S. Eddington describes the same problem in these words: "And yet, in regard to the nature of
things, this knowledge is only an empty shell—a form of
symbols. It is knowledge of structural form, and not knowledge of content. All through the physical world runs that
unknown content, which must surely be the stuff of our
consciousness. Here is a hint of aspects deep within the

world of physics, and yet unattainable by the methods of physics. And, moreover, we have found that where science has progressed the farthest, the mind has but regained from nature that which the mind has put into nature.

' "We have found a strange foot-print on the shores of the unknown. We have devised profound theories, one after another, to account for its origin. At last, we have succeeded in reconstructing the creature that made the foot-print. And Lo! it is our own."

'Dr. Alexis Carrel formulated the same difficulty differently, but just as aptly: "To progress again man must remake himself. And he cannot remake himself without suffering. For he is both the marble and the sculptor." '

Those self-reflexive and circular mechanisms are *the uniquely human types of reaction* which made our human achievements possible. With the new formulations, the consciousness of this special capacity with its profound implications has become generally teachable on all levels, that of uneducated people and children included, and this consciousness may now mark a new period in our evolution.

History, anthropology, and general semantics establish firmly that the enormous majority of humanity so far lived and live on the animal biological level of mere subsistence, without the opportunity to realize their potentialities. For time-binders are not merely biological organisms, but psycho-biological, and this introduces incredible complexities, which so far we did not know how to handle. The old notions about 'man' have hitherto led to a generally sick and bewildered society. We cannot be psycho-logical isolationists and try to be constructive time-binders, or we are bound to be bogged down in an asocial morass of conflicts.

The theory of time-binding and extensional methods of general semantics have been tested in many scientific, educational and managerial fields. Even on the battlefields of World War II they were applied by American physicians, officers and men in thousands of cases of 'battle fatigue', with telling results. Today the new methods are taught in many schools and universities, and there are study groups on all continents.

To conclude, I may quote from my new preface to the third edition of *Science and Sanity*: 'We *need not* blind ourselves with the old dogma that "human nature cannot be changed", for we find that it *can be changed* [if we know how]. We must begin to realize our potentialities as humans, then we may approach the future with some hope. We may feel with Galileo, as he stamped his foot on the ground after recanting the Copernican theory before the Holy Inquisition, *"Eppur si muove!"* The evolution of our human development may be retarded, but it cannot be stopped.'

Alfred Korzybski

Lakeville, Connecticut, U. S. A.
April 1949

Bibliographical Note

The time-binding theory was first propounded in my *Manhood of Humanity: The Science and Art of Human Engineering*, E. P. Dutton, New York, 1921, second edition, with additions, to be published in 1950 by International Non-aristotelian Library Publishing Company, Institute of General Semantics, Distributors. It was further elaborated in my 'Fate and Freedom', *Mathematics Teacher*, May 1923, reprinted in *The Language of Wisdom and Folly* by Irving J. Lee, Harper, New York, 1949, 'The Brotherhood of Doctrines', *The Builder*, April 1924, in my papers read before the International Mathematical Congress in Toronto in 1924, before the Washington Society for Nervous and Mental Diseases in 1925, and before the Washington Psychopathic Society in 1926, when I was studying at St. Elizabeth's Psychiatric Hospital in Washington, D.C. It culminated, after extensive studies of the mechanisms of time-binding, in *Science and Sanity: An Introduction to Non-aristotelian Systems and General Semantics,* The International Non-aristotelian Library Publishing Company, first published in 1933, second edition 1941, third edition 1948, distributed by the Institute of General Semantics. In this book, with a physico-mathematical approach, I introduced for the first time the new appropriate scientific methodology for the time-binding theory, which I called 'extensional method', with principles of essential simplicity.

A.K.

PREFACE

THIS book is primarily a study of Man and ultimately embraces all the great qualities and problems of Man. As a study of Man it takes into consideration *all* the characteristics which make Man what he
is. If some readers do note the absence of certain
expressions familiar to them, it does not mean that
the author does not feel or think as many other people—he does—and very much so; but in this book
an effort has been made to approach the problem of
Man from a scientific-mathematical point of view,
and therefore great pains have been taken *not* to
use words insufficiently defined, or words with many
meanings. The author has done his utmost to use
such words as convey only the meaning intended,
and in the case of some words, such as "spiritual,"
there has been superadded the word "so-called," not
because the author has any belief or disbelief in such
phenomena; there is no need for *beliefs* because some
such phenomena exist, no matter what we may think
of them or by what name we call them; but because
the word "spiritual" is not scientifically defined, and
every individual understands and uses this word in
a personal and private way. To be *im*personal the

author has had to indicate this element by adding "so-called." I repeat once again that this book is not a "materialistic" or a "spiritualistic" book—it is a study of "Man" and therefore does and *should* include materialistic as well as spiritual phenomena because only the complex of these phenomena constitutes the complex of Man.

The problem has not been approached from the point of view of any private doctrine or creed, but from a mathematical, an engineering, point of view, which is impersonal and passionless. It is obvious that to be able to speak about the great affairs of Man, his spiritual, moral, physical, economic, social or political status, it must first be ascertained what Man is—what is his real nature and what are the basic laws of his nature. If we succeed in finding the laws of human nature, all the rest will be a comparatively easy task—the ethical, social, economic and political status of Man should be in accord with the laws of his nature; then civilization will be a human civilization—a permanent and peaceful one—not before.

It is useless to argue if electricity be "natural" or "*super*natural," of "material" or of "spiritual" origin. As a matter of fact we do not ask these questions in studying electricity; we endeavor to find out the natural laws governing it and in handling live wires we do not argue or speculate about them—

we use rubber gloves, etc. It will be the same with
Man and the great affairs of Man—we have, first
of all, to know what Man is.

Though this book has been written with scrupu-
lous care to avoid words or terms of vague meaning—and though it often may seem coldly critical
of things metaphysical, it has not been written
with indifference to that great, perhaps the greatest,
urge of the human heart—the craving for spiritual
truth—our yearning for the higher potentialities of
that which we call "mind," "soul" and "spirit"—but
it has been written with the deep desire to find the
source of these qualities, their scientific significance
and a scientific proof of them, so that they may be
approached and studied by the best minds of the
world without the digressions, and misinterpretations that are caused by the color and the confusion
of personal emotions; and if the book be read with
care, it will be seen that, though the clarifying definition of the classes of life has been chiefly used in
the book for its great carrying power in the *practical*
world, its greatest help will ultimately be in guiding
the investigation, the right valuation and especially
the control and use of the higher human powers.

In writing this book I have been not only introducing new ideas and new methods of analysis, but
I have been using a tongue new to me. The original
manuscript was very crude and foreign in form, and

I am greatly indebted to various friends for their patient kindness in correcting the many errors of my poor English.

I am also under great obligations to Walter Polakov, Doctor of Engineering, for his exceedingly helpful suggestions, not only in giving me a thorough criticism from the point of view of the Engineer, but also in devoting his energies to organizing the first "Time-binding Club" where these problems have been discussed and criticized, with great practical results.

To all those who have read and criticized the manuscript or helped otherwise—Professors E. H. Moore, C. J. Keyser, J. H. Robinson, Burges Johnson, E. A. Ross, A. Petrunkevitch; and Doctors J. Grove-Korski, Charles P. Steinmetz, J. P. Warbasse; Robert B. Wolf, Vice-President of the American Society of Mechanical Engineers; Champlain L. Riley, Vice-President of the American Society of Heating and Ventilating Engineers; Miss Josephine Osborn; to the authors, L. Brandeis, E. G. Conklin, C. J. Keyser, J. Loeb, E. S. Mead, H. O'Higgins, W. Polakov, J. H. Robinson, R. B. Wolf, for their kind permission to quote them, I wish to express my sincere appreciation.

I wish also to acknowledge the deepest gratitude to my wife, formerly Mira Edgerly, who has found in this discovery of the natural law for the human

class of life, the solution of her life long search, and
who, because of her interest in my work, has given
me incomparably inspiring help and valuable criticism. It is not an exaggeration to state that except
for her steady and relentless work and *her time,
which saved my time,* this book could not have been
produced in such a comparatively short time.

Mr. Walter Polakov of New York City, Industrial Counsellor and Industrial Engineer in New
York City, has kindly consented at my request to act,
with my authority, as my representative to whom
any further queries should be addressed in my absence from America.

To all other friends who have helped in many personal ways I express thankfulness, as I wish also to
thank John Macrae, Esq., the Vice-President of E.
P. Dutton & Co., for his unusual attitude toward
publishing the book.

A. K.

*January 17, 1921
New York City.*

ACKNOWLEDGMENT

The author and the publishers acknowledge with gratitude the following permissions to make use of copyright material in this work:

Messrs. D. C. Heath & Company, for permission to quote from "Unified Mathematics," by Louis C. Karpinski, Harry Y. Benedict and John W. Calhoun.

Messrs. G. P. Putnam's Sons, New York and London, for permission to quote from "Organism as a Whole" and "Physiology of the Brain," by Jacques Loeb.

Messrs. Harper & Brothers, for permission to quote from "From the Life, Imaginary Portraits of Some Distinguished Americans," by Harvey O'Higgins.

Messrs. D. Appleton & Company, for permission to quote from "Corporation Finance," by E. S. Mead.

Messrs. J. B. Lippincott Company, for permission to quote from "Forced Movements," by Jacques Loeb.

Princeton University Press, for permission to quote from "Heredity and Environment," by Edwin Grant Conklin.

Columbia University Press, for permission to quote from "The Human Worth of Rigorous Thinking," by C. J. Keyser.

The Rockefeller Institute for Medical Research, for permission to quote from *The Journal of Experimental Medicine,* Vol. 27.

The New School for Social Research, for permission to quote from "An Outline of the History of the Western European Mind," by James Harvey Robinson.

The Engineering Magazine Company, for permission to quote from "Mastering Power Production," by Walter N. Polakov.

CHAPTER I

INTRODUCTION

METHOD AND PROCESSES OF APPROACH TO A NEW CONCEPT OF LIFE

"For a while he trampled with impunity on laws human and divine but, as he was obsessed with the delusion that two and two makes five, he fell, at last a victim to the relentless rules of humble Arithmetic.

"Remember, O stranger, Arithmetic is the first of the sciences and the mother of safety."

BRANDEIS.

IT is the aim of this little book to point the way to a new science and art—the science and art of Human Engineering. By Human Engineering I mean the science and art of directing the energies and capacities of human beings to the advancement of human weal. It need not be argued in these times that the establishment of such a science—the science of human welfare—is an undertaking of immeasurable importance. No one can fail to see that its importance is supreme.

It is evident that, if such a science is to be established it must be founded on ascertained facts—it must accord with what is *characteristic* of Man—it must be based upon a just conception of what Man is—upon a right understanding of Man's place in the scheme of Nature.

No one need be told how indispensable it is to have true ideas—just concepts—correct notions—of the things with which we humans have to deal; everyone knows for example, that to mistake solids for surfaces or lines would wreck the science and art of geometry; anyone knows that to confuse fractions with whole numbers would wreck the science and art of arithmetic; everyone knows that to mistake vice for virtue would destroy the foundation of ethics; everyone knows that to mistake a desert mirage for a lake of fresh water does but lure the fainting traveler to dire disappointment or death. Now, it is perfectly clear that of all the things with which human beings have to deal, the most important by far is Man himself—humankind—men, women and children. It follows that for us human beings nothing else can be quite so important as a clear, true, just, scientific concept of Man—a right understanding of what we as human beings really are. For it requires no great wisdom, it needs only a little reflection, to see that, if we humans radically misconceive the nature of man—if we regard man as being something which he is not, whether it be something higher than man or lower—we thereby commit an error so fundamental and far reaching as to produce

every manner of confusion and disaster in individual
life, in community life and in the life of the race.

The question we have, therefore, to consider first
of all is fundamentally: What is Man? What is a
man? What is a human being? What is the defining or characteristic mark of humanity? To this
question two answers and only two have been given
in the course of the ages, and they are both of them
current to-day. One of the answers is biological—
man is an animal, a certain kind of animal; the other
answer is a mixture partly biological and partly
mythological or partly biological and partly philosophical—man is a combination or *union* of animal
with something supernatural. An important part of
my task will be to show that both of these answers
are radically wrong and that, beyond all things else,
they are primarily responsible for what is dismal in
the life and history of humankind. This done, the
question remains: What is Man? I hope to show
clearly and convincingly that the answer is to be found
in the patent fact that human beings possess in varying
degrees a certain natural faculty or power or capacity
which serves at once to give them their appropriate
dignity as human beings and to discriminate them,
not only from the minerals and the plants but also
from the world of animals, this peculiar or characteristic human faculty or power or capacity I shall

call the *time-binding* faculty or *time-binding* power or *time-binding* capacity. What I mean by time-binding will be clearly and fully explained in the course of the discussion, and when it has been made clear, the question—What Is Man?—will be answered by saying that man is a being naturally endowed with time-binding capacity—that a human being is a time-binder—that men, women and children constitute the time-binding class of life.

There will then remain the great task of indicating and in a measure sketching some of the important ways in which the true conception of man as man will transform our views of human society and the world, affect our human conduct and give us a growing body of scientific wisdom regarding the welfare of mankind including all posterity.

The purpose of this introductory chapter is to consider certain general matters of a preliminary nature—to indicate the spirit of the undertaking—to provide a short course of approach and preparation—to clear the deck, so to speak, and make ready for action.

There are two ways to slide easily through life: Namely, to believe everything, or to doubt everything; both ways save us from thinking. The majority take the line of least resistance, preferring to have their thinking done for them; they accept ready-made individual, private doctrines as their own and follow them more or less blindly. Every generation looks upon its own creeds as true and permanent and has a mingled smile of pity and contempt for the prejudices of the past. For two hundred or more generations of our historical past this attitude has been repeated two hundred or more times, and unless we are very careful our children will have the same attitude toward us.

There can be no doubt that humanity belongs to a class of life which to a large extent determines its own destinies, establishes its own rules of education and conduct, and thus influences every step we are free to take within the structure of our social system. But the power of human beings to determine their own destinies is limited by natural law, Nature's law. It is the counsel of wisdom to discover the laws of nature, including the laws of human nature, and then to live in accordance with them. The opposite is folly.

A farmer must know the natural laws that govern his wheat, or corn, or cow, as otherwise he will not have satisfactory crops, or the quality and abundance of milk he desires, whereas the knowledge of these laws enables him to produce the most favorable conditions for his plants and animals, and thereby to gain the desired results.

Humanity must know the natural laws for humans, otherwise humans will not create the conditions and the customs that regulate human activities which will make it possible for them to have the most favorable circumstances for the fullest human development in life; which means the release of the maximum natural-creative energy and expression in mental, moral, material and spiritual and all the other great fields of human activities, resulting in happiness in life and in work—collectively and individually—because the conditions of the earning of a livelihood influence and shape all our mental processes and activities, the quality and the form of human inter-relationship.

Every human achievement, be it a scientific discovery, a picture, a statue, a temple, a home or a bridge, has to be conceived in the mind first—the plan thought out—before it can be made a reality, and when anything is to be attempted that involves any number of individuals—methods of coordination have to be considered—the methods which have proven to be the best suited for such undertakings are engineering methods—the engineering of *an idea* toward a complete *realization*. Every engineer has to know the materials with which he has to work and the natural laws of these materials, as discovered by observation and experiment and formulated by mathematics and mechanics; else he can not calculate the forces at his disposal; he can not compute the resistance of his materials; he can not determine the capacity and requirements of his power plant; in short, he can not make the most profitable use of his resources. Lately in all industries and particularly during the late World War, which was itself a gigantic industrial process, another factor manifested itself and proved to be of the utmost importance: namely, the human factor, which is not material but is mental, moral, psychological. It has been found that maximum production may be attained when and only when the production is carried on in conformity with certain psychological laws, roughly determined by the analysis of human nature.

Except for productive human labor, our globe is too small to support the human population now upon it. Humanity must produce or perish.

Production is essentially a task for engineers; it essentially depends upon the discovery and the application of natural laws, including the laws of human nature. It is, therefore, not a task for old fashioned philosophical speculation nor for barren metaphysical reasoning *in vacuo;* it is a scientific task and involves the coordination and cooperation of all the sciences. This is why it is an engineering task.

For engineering, rightly understood, is the coordinated sum-total of human knowledge gathered through the ages, with mathematics as its chief instrument and guide. Human Engineering will embody the theory and practice—the science and art—of all engineering branches united by a common aim—the understanding and welfare of mankind.

Here I want to make it very clear that mathematics is not what many people think it is; it is not a system of mere formulas and theorems; but as beautifully defined by Professor Cassius J. Keyser, in his book *The Human Worth of Rigorous Thinking* (Columbia University Press, 1916), mathematics is the science of "Exact thought or rigorous thinking," and one of its distinctive characteristics is "precision, sharpness, completeness of definitions." This quality alone is sufficient to explain why people generally do not like mathematics and why even some scientists bluntly refuse to have anything to do with problems wherein mathematical reasoning is involved. In the meantime, mathematical philosophy has very little, if anything, to do with mere calculations or with numbers as such or with formulas; it is a philosophy wherein precise, sharp and rigorous thinking is essential. Those who deliberately refuse to think "rigorously"—that is mathematically—in connections where such thinking is possible, commit the sin of preferring the worse to the better; they deliberately violate the supreme law of intellectual rectitude.

Here I have to make it clear that for the purpose of Human Engineering the old concepts of matter, space and time are sufficient to start with; they are sufficient in much the same way as they have been sufficient in the old science of mechanics. Figuratively speaking Human Engineering is a higher order of bridge engineering—it aims at the spanning of a gap in practical life as well as in knowledge. The old meanings of matter, space and time were good enough to prevent the collapse of a bridge; the same understanding of space and time as used in this book will protect society and humanity from periodical collapses. The old mechanics lead directly to such a knowledge of the intrinsic laws governing the universe as to suggest the new mechanics. Human Engineering will throw a new light on many old conceptions and will help the study and understanding of matter, space and time in their relative meanings, and perhaps will ultimately lead to an understanding of their absolute meanings.

Philosophy in its old form could exist only in the absence of engineering, but with engineering in existence and daily more active and far reaching, the old verbalistic philosophy and metaphysics have lost their reason to exist. They were no more able to understand the "production" of the universe and life than they are now able to understand or grapple with "production" as a means to provide a happier existence for humanity. They failed because their venerated method of "speculation" can not *produce,* and its place must be taken by mathematical thinking. Mathematical reasoning is displacing meta-physical reasoning. Engineering is driving verbal-istic philosophy out of existence and humanity gains decidedly thereby. Only a few parasites and "spec-ulators" will mourn the disappearance of their old companion "speculation." The world of producers —the predominating majority of human beings— will welcome a philosophy of ordered thought and production.

The scientists, all of them, have their duties no doubt, but they do not fully use their education if they do not try to broaden their sense of responsi-bility toward all mankind instead of closing them-selves up in a narrow specialization where they find their pleasure. Neither engineers nor other scientific men have any right to prefer their own personal peace to the happiness of mankind; their place and their duty are in the front line of struggling human-ity, not in the unperturbed ranks of those who keep themselves aloof from life. If they are indifferent, or discouraged because they feel or think that they know that the situation is hopeless, it may be proved that undue pessimism is as dangerous a "religion" as any other blind creed. Indeed there is very little difference in kind between the medieval fanaticism of the "holy inquisition," and modern intolerance toward new ideas. All kinds of intellect must get together, for as long as we presuppose the situation to be hopeless, the situation will indeed be hopeless. The spirit of Human Engineering does not know the word "hopeless"; for engineers know that wrong methods are alone responsible for disastrous results, and that every situation can be successfully handled by the use of proper means. The task of engineering science is not only to know but to know how. Most of the scientists and engineers do not yet realize that their united judgment would be invincible; no system or class would care to disregard it. Their knowledge is the very force which makes the life of humanity pulsate. If the scientists and the engineers have had no common base upon which to unite, a common base must be provided. To-day the pressure of life is such that we cannot go forward without their coordinating guidance. But first there must be the desire to act. One aim of this book is to furnish the required stimulus by showing that Human Engineering will rescue us from the tangle of private opinions and enable us to deal with all the problems of life and human society upon a scientific basis.

If those who know why and how neglect to act, those who do not know will act, and the world will continue to flounder. The whole history of mankind and especially the present plight of the world show only too sadly how dangerous and expensive it is to have the world governed by those who do not know.

In paying the price of this war, we have been made

to realize that even the private individual can not afford to live wrapped up in his own life and not take his part in public affairs. He must acquire the habit of taking his share of public responsibility. This signifies that a very great deal of very simple work, all pointing in the direction of a greater work, must be done in the way of educating, not engineers and scientific men only, but the general public to co-operate in establishing the practice of Human Engineering in all the affairs of human society and life.

In writing this book I have had to wrestle with tremendous difficulties in expressing new thoughts and in indicating new methods. The reader who stops to criticize words or expressions because of their more or less happy or unhappy use will miss the whole point of the work. The reading of it should be done with a view to seeing how much can be found in it of what is new and good that may be elaborated further, and put into better form. This new enterprise is too difficult and too vast for the unaided labor of one man—life is too short.

The method used in this book in analysing life phenomena is essentially an engineering method, and as physics and mechanics always suggest to mathematicians new fields for analysis, it is not improbable that Human Engineering will give mathematicians new and interesting fields for research. The humblest rôle of mathematicians in Human Engineering may be likened to that of "Public accountants" who put *in order* the affairs of business.

In relation to mathematics Bertrand Russell has said: "Logic is the youth of mathematics, mathematics is the manhood of logic." This brilliant *mot* of the eminent philosopher of mathematics is no doubt just and is profoundly significant; the least it can teach us is that it is useless to try to find a dividing line between logic and mathematics, for no such line exists; to seek for one serves merely to betray one's ignorance of mathematical philosophy. Elsewhere Mr. Russell says: "The hope of satisfaction to our more human desires, the hope of demonstrating that the world has this or that ethical characteristic, is not one which, so far as I can see, philosophy can do anything whatever to satisfy." By "philosophy" he means mathematical philosophy—a philosophy that is rigorously scientific, not vaguely speculative. I am entirely unable to agree with him that such a philosophy can make no contribution to ethics. On the contrary, I contend, and in this book I hope to show, that by mathematical philosophy, by rigorously scientific thinking, we can arrive at the true conception of what a human being really is and that in thus discovering the characteristic nature of man we come to the secret and source of ethics. Ethics as a science will investigate and explain the essential nature of man and the obligations which the essential nature of man imposes upon human beings. It will be seen that to live righteously, to live ethically, is to live in accordance with the laws of human nature; and when it is clearly seen that man is a natural being, a part of nature literally, then it will be seen that the laws of human nature—the only possible rules for ethical conduct—are no more *super*natural and no more *man*-made than is the law of gravitation, for example, or any other natural law.

It is no cause for wonder that mathematical thinking should lead to such a result; for Man is a *natural* being, man's mind is a *natural agency,* and the results of rigorous thinking, far from being artificial fictions, are natural facts—natural revelations of natural law.

I hope I have not given the impression, by repeated allusion to mathematical science, that this book is to be in any technical sense a mathematical treatise. I have merely wished to indicate that the task is conceived and undertaken in the mathematical spirit, which must be the guiding spirit of Human Engineering; for no thought, if it be non-mathematical in spirit, can be trusted, and, although mathematicians sometimes make mistakes, the spirit of mathematics is always right and always sound.

Whilst I do not intend to trouble the reader with any highly technical mathematical arguments, there are a few simple mathematical considerations which anyone of fair education can understand, which are of exceedingly great importance for our purpose, and to which, therefore, I ask the reader's best attention. One of the ideas is that of an *arithmetical progression;* another one is that of a *geometrical progression.* Neither of them involves anything more difficult than the most ordinary arithmetic of the secondary school or the counting house, but it will be seen that they throw a flood of light upon many of the most important human concerns.

Because we are human beings we are all of us interested in what we call progress—progress in law, in government, in jurisprudence, in ethics, in philosophy, in the natural sciences, in economics, in the fine arts, in the practical arts, in the production and distribution of wealth, in all the affairs affecting the welfare of mankind. It is a fact that all these great matters are interdependent and interlocking; it is therefore a fact of the utmost importance that progress in each of the cardinal matters must keep abreast of progress in the other cardinal matters in order to keep a just equilibrium, a proper balance, and so to maintain the integrity and continued prosperity of the whole complex body of our social life; it is a fact, a fact of observation, that in some of the great matters progress proceeds in accordance with one law and one rate of advancement and in others in accordance with a very different law and rate; it is

a fact, a fact of observation and sad experience, a
fact attested by all history and made evident by reason, that owing to the widely differing laws and rates
of progress in the great essential concerns of humanity, the balance and equilibrium among the parts is
disturbed, the strain gradually increases until a violent break ensues in the form of social conflicts,
insurrections, revolutions and war; it is a fact that
the readjustment that follows, as after an earthquake, does indeed establish a kind of new equilibrium, but it is an equilibrium born of violence, and
it is destined to be again disturbed periodically without end, unless by some science and art of Human
Engineering progress in all the great matters essential to human weal can be made to proceed in accordance with one and the same law having its validity
in the nature of man.

Taken in combination, the facts just stated are so
extremely important that they deserve to be stated
with the utmost emphasis and clarity. To this end
I beg the reader to consider very carefully and side
by side the two following series of numbers. The
first one is a simple geometrical progression—
denoted by (GP); the second one is a simple arithmetical progresson—denoted by (AP):

GP : 2, 4, 8, 16, 32, 64, 128, 256, 512, 1024, etc.;

AP : 2, 4, 6, 8, 10, 12, 14, 16, 18, 20, etc.

For convenience of comparison I let them begin
with the same number and for simplicity I have
taken 2 for this initial term; observe that in the
(GP) each term is got from the preceding term by
multiplying by 2 and that in the (AP) each term
is got from its predecessor by adding 2; in the first
series the multiplier 2 is called the common *ratio* and
in the second series the repeatedly added 2 is called
the common *difference;* it is again for the convenience
of comparison that I have chosen the same number
for both common ratio and common difference and
for the sake of simplicity that I have taken for this
number the easy number 2. Other choices would
be logically just as good.

Why have I introduced these two series? Because
they serve to illustrate perfectly two widely different
laws of progress—two laws representing vastly different *rates* of growth, increase, or *advancement.*

Do not fail to observe in this connection the following two facts. One of them is that the magnitude of the terms of any geometric progression whose
ratio (no matter how small) is 2 or more will over-
take and surpass the magnitude of the corresponding terms of any arithmetical progression, no matter
how large the common difference of the latter may
be. The other fact to be noted is that the greater
the ratio of a geometric progression, the more
rapidly do its successive terms increase; so that the

terms of one geometric progression may increase a thousand or a million or a billion times faster than the corresponding terms of another geometric progression. As any geometric progression (of ratio equal to 2 or more), no matter how slow, outruns every arithmetic progression, no matter how fast, so one geometric progression may be far swifter than another one of the same type.

To every one it will be obvious that the two progressions differ in pace; and that the difference between their corresponding terms becomes increasingly larger and larger the farther we go; for instance, the sum of the first six terms of the geometrical progression is 126, whereas the sum of the first six terms of the arithmetical progression is only 42, the difference between the two sums being 84; the sum of 8 terms is 510 for the (GP) and 72 for the (AP), the difference between these sums (of only 8 terms each) being 438, already much larger than before; if now we take the sums of the first 10 terms, they will be 2046 and 110 having a difference of 1936; etc., etc.

Consider now any two matters of great importance for human weal—jurisprudence for example, and natural science—or any other two major concerns of humanity. It is as plain as the noon-day sun that, if progress in one of the matters advances according to the law of a geometric progression and

the other in accordance with a law of an arithmetical
progression, progress in the former matter will very
quickly and ever more and more rapidly outstrip
progress in the latter, so that, if the two interests
involved be interdependent (as they always are), a
strain is gradually produced in human affairs, social
equilibrium is at length destroyed; there follows a
period of readjustment by means of violence and
force. It must not be fancied that the case supposed
is merely hypothetical. The whole history of mankind and especially the present condition of the world
unite in showing that far from being merely hypothetical, the case supposed has always been actual and is
actual to-day on a vaster scale than ever before. My
contention is that while progress in some of the great
matters of human concern has been long proceeding
in accordance with the law of a rapidly increasing
geometric progression, progress in the other matters
of no less importance has advanced only at the rate
of an arithmetical progression or at best at the rate
of some geometric progression of relatively slow
growth. To see it and to understand it we have to
pay the small price of a little observation and a little
meditation.

Some technological invention is made, like that of
a steam engine or a printing press, for example; or
some discovery of scientific method, like that of
analytical geometry or the infinitesimal calculus; or

some discovery of natural law, like that of falling
bodies or the Newtonian law of gravitation. What
happens? What is the effect upon the progress of
knowledge and invention? The effect is stimulation.
Each invention leads to new inventions and each discovery to new discoveries; invention breeds invention, science begets science, the children of knowledge
produce their kind in larger and larger families; the
process goes on from decade to decade, from generation to generation, and the spectacle we behold is that
of advancement in scientific knowledge and technological power according to the law and rate of a
rapidly increasing geometric progression or logarithmic function.

And now what must we say of the so-called sciences—the pseudo sciences—of ethics and jurisprudence and economics and politics and government?
For the answer we have only to open our eyes and
behold the world. By virtue of the advancement
that has long been going on with ever accelerated
logarithmic rapidity in invention, in mathematics, in
physics, in chemistry, in biology, in astronomy and
in applications of them, time and space and matter
have been already conquered to such an extent that
our globe, once so seemingly vast, has virtually
shrunken to the dimensions of an ancient province;
and manifold peoples of divers tongues and traditions and customs and institutions are now con-

strained to live together as in a single community.
There is thus demanded a new ethical wisdom, a
new legal wisdom, a new economical wisdom, a new
political wisdom, a new wisdom in the affairs of government. For the new visions our anguished times
cry aloud but the only answers are reverberated
echoes of the wailing cry mingled with the chattering
voices of excited public men who know not what to
do. Why? What is the explanation? The question is double: Why the disease? And why no remedy at hand? The answer is the same for both. And
the answer is that the so-called sciences of ethics and
jurisprudence and economics and politics and government have not kept pace with the rapid progress
made in the other great affairs of man; they have
lagged behind; it is because of their lagging that the
world has come to be in so great distress; and it is
because of their lagging that they have not now
the needed wisdom to effect a cure.

Do you ask why it is that the "social" sciences—
the so-called sciences of ethics, etc.—have lagged
behind? The answer is not far to seek nor difficult
to understand. They have lagged behind, partly
because they have been hampered by the traditions
and the habits of a bygone world—they have looked
backward instead of forward; they have lagged behind, partly because they have depended upon the
barren methods of verbalistic philosophy — they

have been metaphysical instead of scientific; they
have lagged behind, partly because they have been
often dominated by the lusts of cunning "politicians"
instead of being led by the wisdom of enlightened
statesmen; they have lagged behind, partly because
they have been predominantly concerned to protect
"vested interests," upon which they have in the main
depended for support; the *fundamental* cause, however, of their lagging behind is found in the astonishing fact that, despite their being by their very
nature most *immediately* concerned with the affairs
of mankind, they have not discovered what Man
really is but have from time immemorial falsely regarded human beings either as animals or else as
combinations of animals and something supernatural.
With these two monstrous conceptions of the essential nature of man I shall deal at a later stage of this
writing.

At present I am chiefly concerned to drive home
the fact that it is the great *disparity* between the
rapid progress of the natural and technological
sciences on the one hand and the slow progress of
the metaphysical, so-called social "sciences" on the
other hand, that sooner or later so disturbs the
equilibrium of human affairs as to result periodically
in those social cataclysms which we call insurrections, revolutions and wars. The reader should note
carefully that such cataclysmic changes—such
"jumps," as we may call them—such violent read-

justments in human affairs and human relationships
—are recorded throughout the history of mankind.
And I would have him see clearly that, because the
disparity which produces them increases as we pass
from generation to generation—from term to term
of our progressions—the "jumps" in question occur
not only with increasing violence but with increasing
frequency.   This highly significant fact may be
graphically illustrated in the following figure:

Geometric evolution of the natural and technological sciences.
—Peaceful progress.

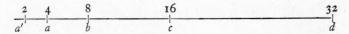

Arithmetical evolution of the so-called social "sciences,"
accelerated by violent "jumps."—Non-peaceful social progress.

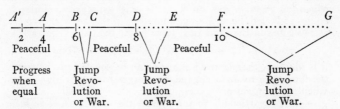

$a'2$, $2a$, ab, bc, cd, represent the geometrical law
of progression in the natural and technological
sciences (peaceful evolution).

$A'2$, $2A$, AB, CD, EF, represent the lagging
arithmetical law of progression in the so-called social
sciences (peaceful evolution).

Both of these during the same periods of time.

BC, DE, FG, represent revolutions or wars, with the aftermath of revolution of ideas—the "jump"—violent readjustment of ideas to facts—forced by events.

ab, bc, cd, and *AB, CD, EF,* take the same amount of time, but the second progression being much slower than the first one, the "jumps" or revolutions occur at shorter intervals as time goes on and thus more frequently force us to coordinate our ideas to facts. Periods of peace or seeming peace alternate more and more frequently with periods of violence; the mentioned *disparity* of progress in peaceful times is the hatching seed of future violence.*

* To digress a bit, it may be interesting to add, that population and the need of people increase in a geometrical progression; and also that the growth of individuals is limited by the fact, that they have to absorb their food through surfaces which as growth goes on increase only as *squares*, while the bodies to be fed, being volumes, increase in size as *cubes* increase, as the cubes of the same base grow faster than the squares,

$$2^2 = 4, \quad 2^3 = 8, \quad 3^2 = 9, \quad 3^3 = 27, \quad \text{and so on,}$$

it is obvious, that in the infancy of an organism only a part of the food goes to maintain life, the larger part goes for growth; when the organism becomes larger, the absorbing surfaces growing proportionally to the square, the food is spent to build the mass of the volume of the body and is spent proportionally to the cube. Suppose our organism has grown to a size twice as large, its absorbing capacity has become four times larger, its volume eight times larger. In case of 3 times, the difference will be 9 and 27. It is obvious that at some point, all the absorbed food will be used to maintain life and none will be left for growth, and this last process will stop. This is another example which explains how the theory of dimensions is vitally important in life and shows why it is absolutely essential to take account of dimensions in the study of life problems.

As a matter of fact these few mathematical considerations can hardly be called mathematics or mathematical philosophy; nevertheless, without bringing attention to these very simple mathematical ideas we should not be able to proceed any further than in the past. Our life problems have always been "solved" by verbalists and rhetorical metaphysicians who cleverly played with vague words and who always ignored the supremely important matter of dimensions because they were ignorant of it. There was no possible way to arrive at an agreement on the significance of words, or even the understanding of them. Let us take, for instance, such words as "good" or "bad" or "truth"; volumes upon volumes have been written about them; no one has reached any result universally acceptable; the effect has been to multiply warring schools of philosophy—sectarians and partisans. In the meantime *something* corresponding to each of the terms "good," "bad," "truth" exists as matter of fact; but what that something is still awaits scientific determination. If only these three words could be scientifically defined, philosophy, law, ethics and psychology would cease to be "private theories" or verbalism and they would advance to the rank and dignity of sciences.

Here I may quote a characteristic of life as expressed by one of the "heroes" of my esteemed friend Harvey O'Higgins, in his book, *From the*

Life, Imaginary Portraits of Some Distinguished Americans (Harper, N. Y.).

"Warren never philosophized; he handled facts as an artisan handles his tools; but if he *had* philosophized, his theory of life would probably have been something like this: 'There is no justice, there is no morality, in nature or in natural laws; justice and morality are laws only of human society. But society, natural life, and all civilization are subject in their larger aspects to natural laws—which contradict morality and outrage justice—and the statesman has to move with those laws and direct his people in accordance with them, despite the lesser by-laws of morality and justice.'"

If such are the creeds of "distinguished people" anywhere, what better can we expect than that which we see in the history of humanity?

But the fact that the old philosophy, law, ethics, psychology, politics and sociology could not solve the practical problems of humanity, is not any reason whatsoever why we should despair. The problems can be solved.

To follow the reasoning of this book, it is not necessary to be a highly trained specialist; the only qualifications required are candor, an open mind, freedom from blinding prejudice, thoughtfulness, a real desire for truth, and enough common sense to understand that to talk of adding three quarts of milk to three-quarters of a mile is to talk nonsense.

CHAPTER II

CHILDHOOD OF HUMANITY

THE conclusion of the World War is the closing of the period of the childhood of humanity. This childhood, as any childhood, can be characterized as devoid of any real understanding of values, as is that of a child who uses a priceless chronometer to crack nuts.

This childhood has been unduly long, but happily we are near to the end of it, for humanity, shaken by this war, is coming to its senses and must soon enter its manhood, a period of great achievements and rewards in the new and real sense of values dawning upon us.

The sacred dead will not have died for naught; the "red wine of youth," the wanton waste of life, has shown us the price of life, and we will have to keep our oath to make the future worthy of their sweat and blood.

Early ideas are not necessarily true ideas.

There are different kinds of interpretations of history and different schools of philosophy. All of them have contributed something to human progress, but none of them has been able to give the world a

basic philosophy embracing the whole progress of
science and establishing the life of man upon the
abiding foundation of Fact.

Our life is bound to develop according to evident
or else concealed laws of nature. The evident laws
of nature were the inspiration of genuine science in
its cradle; and their interpretations or misinterpretations have from the earliest times formed systems
of law, of ethics, and of philosophy.

Human intellect, be it that of an individual or
that of the race, forms conclusions which have to be
often revised before they correspond approximately
to facts. What we call progress consists in coordinating ideas with realities. The World War has
taught something to everybody. It was indeed a
great reality; it accustomed us to think in terms of
reality and not in those of phantom speculation.
Some unmistakable truths were revealed. Facts and
force were the things that counted. Power had to
be produced to destroy hostile power; it was found
that the old political and economic systems were not
adequate to the task put upon them. The world had
to create new economic conditions; it was obliged
to supplement the old systems with special boards
for food, coal, railroads, shipping, labor, etc. The
World War emergency compelled the nations to or-
ganize for producing greater power in order to conquer power already great.

If there is anything which this war has proved, it is the fact that the most important asset a nation or an individual can have, is the ability "to do things."

"In Flanders Fields the poppies blow . . .," that is too true; they blow and they are strong and red. But the purpose of this writing is not the celebration of poetry, but the elucidation and right use of facts.

Normally, thousands of rabbits and guinea pigs are used and killed, in scientific laboratories, for experiments which yield great and tangible benefits to humanity. This war butchered millions of people and ruined the health and lives of tens of millions. Is this climax of the pre-war civilization to be passed unnoticed, except for the poetry and the manuring of the battle fields, that the "poppies blow" stronger and better fed? Or is the death of ten men on the battle field to be of as much worth in knowledge gained as is the life of one rabbit killed for experiment? Is the great sacrifice worth analysing? There can be only one answer—yes. But, if truth be desired, the analysis must be scientific.

In science, "opinions" are tolerated when and only when facts are lacking. In this case, we have all the facts necessary. We have only to collect them and analyse them, rejecting mere "opinions" as cheap and unworthy. Such as understand this lesson will know how to act for the benefit of all.

At present the future of mankind is dark. "Stop, look, and listen"—the prudent caution at railroad crossings—must be amended to read "stop, look, listen, and THINK"; not for the saving of a few lives in railroad accidents, but for the preservation of the life of humanity. Living organisms, of the lower and simpler types, in which the differentiation and the integration of the vital organs have not been carried far, can move about for a considerable time after being deprived of the appliances by which the life force is accumulated and transferred, but higher organisms are instantly killed by the removal of such appliances, or even by the injury of minor parts of them; even more easily destroyed are the more advanced and complicated *social* organizations.

The first question is: what are to be the scientific methods that will eliminate diverse opinions and creeds from an analysis of facts and ensure correct deductions based upon them? A short survey of facts concerning civilization will help to point the way.

Humanity, in its cradle, did not have science; it had only the faculties of observation and speculation. In the early days there was much speculative thinking, but it was without any sufficient basis of facts. Theology and philosophy flourished; their speculations were often very clever, but all their primitive notions about facts—such as the structure of the heavens, the form of the earth, mechanical principles, meteorological or physiological phenomena—were almost all of them wrong.

What is history? What is its significance for humanity? Dr. J. H. Robinson gives us a precise answer: "Man's abject dependence on the past gives rise to the continuity of history. Our convictions, opinions, prejudices, intellectual tastes; our knowledge, our methods of learning and of applying for information we owe, with slight exceptions, to the past—often to the remote past. History is an expansion of memory, and like memory it alone can explain the present and in this lies its most unmistakable value." *

The savage regards every striking phenomenon or group of phenomena as caused by some personal agent, and from remotest antiquity the mode of thinking has changed only as fast as the relations among phenomena have been established.†

---

* *An Outline of the History of the Western European Mind*, by James Harvey Robinson. The New School for Social Research, New York, 1919. This little volume gives condensed statements, as in a nutshell, of the historical developments of the human mind and contains a long list of the most substantial modern books on historical questions. All the further historical quotations will be taken from this exceptionally valuable little book, and for convenience they will simply be marked by his initials—J. H. R.

† (J. H. R.) "Late appearance of a definite theory of progress. Excessive conservatism of primitive peoples. The Greeks speculated on the origin of things, but they did not have a conception of the possibility of indefinite progress . . . Progress

Human nature was always asking "why"? and not
being able to answer why, they found their answer

of man from the earliest time till the opening of the 17th century
almost altogether unconscious. . . . Fundamental weakness of
Hellenic learning. It was an imposing collection of speculation,
opinions, and guesses, which, however brilliant and ingenious
they might be, were based on a very slight body of exact knowledge, and failed to recognize the fundamental necessity of
painful scientific research, aided by apparatus. There was no
steady accumulation of knowledge to offset the growing emotional distrust of reason. . . . Unfulfilled promise of Hellenistic
science. Influence of slavery in checking the development of
science. . . . The deficiencies of Medieval culture. All the
weaknesses of the Hellenic reasoning, combined with those of
the Christian Fathers, underlay what appeared to be a most
logically elaborated and definitive system of thought. Defects
of the university education. . . . Little history of Natural
science, in our sense of the word, taught in the universities. . . .
Copernicus, 'De Revolutionibus Orbium Coelestium.' Libri
VI, 1543. . . . Copernicus' own introduction acknowledges
his debt to ancient philosophers. Still believed in fixed Starry
Sphere. His discovery had little immediate effect on prevailing notions. Giordano Bruno (1548–1600) made it his chief
business to think out and set forth in Latin and Italian the
implications of the discovery of Copernicus. . . . Bruno burned
by the Inquisition at Rome. . . . Keppler (1571–1630) and
his discovery of the elliptical orbits of the planets. Galileo
(1564–1642). His telescope speedily improved so as to magnify
32 diameters. His attitude toward the Copernican theory,
which was condemned by Roman Inquisition 1616. . . .
Galileo's chief discoveries were in physics and mechanics.
Isaac Newton (1642–1727) proved that the laws of falling
bodies apply to the heavens. This made a deep impression
and finally the newer conceptions of the universe began to be
popularized. . . . Lord Bacon (1561–1626), the 'Buccinator'
of experimental and applied modern science. . . . His lively
appreciation of the existing obstacles to scientific advance; the
idols of the tribe, cave, market-place, and theatre. . . . Necessity of escaping from the scholastic methods of 'tumbling up
and down in our reasons and conceits,' and studying the world
about us. Undreamed of achievements possible if only the
right method of research be followed . . . the distrust of

through another factor "who." The unknown was called, Gods or God. But with the progress of science the "why" became more and more evident, and the question came to be "how." From the early days of humanity, dogmatic theology, law, ethics, and science in its infancy, were the monopolies of one class and the source of their power.*

ancient authority. . . . Descartes (1596–1650), . . . he proposed to reach the truth through analysis and clear ideas, on the assumption that God will not deceive. . . . His fundamental interest in mathematics. . . . His claim to originality and his rejection of all authority. . . . Obstacles to scientific advance; the universities still dominated by Aristotle; the theological faculties; the censorship of the press exercised by both church and state; . . ."

* (J. H. R.) "Phases of religious complex. 'Religious,' a vague and comprehensive term applied to: (1) certain classes of emotions (awe, dependence, self-distrust, aspirations, etc.); (2) Conduct, which may take the form of distinctive religious acts (ceremonies, sacrifices, prayers, 'good works') or the observance of what in primitive conditions are recognized as 'taboos'; (3) Priestly, or ecclesiastical organizations; (4) Beliefs about supernatural beings and man's relations to them: the latter may take the form of revelation and be reduced to creeds and become the subject of elaborate theological speculations.

"Association of religion with the supernatural; religion has always had for its primary object the attainment of a satisfactory adjustment to, or a successful control over, the supernatural. . . . The cultural mind viewed as the product of a long and hazardous process of accumulation. . . . Spontaneous generation of superstitions. Prevalence of symbolism, mana, animism, magic, fetishism, totemism; the taboo (cf. our modern idea of 'principle'), the sacred, clean and unclean; 'dream logic'— spontaneous rationalizing or 'jumping at conclusions'; . . . The 16th book of the Theodosian Code contains edicts relating to the Church issued by the Roman Emperors during the 4th and 5th centuries. They make it a crime to disagree with the Church; they provide harsh penalties for heretical

The first to break this power were the exact sciences. They progressed too rapidly to be bound and limited by obscure old writings and prejudices; life and realities were their domain. Science brushed aside all sophistry and became a reality. Ethics is too fundamentally important a factor in civilization to depend upon a theological or a legal excuse;

teaching and writing, and grant privileges to the orthodox clergy (exemptions from regular taxes and benefit of the clergy). . . . Christianity becomes a monopoly defended by the state. . . . Psychological power and attraction in the elaborate symbolism and ritual of the church. . . . Allegory put an end to all literary criticism. . . . Flourishing of the miraculous; any unusual or startling occurrence attributed to the intervention of either God or the Devil. . . . Older conceptions of disease as caused by the Devil. . . . Our legal expression 'act of God' confined to unforseeable natural disasters. How with a growing appreciation for natural law and a chastened taste in wonders, miracles have tended to become a source of intellectual distress and bewilderment. . . . Protestants shared with Roman Catholics the horror of 'rationalists' and 'free-thinkers.' The leaders of both parties agreed in hampering and denouncing scientific discoveries. . . . Witchcraft in its modern form emerges clearly in the 15th century. . . . Great prevalence of witchcraft during the 16th and 17th centuries in Protestant and Catholic countries, alike. . . . Trial of those suspected of sorcery. Tortures to force confession. The witches' mark. Penalties, burning alive, strangling, hanging. Tens of thousands of innocent persons perished. . . . Those who tried to discredit witchcraft denounced as 'Sadducees' and atheists. . . . The psychology of intolerance. Fear, vested interests, the comfortable nature of the traditional and the habitual. The painful appropriation of new ideas. . . . The intolerance of the Catholic Church: a natural result of its state-like organization and claims. . . . Its doctrine of exclusive salvation and its conception of heresy both sanctioned by the state. Doubt and error regarded as sinful. . . . Beginnings of censorship of the press after the invention of printing, licensing of ecclesiastical and civil authorities. . . . Protestants of 16th century accept the theory of intolerance."

ethics must conform to the *natural* laws of human *nature*.

Laws, legal ideas, date from the beginning of civilization. Legal speculation was wonderfully developed in parallel lines with theology and philosophy before the natural and exact sciences came into existence. Law was always made by the few and in general for the purpose of preserving the "existing order," or for the reestablishment of the old order and the punishment of the offenders against it.

Dogmatic theology is, by its very nature, unchangeable. The same can be said in regard to the spirit of the law. Law was and is to protect the past and present status of society and, by its very essence, must be very conservative, if not reactionary. Theology and law are both of them static by their nature.*

*(J. H. R.) "The Socio-psychological foundations of conservatism: Primitive natural reverence for the familiar and habitual greatly reenforced by religion and law. Natural conservatism of all professions. Those who suffer most from existing institutions commonly, helplessly accept the situation as inevitable. Position of the conservative; he urges the impossibility of altering 'human nature' and warns against the disasters of revolution. Conservatism in the light of history: History would seem to discredit conservatism completely as a working principle in view of the past achievements of mankind in the recent past and the possibilities which opened before us. . . . Futility of the appeal of the conservative to human nature as an obstacle to progress. . . . Culture can not be transmitted hereditarily but can be accumulated through education and modified indefinitely."

Philosophy, law and ethics, to be effective in a dynamic world must be dynamic; they must be made vital enough to keep pace with the progress of life and science. In recent civilization ethics, because controlled by theology and law, which are static, could not duly influence the dynamic, revolutionary progress of technic and the steadily changing conditions of life; and so we witness a tremendous downfall of morals in politics and business. Life progresses faster than our ideas, and so medieval ideas, methods and judgments are constantly applied to the conditions and problems of modern life. This discrepancy between facts and ideas is greatly responsible for the dividing of modern society into different warring classes, which do not understand each other. Medieval legalism and medieval morals—the basis of the old *social* structure—being by their nature conservative, reactionary, opposed to change, and thus becoming more and more unable to support the mighty social burden of the modern world, must be adjudged responsible in a large measure for the circumstances which made the World War inevitable.

Under the flash of explosives some of the workings of those antiquated ideas were exposed or crushed. The World War has profoundly changed economic conditions and made it necessary to erect new standards of values. We are forced to realize that evolution by transformation is a cosmic process and that reaction, though it may retard it, can not entirely stop it.*

The idea that organic species are results of special creation has no scientific standard whatever. There is not one fact tending to prove special or separate creation; the evidence, which is overwhelming, is all of it on the other side. The hypothesis of special creation is a mere fossil of the past. Evolution is the only theory which is in harmony with facts and with all branches of science; life is dynamic, not static.

Philosophy, as defined by Fichte, is the "science of sciences." Its aim was to solve the problems of the world. In the past, when all exact sciences were in their infancy, philosophy had to be purely speculative, with little or no regard to realities. But if

* (J. H. R.) "Formulation and establishment of the evolutionary hypothesis. Discovery of the great age of the earth; . . . gradual development of the evolutionary theory. . . . Darwin's 'Origin of the Species,' 1859. Herbert Spencer (1820–1903). . . . Haeckel (1834–1919) and others clarify, defend and popularize the new doctrine. Subsequent development of the evolutionary doctrine by Mendel, Weisman, DeVries and others. Weakening of the special creation theory by other evidence such as archeology and biblical criticism. The significance of the doctrine for intellectual history. Character of the opposition to the evolutionary theory. Popular confusion of 'Darwinism' with 'evolution.' Revolutionary effects of the new point of view. Does away with conception of fixed species (Platonic ideas) that had previously dominated speculation. The genetic method adopted in all the organic sciences, including the newer social sciences. Problem of adjusting history to the discoveries of the past 50 years. Bearing of evolution on the theory of progress. Organic evolution and social evolution."

we regard philosophy as a Mother science, divided
into many branches, we find that those branches have
grown so large and various, that the Mother science
looks like a hen with her little ducklings paddling
in a pond, far beyond her reach; she is unable to
follow her growing hatchlings. In the meantime,
the progress of life and science goes on, irrespective
of the cackling of metaphysics. Philosophy does not
fulfill her initial aim to bring the results of experimental and exact sciences together and to solve world
problems. Through endless, scientific specialization
scientific branches multiply, and for want of coordination the great world-problems suffer. This failure
of philosophy to fulfill her boasted mission of scientific coordination is responsible for the chaos in the
world of general thought. The world has no collective or organized higher ideals and aims, nor
even fixed general purposes. Life is an accidental
game of private or collective ambitions and greeds.*

---

* (J. H. R.) "The Deists and philosophers destroy the older
theological anthropology and reassert the dignity of man; the
growth of criticism and liberalism has made the analysis of
social institutions somewhat less dangerous; the general growth
of knowledge has reacted in a stimulating way upon the sciences
of society; the great increase in the number, complexity and
intensity of social problems has proved a strong incentive to
social science; The Darwinian hypothesis has rendered pre-
posterous any conception of a wholly static social system. However, the modern social sciences in our capitalistic order meet
much the same resistance from the 'vested interests' that
theological radicalism encountered in the Middle Ages and
social science has in no way approached the objectivity and

Systematic study of chemical and physical phenomena has been carried on for many generations and these two sciences now include: (1) knowledge of an enormous number of facts; (2) a large body of natural laws; (3) many fertile working hypotheses respecting the causes and regularities of natural phenomena; and finally (4) many helpful theories held subject to correction by further testing of the hypotheses gi. 'ng rise to them. When a subject is spoken of as a ⸗ience, it is understood to include all of the above mentioned parts. Facts alone do not constitute a science any more than a pile of stones constitutes a house, not even do facts and laws alone; there must be facts, hypotheses, theories and laws before the subject is entitled to the rank of a science.

The primal function of a science is to enable us to anticipate the future in the field to which it relates.

progressiveness of present day natural science. . . . Grave effects of vested rights in hampering experiments and readjustments. . . . Obstacles to readjustment presented by consecrated traditions. . . . Influence of modern commercialism in the inordinate development of organization and regimentation in our present educational system. Psychological disadvantages of our conventional examination system. As yet our education has not been brought into close relation with prevailing conditions of our ever increasing knowledge. . . . Excellent aims and small achievements of sociology in practical results. (*Because of absolute lack of any scientific base.* Author.) General nature of the problem of social reform: psychological problems involved in social reform movements: violent resistance of the group to that criticism of the existing institutions, which must precede any effective social reform. . . . "

Judged by this standard, neither philosophy nor its kindred—the so-called social sciences—have in the past been very effective. There was, for example, no official warning of the coming of the World War —the greatest of catastrophies. The future was not anticipated because political philosophers did not possess the necessary basis of knowledge. To be just we must admit that philosophy has been but little aided financially because it is commonly regarded as unnecessary. The technical branches of science have been strongly backed and generally supported by those to whom they have brought direct profit; and so they have had better opportunities for development.

Ethics in the stifling grip of myth and legalism is not convincing enough to exercise controlling influence. Such is the situation in which we find ourselves. Being still in our childhood and thinking like savages, we looked upon the World War as a personal creation of a "war-lord," because those interested in it told us so. We neglected to use our common sense and look deeper into its origins; to perform for ourselves the duty which political philosophy did not perform for us—the duty of thinking in terms of facts and not in terms of metaphysical speculations. Knowledge of facts would have told us that the war lords were only the representatives of the ruling classes. A system of social and economic order built exclusively on selfishness, greed, "survival of the fittest," and ruthless competition, must cease to exist, or exist by means of war. The representatives of this system determined to continue to exist, and so war was the consequence. The ruling classes carried the whole system under which they lived to its logical conclusion and natural issue, which is "grab what you can." This motto is not peculiar to any one country; it is the motto of our whole civilization and is the inevitable outcome of our stupid philosophy regarding the characteristic nature of man and the proper potentialities of human life. Where are we to find the true doctrines? Where the true philosophy? If we go back over the history of civilization, we find that in all "sciences," except the exact ones, private opinions and theories have shaped our beliefs, colored our mental processes and controlled our destinies; we see, for example, pessimism opposed to optimism, materialism to spiritualism, realism to idealism, capitalism to socialism, and so on endlessly. Each of the disputatious systems has a large number of followers and each faction looks upon the others as deprived of truth, common sense and knowledge. All of them play with the words "natural law" which they ignorantly presume to have as the basis and content of their own particular doctrine.

It is the same in the realm of religions; there are

approximately 291 million Confucianists, or Taoists, 261 million Roman Catholics, 211 million Mohammedans, 209 million Hindus, 177 million Protestants, 157 million Animists, 137 million Buddhists, 115 million Orthodox Christians—to speak only of the most important religions. Each group, and they are rather large groups, believes its theory or its faith to be infallible and all the others to be false.

Bacon seems a bit remote, but the idols and medieval fetishes which he so masterfully describes are equally venerated to-day.

(*Novum Organum,* by Francis Bacon.)

34. "Four species of idols beset the human mind, to which (for distinction's sake) we have assigned names, calling the first Idols of the Tribe, the second Idols of the Den, the third Idols of the Market, the fourth Idols of the Theatre.

40. "The information of notions and axioms on the foundation of true induction is the only fitting remedy by which we can ward off and expel these idols. It is, however, of great service to point them out; for the doctrine of idols bears the same relation to the interpretation of nature as that of the confutation of sophisms does to common logic.

41. "The idols of the tribe are inherent in human nature and the very tribe or race of man; for man's sense is falsely asserted to be the standard of things; on the contrary, all the perceptions both of the senses and the mind bear reference to man and not to the Universe, and the human mind resembles these uneven mirrors which impart their own properties to different objects, from which rays are emitted and distort and disfigure them.

42. "The idols of the den are those of each individual; for everybody (in addition to the errors common to the race

of man) has his own individual den or cavern, which intercepts and corrupts the light of nature, either from his own peculiar and singular disposition, or from his education and intercourse with others, or from his reading, and the authority acquired by those whom he reverences and admires, or from the different impressions produced on the mind, as it happens to be preoccupied and predisposed, or equable and tranquil, and the like; so that the spirit of man (according to its several dispositions), is variable, confused, and, as it were, actuated by chance; and Heraclitus said well that men search for knowledge in lesser worlds, and not in the greater or common world.

43. "There are also idols formed by the reciprocal intercourse and society of man with man, which we call idols of the market, from the commerce and association of men with each other; for men converse by means of language, but words are formed at the will of the generality, and there arises from a bad and unapt formation of words a wonderful obstruction to the mind. Nor can the definitions and explanations with which learned men are wont to guard and protect themselves in some instances afford a complete remedy—words still manifestly force the understanding, throw everything into confusion, and lead mankind into vain and innumerable controversies and fallacies.

44. "Lastly, there are idols which have crept into men's minds from the various dogmas of peculiar systems of philosophy, and also from the perverted rules of demonstration, and these we denominate idols of the theatre: for we regard all the systems of philosophy hitherto received or imagined, as so many plays brought out and performed, creating fictitious and theatrical worlds. Nor do we speak only of the present systems, or of the philosophy and sects of the ancients, since numerous other plays of a similar nature can be still composed and made to agree with each other, the causes of the most opposite errors being generally the same. Nor,

again, do we allude merely to general systems, but also to
many elements and axioms of sciences which have become
inveterate by tradition, implicit credence, and neglect." *

Metaphysical speculation and its swarming prog-
eny of blind and selfish political philosophies, private
opinions, private "truths," and private doctrines,
sectarian opinions, sectarian "truths" and sectarian
doctrines, querulous, confused and blind—such is
characteristic of the *childhood* of humanity. The
period of humanity's *manhood* will, I doubt not, be
a scientific period—a period that will witness the
gradual extension of scientific method to all the in-

---

* (J. H. R.) "During the past two centuries the application
of the scientific discoveries to daily life has revolutionized
our methods of supplying our economic needs, our social and
intellectual life, and the whole range of the relations of mankind.
The impulse of invention, iron, coal, and steam essential to the
development of machinery on a large scale; machinery has in
turn begotten the modern factory with its vast organized labor,
the modern city and finally, our well nigh perfect means of
rapid human inter-communication. The tremendous increase
in the production of wealth and the growing interdependence of
nations has opened up a vast range of speculation in regard to
the betterment of mankind to the abolition or reduction of pov-
erty, ignorance, disease, and war. . . . Man advances from a
tool-using to a machine-controlling animal. The rise of the
factory system; the concentration and localization of industry;
increased division of labor and specialization of industrial processes. The great increase in the volume of capital and in the
extent of investments; the separation of capital and labor and
the growth of impersonal economic relationship. Problems of
capital and labor; unemployment and the labor of women and
children; labor organizations. Increased productivity and the
expansion of commerce. Industrial processes become dynamic
and everchanging—a complete reversal of the old stability, repetition and isolation."

terests of mankind—a period in which man will discover the essential nature of man and establish, at length, the science and art of directing human energies and human capacities to the advancement of human weal in accordance with the laws of human nature.

CHAPTER III

CLASSES OF LIFE

THE problems to be dealt with in this chapter are not easy, but they are exceedingly important. To classify phenomena correctly, they must be correctly analysed and clearly defined. For the sake of clearness I will use the simplest illustrations and, avoiding as much as possible the difficulties of technical terms, will use language easily to be understood by every one. In some cases the words will indeed have a technical meaning and it will be necessary to exercise great care against the danger of giving false impressions; for clear ideas are essential to sound thinking. As a matter of fact our common daily speech is ill adapted for the precise expression of thought; even so-called "scientific" language is often too vague for the purpose and requires further refining. Some may say that it is useless and unnecessary to lay so much stress on correct thinking and precise expression; that it has no practical value; for they say that "business" language is good enough to "talk business," or to put "something over"—the other fellow. But a little explanation will show that precision is often of the greatest importance.

Humanity is a peculiar class of life which, in some degree, determines its own destinies; therefore in practical life *words* and *ideas* become *facts*—facts, moreover, which bring about important practical consequences. For instance, many millions of human beings have defined a stroke of lightning as being the "punishment of God" of evil men; other millions have defined it as a "natural, casual, periodical phenomenon"; yet other millions have defined it as an "electric spark." What has been the result of these "non-important" definitions in practical life? In the case of the first definition, when lightning struck a house, the population naturally made no attempt to save the house or anything in it, because to do so would be against the "definition" which proclaims the phenomenon to be a "punishment for evil," any attempt to prevent or check the destruction would be an impious act; the sinner would be guilty of "resisting the supreme law" and would deserve to be punished by death.

Now in the second instance, a stricken building is treated just as any tree overturned by storm; the people save what they can and try to extinguish the fire. In both instances, the behavior of the populace is the same in one respect; if caught in the open by a storm they take refuge under a tree—a means of safety involving maximum danger but the people do not know it.

Now in the third instance, in which the population have a scientifically correct definition of lightning, they provide their houses with lightning rods; and if they are caught by a storm in the open they neither run nor hide under a tree; but when the storm is directly over their heads, they put themselves in a position of minimum exposure by lying flat on the ground until the storm has passed.

Such examples could be given without end, but there is another example of sufficient vital importance to be given here, as it has to do with our conception of the social and economic system, and the state. If our institutions are considered "God-given"—sacred and therefore static—every reformer or advocate of change should be treated as a criminal or "a danger to the existing order" and hanged or at least put in jail for life. But now, if our institutions are "man made," imperfect and often foolish, and subject to change all the time steadily and dynamically in obedience to some known or unknown law; then of course all reactionaries would be a "danger to the natural order" and they should be treated the same way. The importance of definitions can be seen in all other fields of practical life; definitions create conditions. To know the world in which we live, we have to analyse facts by help of such facts as we know in daily practice and such facts as are established in scientific laboratories where men do not jump to conclusions. In some places it will be necessary to make statements that will have to await full justification at a later stage of the discussion. This will be necessary to indicate the trend of the analysis.

The aim of the analysis is to give us just conceptions, correct definitions, and true propositions. The process is slow, progressive, and endless. The problems are infinitely many, and it is necessary to select. Fortunately the solution of a few leads automatically to the solution of many others. Some of the greatest and most far-reaching scientific discoveries have been nothing else than a few correct definitions, a few just concepts and a few true propositions. Such, for example, was the work of Euclid, Newton and Leibnitz—a few correct definitions, a few just concepts, a few true propositions; but these have been extended and multiplied, sometimes by men of creative genius, and often almost automatically by men of merely good sense and fair talent.

The matter of definition, I have said, is very important. I am not now speaking of *nominal* definitions, which for convenience merely give names to known objects. I am speaking of such definitions of phenomena as result from correct analysis of the phenomena. Nominal definitions are mere conveniences and are neither true nor false; but analytic definitions are definitive *propositions* and are true or else false. Let us dwell upon the matter a little more.

In the illustration of the definitions of lightning, there were three; the first was the most mistaken and its application brought the most harm; the second was less incorrect and the practical results less bad; the third under the present conditions of our knowledge, was the "true one" and it brought the maximum benefit. This lightning illustration suggests the important idea of *relative* truth and *relative* falsehood—the idea, that is, of degrees of truth and degrees of falsehood. A definition may be neither absolutely true nor absolutely false; but of two definitions of the same thing, one of them may be truer or falser than the other.

If, for illustration's sake, we call the first "truth" A_1 (alpha 1), the second one A_2 (alpha 2), the third one A_3 (alpha 3), we may suppose that a genius appears who has the faculty to surpass all the other relative truths $A_1, A_2, A_3, \ldots A_n$ and gives us an absolute or final truth, VALID IN INFINITY (A_∞) say a final definition, that lightning is so . . . and so . . ., a kind of energy which flows, let us say, through a glass tube filled with charcoal. Then of course this definition would immediately make obvious what use could be made of it. We could erect glass towers filled with charcoal and so secure an unlimited flow of available free energy and our whole life would be affected in an untold degree. This example explains the importance of correct definitions.

But to take another example: there is such a thing as a phenomenon called the "color" red. Imagine how it might be defined. A reactionary would call it a "Bolshevik" (A_1); a Bolshevik would say "My color" (A_2); a color-blind person would say "such a thing does not exist" (A_3); a Daltonist would say "that is green" (A_4); a metaphysician would say "that is the soul of whiskey" (A_5); an historian would say "that is the color of the ink with which human history has been written" (A_6); an uneducated person would say "that is the color of blood" (A_7); the modern scientist would say "it is the light of such and such wave length" (A_n). If this last definition be "valid in infinity" or not we do not know, but it is, nevertheless, a "scientific truth" in the present condition of our knowledge.

This final but unknown "truth valid in infinity" is somehow perceived or felt by us as an ideal, for in countless years of observation we have formed a series of less and less false, more and more nearly true "ideas" about the phenomenon. The "ideas" are *reflections* of the phenomenon, reflected in our midst as in a mirror; the reflections may be distorted, as in a convex or concave mirror, but they suggest an ideal reflection valid in infinity. It is of the utmost importance to realize that the words which are used to express the ideas and the ideals are THE REPRESENTATIONS of the ideas and ideal; it is only by words that we are enabled to give to other human beings an exact or nearly exact impression which we have had of the phenomenon.

It may be helpful to illustrate this process by an example. Let us suppose that a man makes an experiment of doing his own portrait from a mirror, which may be plane, concave or convex. If he looks into a plane mirror, he will see his true likeness; even so, if he be a poor designer, he will draw the likeness badly. Let us suppose that the man has beautiful features but because the drawing is very poor, it will not convey the impression that the features of the original were beautiful. If this poor designer were to look into and work from a concave or convex mirror, the drawing of his likeness would have practically no resemblance to his original features.

For correct analysis and true definitions of the cardinal classes of life in our world it is necessary to have some just ideas about dimensions or dimensionality. The Britannica gives us some help in this connection. I will explain briefly by an example. Measurable entities of different kinds can not be compared directly. Each one must be measured in terms of a unit of its own kind. A line can have only length and therefore is of one dimension: a surface has length and width and is therefore said to have two dimensions; a volume has length, width and thickness and is, therefore, said to have three dimensions. If we take, for example, a volume—say a cube—we see that the cube has surfaces and lines and points, but a volume is not a surface nor a line nor a point. Just these dimensional differences have an enormous unrealized importance in practical life, as in the case of taking a line of five units of length and building upon it a square, the measure of this square (surface) will not be 5, it will be 25; and the 25 will not be 25 linear units but 25 square or surface units. If upon this square we build a cube, this cube will have neither 5 nor 25 for its measure; it will have 125, and this number will not be so many units of length nor of surface but so many solid or cubic units.

It is as plain as a pike staff that, if we confused *dimensions* when computing lengths and areas and volumes, we would wreck all the architectural and engineering structures of the world, and at the same time show ourselves stupider than block-heads.

To analyse the classes of life we have to consider two very different kinds of phenomena: the one embraced under the collective name — Inorganic chemistry—the other under the collective name—

Organic chemistry, or the chemistry of hydro-carbons. These divisions are made because of the peculiar properties of the elements chiefly involved in the second class. The properties of matter are so distributed among the elements that three of them—Oxygen, Hydrogen, and Carbon—possess an ensemble of unique characteristics. The number of reactions in inorganic chemistry are relatively few, but in organic chemistry—in the chemistry of these three elements the number of different compounds is practically unlimited. Up to 1910, we knew of more than 79 elements of which the whole number of reactions amounted to only a few hundreds, but among the remaining three elements—Carbon, Hydrogen and Oxygen—the reactions were known to be practically unlimited in number and possibilities; this fact must have very far reaching consequences. As far as energies are concerned, we have to take them as nature reveals them to us. Here more than ever, mathematical thinking is essential and will help enormously. The reactions in inorganic chemistry always involve the phenomenon of heat, sometimes light, and in some instances an unusual energy is produced called electricity. Until now, the radio-active elements represent a group too insufficiently known for an enlargement here upon this subject.

The organic compounds being unlimited in number and possibilities and with their unique characteristics, represent of course, a different class of phenomena, but being, at the same time, *chemical* they include the basic chemical phenomena involved in all chemical reactions, but being unique in many other respects, they also have an infinitely vast field of unique characteristics. Among the energetic phenomena of organic chemistry, besides the few mentioned above there are NEW AND UNIQUE energetic phenomena occurring in this dimension.

Of these phenomena, mention may be made of the phenomenon "life," the phenomenon of the "instincts" and of the "mind" in general. These energetic phenomena are unique for the unique chemistry of the three unique elements. It is obvious that this "uniqueness" is the reason why these phenomena must be classified as belonging to or having a higher dimensionality than belongs to the phenomena of inorganic chemistry just as the uniqueness of the properties of a volume as compared with surface properties depends upon the fact that a volume has a higher dimensionality than a surface. Just as this difference of dimensions makes the whole difference between the geometry of volumes and the geometry of surfaces, the difference between the two chemistries involves a difference of dimensionality.

The higher energies of the chemistries of the higher dimensionality are very difficult to define; my descriptions are no better than the description of

life given by Professor Wilhelm Roux, in his *Der
Kampf der Teile im Organismus,* Leipzig, 1881,
which are equally unsatisfactory. In want of a better, I quote him. He defines a living being as a natural object which possesses the following nine characteristic autonomous activities: Autonomous change,
Autonomous excretion, Autonomous ingestion, Au-
tonomous assimilation, Autonomous growth, Auton-
omous movement, Autonomous multiplication, Au-
tonomous transmission of hereditary characteristics
and Autonomous development. The words "Autonomous activities" are important because they hint
at the dimensional differences of these energies. But
a better word should be found to define the dimensional differences between the activities found in
inorganic chemistry and those found in organic
chemistry. We see it is a mistake to speak about
"life" in a crystal, in the same sense in which we
use the word life to name the curious AUTONOMOUS
phenomenon of ORGANIC CHEMISTRY, WHICH IS OF
ANOTHER DIMENSION than the activities in inorganic
chemistry. For the so-called life in the crystals—
the *not* AUTONOMOUS (or anautonomous) activities
of crystals—another word than life should be found.
In the theory of crystals the term life is purely
rhetorical: its use there is very injurious to sound
science. These old ideas of "life" in crystals are
profoundly unscientific and serve as one of the best

examples of the frequent confusion or intermixing
of dimensions—a confusion due to unmathematical,
logically incorrect ways of thinking. If crystals
"live," then *volumes are surfaces,* and 125 cubic
units=25 square units—absurdities belonging to the
"childhood of humanity."

"Crystals can grow in a proper solution, and can regen-
erate their form in such a solution when broken or injured;
it is even possible to prevent or retard the formation of
crystals in a supersaturated solution by preventing 'germs'
in the air from getting into the solution, an observation which
was later utilized by Schroeder and Pasteur in their experiments on spontaneous generation. However, the analogies
between a living organism and a crystal are merely superficial
and it is by pointing out the fundamental differences between
the behavior of crystals and that of living organisms that
we can best understand the specific difference between non-
living and living matter. It is true that a crystal can grow,
but it will do so only in a supersaturated solution of its own
substance. Just the reverse is true for living organisms. In
order to make bacteria or the cells of our body grow, solutions of the split products of the substances composing them
and not the substances themselves must be available to the
cells; second, these solutions must not be supersaturated, on
the contrary, they must be dilute; and third, growth leads
in living organisms to cell division as soon as the mass of
the cell reaches a certain limit. This process of cell division
can not be claimed even metaphorically to exist in a crystal.
A correct appreciation of these facts will give us an insight
into the specific difference between non-living and living matter. The formation of living matter consists in the synthesis
of the proteins, nucleins, fats, and carbohydrates of the cells,
from split products. . . .

"The essential difference between living and non-living matter consists then in this: the living cell synthesizes its own complicated specific material from indifferent or non-specific simple compounds of the surrounding medium, while the crystal simply adds the molecules found in its super-saturated solution. This synthetic power of transforming small 'building stones' into the complicated compounds specific for each organism is the 'secret of life' or rather one of the secrets of life." (*The Organism as a Whole*, by Jacques Loeb.)

It will be explained later that one of the energetic phenomena of organic chemistry—the "mind," which is one of the energies characteristic of this class of phenomena, is "autonomous," is "selfpro-pelling" and true to its dimensionality. If we analyse the classes of life, we readily find that there are three cardinal classes which are radically distinct in function. A short analysis will disclose to us that, though minerals have various activities, they are not "living." The plants have a very definite and well known function—the transformation of solar energy into organic chemical energy. They are a class of life which appropriates one kind of energy, converts it into another kind and stores it up; in that sense they are a kind of storage battery for the solar energy; and so I define THE PLANTS AS THE CHEM-ISTRY-BINDING class of life.

The animals use the highly dynamic products of the *chemistry-binding* class—the plants—as food, and those products—the results of plant-transformation—undergo in animals a further transformation into yet higher forms; and the animals are correspondingly a more dynamic class of life; their energy is kinetic; they have a remarkable freedom and power which the plants do not possess—I mean the freedom and faculty to move about in *space;* and so I define ANIMALS AS THE SPACE-BINDING CLASS OF LIFE.

And now what shall we say of *human* beings? What is to be our definition of Man? Like the animals, human beings do indeed possess the *space-binding* capacity but, over and above that, human beings possess a most remarkable capacity which is entirely peculiar to them—I mean the capacity to summarise, digest and appropriate the labors and experiences of the past; I mean the capacity to use the fruits of past labors and experiences as intellectual or spiritual capital for developments in the present; I mean the capacity to employ as instruments of increasing power the accumulated achievements of the all-precious lives of the past generations spent in trial and error, trial and success; I mean the capacity of human beings to conduct their lives in the ever increasing light of inherited wisdom; I mean the capacity in virtue of which man is at once the heritor of the by-gone ages and the trustee of posterity. And because humanity is just this magnifi-

cent natural agency by which the past lives in the
present and the present for the future, I define
HUMANITY, in the universal tongue of mathematics
and mechanics, to be the TIME-BINDING CLASS OF
LIFE.

These definitions of the cardinal classes of life
are, it will be noted, obtained from direct observation; they are so simple and so important that I cannot over-emphasize the necessity of grasping them
and most especially the definition of Man. For these
simple definitions and especially that of Humanity
will profoundly transform the whole conception of
human life in every field of interest and activity;
and, what is more important than all, the definition
of Man will give us a starting point for discovering
the *natural* laws of human nature—of the human
class of life. The definitions of the classes of life
represent the different classes as distinct in respect
to dimensionality; and this is extremely important
for no measure or rule of one class can be applied
to the other, *without making grave mistakes*. For
example, to treat a human being as an animal—as
a mere space-binder—because humans have certain
animal propensities, is an error of the same type and
grossness as to treat a cube as a surface because it
has surface properties. It is absolutely essential to
grasp that fact if we are ever to have a science
of human nature.

We can represent the different classes of life in three life coordinates. The minerals, with their inorganic activities would be the Zero (o) dimension of "life"—that is the *lifeless* class—here represented by the point *M*.

The plants, with their "autonomous" growth, to be represented by the ONE DIMENSIONAL line *MP*.

The animals, with their "autonomous" capacity to grow and to be active in space by the TWO DIMENSIONAL plane *PAM*.

The humans, with their "autonomous" capacity to grow, to be active in space AND TO BE ACTIVE IN TIME, by the THREE DIMENSIONAL region *MAPH*.

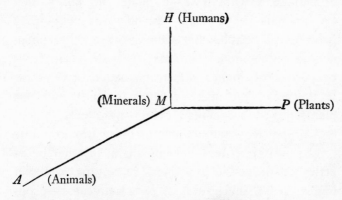

Such diagrammatic illustrations must not be taken too literally; they are like figures of speech—helpful if understood—harmful if not understood. The reader should reflect upon the simple idea of dimen-

sions until he sees clearly that the idea is not merely
a thing of interest or of convenience, but is absolutely essential as a means of discriminating the cardinal classes of life from one another and of conceiving each class to be what it is instead of mixing
it confusedly with something radically different. It
will greatly help the reader if he will retire to the
quiet of his cloister and there meditate about as
follows. A line has one dimension; a plane has two;
a plane contains lines and so it has line properties—
one-dimensional properties—but it has other properties—*two*-dimensional properties—and it is these
that are peculiar to it, give it its own character,
and make it what it is—a plane and not a line.
So animals have some plant properties—they
grow, for example—but animals have other properties—autonomous mobility, for example,—
properties of higher dimensionality or type—and
it is these that make animals *animals* and not
plants. Just so, human beings have certain animal properties—autonomous mobility, for example,
or physical appetites—but humans have other properties or propensities—ethical sense, for example,
logical sense, inventiveness, progressiveness—properties or propensities of higher dimensionality, level,
or type—and it is these propensities and powers
that make human beings *human* and *not* animal.
When and only when this fact is clearly seen and

keenly realized, there will begin the *science of man* —the science and art of *human nature*—for then and only then we shall begin to escape from the age-long untold immeasurable evils that come from re-garding and treating human beings as animals, as mere binders of space, and we may look forward to an ethics, a jurisprudence and economics, a governance—a science and art of human life and so-ciety—based upon the laws of human nature because based upon the just conception of humanity as the time-binding class of life, creators and improvers of good, destined to endless advancement, in accord with the potencies of Human Nature.*

* It may be contended by some that animals have been making "progress" or some may say that animals also "bind-time." This use of words would again become mere verbalism, a mere talking about words—mere speculation having nothing to do with *facts* or with correct thinking, in which there is no inter-mixing of dimensions. The peculiar faculty belonging exclusively to humans which I designate as "time-binding" I have clearly defined as an *exponential function* of *time* in the following chapter. If people are pleased to talk about the "progress" of animals, they can hardly fail to see clearly that it differs both in function and in type or dimension from what is rightly meant by human progress; human time-binding capacity lies in an entirely dif-ferent dimension from that of animals. So, if any persons wish to talk of animal "progress" or animal "time-binding," they should invent a suitable word for it to save them from the blunder of confusing types or mixing dimensions.

This mathematical discrimination between classes, types, dimensions is of the utmost importance in the natural sciences, because of the transmutation of species. To adjust the Darwin theory to dimensionality is a somewhat more difficult problem; it involves the concept of the "continuum"; but with the modern theory of de Vries, these things are self evident. If animals really progress, which is doubtful because they are an

Humanity is still in its childhood; we have "bound" so little time in the course of the centuries, which are so brief in the scheme of the universe. At the bottom of every human activity, historical fact or trend of civilization, there lies some doctrine or conception of so-called "truth." Apples had fallen from trees for ages, but without any important results in the economy of humanity. The fact that a fallen apple hit Newton, led to the discovery of the theory of gravitation; this changed our whole world conception, our sciences and our activities; it powerfully stimulated the development of all the branches of natural and technological knowledge. Even in the event of the Newtonian laws being proved to be not quite correct, they have served a great purpose in enabling us to understand natural phenomena in a sufficiently approximate way to make it possible to build up modern technology and to develop our physical science to the point where it was necessary and possible to make a correction of the Newtonian laws.

A similar organic change in our conception of human life and its phenomena is involved in the foregoing definitions of the classes of life; they will replace basic errors with scientific truths of fundamen-

older form of life than humans and they have not shown any noticeable progress to the knowledge of man, their progress is so small in comparison with man's that it may be said, in mathematical terms, to be *negligible* as an infinitesimal of higher order.

tal importance; they will form the basis for scientific development of a permanent civilization in place of the periodically convulsive so-called civilizations of the past and present. To know the cause of evil and error is to find the cure.

CHAPTER IV

WHAT IS MAN?

MAN has ever been the greatest puzzle to man. There are many and important reasons for this fact. As the subject of this book is not a theoretical, academic study of man, of which too many have already been written, I will not recount the reasons, but will confine myself to the more pressing matters of the task in hand, which is that of pointing the way to the science and art of Human Engineering. The two facts which have to be dealt with first, are the two which have most retarded human progress: (1) there has never been a true definition of man nor a just conception of his rôle in the curious drama of the world; in consequence of which there has never been a proper principle or starting point for a science of humanity. It has never been realized that man is a being of a dimension or type different from that of animals and the characteristic nature of man has not been understood; (2) man has always been regarded either as an animal or as a supernatural phenomenon. The facts are that man is not *super*natural but is literally a part of nature

66

and that human beings are not animals. We have seen that the animals are truly characterized by their autonomous mobility—their space-binding capacity—animals are space-binders. We have seen that human beings are characterized by their creative power, by the power to make the past live in the present and the present for the future, by their capacity to bind time—human beings are time-binders. These concepts are basic and impersonal; arrived at mathematically, they are mathematically correct.

It does not matter at all *how* the first man, the first time-binder, was produced; the fact remains that he was somewhere, somehow produced. To know anything that is to-day of fundamental interest about man, we have to analyse man in three coordinates—in three capacities; namely, his chemistry, his activities in space, and especially his activities in time; whereas in the study of animals we have to consider only two factors: their chemistry and their activities in space.

Let us imagine that the aboriginal—original human specimen was one of two brother apes, *A* and *B;* they were alike in every respect; both were animal space-binders; but something strange happened to *B;* he became the first time-binder, a human. No matter how, this "something" made the change in him that lifted him to a higher dimension; it is enough that in some-wise, over and above his animal capacity for binding space, there was superadded the marvelous new capacity for binding-time. He had thus a new faculty, he belonged to a new dimension; but, of course, he did not realize it; and because he had this new capacity he was able to analyze his brother *"A"*; he observed *"A* is my brother; he is an animal; but he is my brother; therefore, *I* AM AN ANIMAL." This fatal first conclusion, reached by false analogy, by neglecting a fact, has been the chief source of human woe for half a million years and it still survives. The time-binding capacity, first manifest in *B,* increased more and more, with the days and each generation, until in the course of centuries man felt himself increasingly somehow different from the animal, but he could not explain. He said to himself, "If I am an animal there is also in me something higher, a spark of some thing *super*natural."

With this conclusion he estranged himself, as something apart from nature, and formulated the impasse, which put him in a cul-de-sac of a double life. He was neither true to the "supernatural" which he could not know and therefore, could not emulate, nor was he true to the "animal" which he scorned. Having put himself outside the "natural laws," he was not really true to any law and condemned himself to a life of hypocrisy, and established speculative, artificial, unnatural laws.

"How blind our familiar assumptions make us! Among the animals, man, at least, has long been wont to regard himself as a being quite apart from and not as part of the cosmos round about him. From this he has detached himself in thought, he has estranged and objectified the world, and lost the sense that he is of it. And this age-long habit and point of view, which has fashioned his life and controlled his thought, lending its characteristic mark and color to his whole philosophy and art and learning, is still maintained, partly because of its convenience, no doubt, and partly by force of inertia and sheer conservatism, in the very teeth of the strongest probabilities of biological science. Probably no other single hypothesis has less to recommend it, and yet no other so completely dominates the human mind." (Cassius J. Keyser, loc. cit.) And this monstrous conception is current to-day: millions still look upon man as a mixture of animal and something supernatural.

There is no doubt that the engineering of human society is a difficult and complicated problem of tremendous ethical responsibility, for it involves the welfare of mankind throughout an unending succession of generations. The science of Human Engineering can not be built upon false conceptions of human nature. It can not be built on the conception of man as a kind of animal; it can not be built on the conception of man as a mixture of natural and supernatural. It must be built upon the conception of man as being at once natural and higher in dimensionality than the animals. It must be built upon the scientific conception of mankind as characterized by their time-binding capacity and function. This conception radically alters our whole view of human life, human society, and the world.

It must be obvious to any one that time-binding is the only natural criterion and standard for the time-binding class of life. This mighty term—time-binding—when comprehended, will be found to embrace the WHOLE of the natural laws, the natural ethics, the natural philosophy, the natural sociology, the natural economics, the natural governance, to be brought into the education of time-binders; then really peaceful and progressive civilization, without periodical collapses and violent readjustments, will commence; not before. Everything which is really "time-binding" *is in* the HUMAN DIMENSION; therefore, it will represent every quality that is implied in such words as—*good, just, right, beautiful;* while everything that is merely space-binding will be classified as "animal" and be thus assessed at its proper value. Those ignorant "masters of our destinies" who regard humans as animals or as monstrous hybrids of natural and supernatural must be dethroned by scientific education.

Humans can be literally poisoned by false ideas
and false teachings. Many people have a just horror
at the thought of putting poison into tea or coffee,
but seem unable to realize that, when they teach false
ideas and false doctrines, they are poisoning the
time-binding capacity of their fellow men and women.
One has to stop and think! There is nothing mystical
about the fact that ideas and words are energies
which powerfully affect the physico-chemical base of
our time-binding activities. Humans are thus made
untrue to "human nature." Hypnotism is a known
fact. It has been proved that a man can be so
hypnotized that in a certain time which has been
suggested to him, he will murder or commit arson
or theft; that, under hypnotic influence, the personal
morale of the individual has only a small influence
upon his conduct; the subject obeys the hypnotic suggestions, no matter how immoral they are. The
conception of man as a mixture of animal and supernatural has for ages kept human beings under the
deadly spell of the suggestion that, animal selfishness and animal greediness are their essential character, and the spell has operated to suppress their
REAL HUMAN NATURE and to prevent it from expressing itself naturally and freely.

On the other hand, when human beings are educated to a lively realization that they are by *nature*
time-binding creatures, then they will spontaneously

live in accordance with their time-binding nature,
which, as I have said, is the source and support of
the highest ideals.

What is achieved in blaming a man for being selfish and greedy if he acts under the influence of a
social environment and education which teach him
that he is an animal and that selfishness and greediness are of the essence of his nature?

Even so eminent a philosopher and psychologist as
Spencer tells us: "Of self-evident truths so dealt
with, the one which here concerns us is that a creature must live before it can act. . . . Ethics has to
recognize the truth that egoism comes before altru-
ism." This is true for ANIMALS, because animals
die out from lack of food when their natural supply
of it is insufficient because they have NOT THE
CAPACITY TO PRODUCE ARTIFICIALLY. But it is not
true for the HUMAN DIMENSION.

Why not? Because humans through their time-
binding capacity are first of all *creators* and so their
number is not controlled by the supply of unaided
nature, but only by men's artificial productivity,
which is THE MATERIALIZATION OF THEIR TIME-
BINDING CAPACITY.

Man, therefore, by the very intrinsic character of
his being, MUST ACT FIRST, IN ORDER TO BE ABLE
TO LIVE (through the action of parents—or society)
which is not the case with animals. The misunder-

standing of this simple truth is largely accountable
for the evil of our ethical and economic systems or
lack of systems. As a matter of fact, if humanity
were to live in *complete* accord with the animal conception of man, artificial production—time-binding
production—would cease and ninety per cent of
mankind would perish by starvation. It is just
because human beings are not animals but are time-
binders—not mere finders but creators of food and
shelter—that they are able to live in such vast
numbers.

Here even the blind must see the effect of higher
dimensionality, and this effect becomes in turn the
cause of other effects which produce still others, and
so on in an endless chain. WE LIVE BECAUSE WE
PRODUCE, BECAUSE WE ARE ACTING IN TIME AND
ARE NOT MERELY ACTING IN SPACE—BECAUSE MAN
IS NOT A KIND OF ANIMAL. It is all so simple, if
only we apply a little sound logic in our thinking
about human nature and human affairs. If human
ethics are to be human, are to be in the human
dimension, the postulates of ethics must be changed;
FOR HUMANITY IN ORDER TO LIVE MUST ACT FIRST;
the laws of ethics—the laws of right living—are
natural laws—laws of human nature—laws having
their whole source and sanction in the time-binding
capacity and time-binding activity peculiar to man.
Human excellence is excellence in time-binding, and

must be measured and rewarded by time-binding standards of worth.

Humanity, in order to live, must produce creatively and therefore must be guided by applied science, by technology; and this means that the so-called social sciences of ethics, jurisprudence, psychology, economics, sociology, politics, and government must be emancipated from medieval metaphysics; they must be made scientific; they must be *technologized;* they must be made to progress and to function in the proper dimension—the human dimension and not that of animals: they must be made time-binding sciences.

Can this be done? I have no doubt that it can. For what is human life after all?

To a general in the battlefield, human life is a factor which, if properly used, can destroy the enemy. To an engineer human life is an equivalent to energy, or a capacity to do work, mental or muscular, and the moment something is found to be a source of energy and to have the capacity of doing work, the first thing to do, from the engineer's point of view, is to analyse the generator with a view to discovering how best to conserve it, to improve it, and bring it to the level of maximum productivity. Human beings are very complicated energy-producing batteries differing widely in quality and magnitude of productive power. Experience has shown that these batteries are, first of all, chemical batteries producing a mysterious energy. If these batteries are not supplied periodically with a more or less constant quantity of some chemical elements called food and air, the batteries will cease to function—they will die. In the examination of the structure of these batteries we find that the chemical base is very much accentuated all through the structure. This chemical generator is divided into branches each of which has a very different rôle which it must perform in harmony with all the others. The mechanical parts of the structure are built in conformity to the rules of mechanics and are automatically furnished with lubrication and with chemical supplies for automatically renewing worn-out parts. The chemical processes not only deposit particles of mass for the structure of the generator but produce some very powerful unknown kinds of energies or vibrations which make all the chemical parts function; we find also a mysterious apparatus with a complex of wires which we call brain, glands, and nerves; and, finally, these human batteries have the remarkable capacity of reproduction.

These functions are familiar to everybody. From the knowledge of other physical, mechanical and chemical phenomena of nature, we must come to the conclusion, that this human battery is the most perfect example of a complex engine; it has all the peculiarities of a chemical battery combined with a generator of a peculiar energy called life; above all, it has mental or spiritual capacities; it is thus equipped with both mental and mechanical means for producing work. The parts and functions of this marvelous engine have been the subject of a vast amount of research in various special branches of science. A very noteworthy fact is that both the physical work and the mental work of this human engine are always accompanied by both physical and chemical changes in the structure of its machinery— corresponding to the wear and tear of non-living engines. It also presents certain sexual and spiritual phenomena that have a striking likeness to certain phenomena, especially wireless phenomena, to electricity and to radium. This human engine-battery is of unusual strength, durability and perfection; and yet it is very liable to damage and even wreckage, if not properly used. The controlling factors are very delicate and so the engine is very capricious. Very special training and understanding are necessary for its control.

The reader may wish to ask: What is the essence of the time-binding power of Man? Talk of essences is metaphysical—it is not scientific. Let me explain by an example.

What is electricity? The scientific answer is: electricity is that which exhibits such and such phe-

nomena. Electricity means nothing but a certain
group of phenomena called electric. We are studying electricity when we are studying those phenomena. Thus it is in physics—there is no talk of
essences. So, too, in Human Engineering—we
shall not talk of the essence of time-binding but only
of the phenomena and the laws thereof. What has
led to the development of electric appliances is
knowledge of electrical phenomena—not metaphysical talk about the electrical essence. And what
will lead to the science and art of Human Engineering is knowledge of time-binding phenomena—not
vain babble about an *essence* of time-binding power.
There is no mystery about the word time-binding.
Some descriptive term was necessary to indicate that
human capacity which discriminates human beings
from animals and marks man as man. For that use
—the appropriateness of the term time-binding
becomes more and more manifest upon reflection.

What are the conditions of life upon this earth?
Is there war or peace in daily life? All living beings
require food; they multiply in a geometrical ratio;
and so the *natural* productivity of the soil becomes
increasingly inadequate. The tendency to increase
in geometrical ratio is true of all life—vegetable,
animal and human, but the tendency is checked by
various counteracting influences, natural and artificial. A short time ago these checks had so operated

to annul the law of increase as almost to stop the growth of human population. It is only by the time-binding capacity of man—by scientific progress and technological invention—that the checks have been overcome. And so in the last century the population of Europe increased more than it had increased in several centuries before. Impoverished soil, excessive heat or cold, excessive moisture, the lack of rainfall, and many other factors are hostile to life. It is evident, therefore, that human life must especially struggle for existence; it must carry on a perpetual contest for self preservation. It seems obvious that, if there is perpetual war in every-day life, war methods must be applied.

We have just passed through a tremendous world-wide *military* war and we developed special ways of producing power to overcome the enemy. We were thus driven to discover some of the hidden sources of power and all of our old habits and ideas were bent toward military methods and military technology. The war of every-day life against hostile elements is war for the subjugation of physical nature and not for the conquest of people. It is a war carried on by the time-binding power of men pitted against natural obstacles, and its progressive triumph means progressive advancement in human weal.

The lesson of the World War should not be

missed through failure to analyse it. When nations
war with nations, the normal daily war of millions
and millions of individuals to subjugate natural resources to human uses is interrupted, and the slow-
gathered fruits of measureless toil are destroyed.

But peaceful war, war for the conquest of nature,
involves the use of methods of technology and, what
is even more important, technological philosophy,
law and ethics.

What I want to emphasize in this little book, is
the need of a thoroughgoing revision of our ideas;
and the revision must be made by engineering minds
in order that our ideas may be made to match facts.
If we are ill, we consult a physician or a surgeon,
not a charlatan. We must learn that, when there is
trouble with the producing power of the world, we
have to consult an engineer, an expert on power.
Politicians, diplomats, and lawyers do not understand
the problem. What I am advocating is that we
must learn to ask those who know how to produce
things, instead of asking those whose profession is
to fight for the division of things produced by nature
or by other human beings.

As a matter of fact our civilization has been for
a long time disorganized to the point of disease.
Lately through the whirl of changing conditions, due
to the great release of power in the new-born giant
technology, the disorganization has become acute.

The sick seldom know the cure for themselves. If the cure is to be enduring, we have to go to the source, and this can be done only by men familiar, not only with effects but also with the causes.

Money is not the wealth of a nation, but production is wealth; so *ordered production* is the main object for humanity. But to have the maximum of production, it is necessary to have production put on a sound basis. No mere preaching of brotherly love, or class hatred, will produce one single brick for the building of the future temple of human victory—the temple of *human* civilization. Ordered production demands analysis of basic facts.

This era is essentially an industrial era. To produce we have to have: (1) raw material or soil; (2) instruments for production—tools and machines; and (3) the application of power.

The three requirements may be briefly characterized and appraised as follows:

(1) Raw material and soil are products of nature; humanity simply took them and had the use of them for nothing, because it is impossible to call a prayer of thanksgiving (if any) addressed to a "creator" as payment to gods or men. But raw material and soil, in the conditions in which nature produces them, are of very little immediate benefit to humanity, because untilled soil produces very little food for humans, and raw material such as

wood, coal, oil, iron, copper, etc., are completely useless to humanity until after human work is applied to them. It is necessary to cut a tree for the making of timber; it is necessary to excavate the minerals, and even then, only by applying further human work is it possible to make them available for any human use. So, it is obvious that even raw materials in the form in which nature has produced them, are mostly of no value and unavailable for use, unless *re*produced through the process of "human creative production." Therefore, we may well conclude that "raw material" must be divided into two very distinct classes: (*a*) raw material as produced by nature—nature's free gift—which in its original form and place has practically no use-value; and (*b*) raw material reproduced by man's mental and muscular activities, by his "time-binding" capacities. Raw materials of the second class have an enormous use-value; indeed they make the existence of humanity possible.

As to the second requirement for production, namely:

(2) Tools and machines, it is obvious that "tools and machines" are made of raw material by human work, mental and muscular.

And, finally:

(3) The application of power. Different sources of natural energy and power are known. The most

important available source of energy for this globe
is the sun—the heat of the sun. This solar heat is
the origin of water power, of wind power, and of
the power bound up in coal, of the chemistry, growth
and transforming agency of plants.*

* It must be remembered here that our world is, first of all, a
dynamic conglomeration of matter and energy, which to-day, as
well as in the first period of primitive organic life, took and takes
different known and unknown forms. One of these forms of
energy is the chemical energy, with its tendency to combinations
and exchanges. Different elements act in different ways. The
history of the earth and its life is simply the history of different
chemical periods, with different transformations of energy. A
strange fact is to be noticed about nitrogen. Nitrogen chemi-
cally has an exceptional inertness toward most other substances,
but once it is a component part of a substance, almost all of these
combinations are a very powerful source of energy, and all of
them have a very strong effect upon organic life. Nitric acid
acts through oxidation, the substances are burned up by the
oxygen given off from the acid. Nitric acid occurs in nature,
in a combination called nitrates. From the soil the nitrates
pass into the plant. Nitrite of amyl acts upon our organs in a
most violent and spasmodic way. Nitrous oxide is the so-called
laughing gas.

Alkaloids are compounds of a vegetable origin, generally of
complex composition and capable of producing marked effects
upon animals. They all contain nitrogen. Explosives which
are a chemical means of storing tremendous amounts of energy,
are mostly of some nitrogenous compound. Albumen is an
organic compound of great importance in life, which, besides
being the characteristic ingredient in the white of an egg, abounds
in the serum of the blood and forms an important part of the
muscles and brain. Albuminoids play the most vital rôle in
plant life and are an extensive class of organic bodies found in
plants and animals, as they are found to form the chief constitu-
ents of blood, nerves. All albuminoids found in animals are
produced by the processes fulfilled in plants. Their exact
constitution is not known; analysis shows that they contain
approximately: Carbon 50–55%, Hydrogen 6.9–7.5%, Nitrogen
15–19%, Oxygen 20–24%, Sulphur 0.3–2.0%. Venous blood

All foods which the animals as well as the humans use are, already, the result of the solar energy transformed into what may be called chemical energy. Transformation of energies is building up of life.

It is to be clearly seen that the only source of energy which can be directly appropriated and used by man or animal is vegetable food found in the wilderness; no other sources of power are avail-

contains in 100 volumes: Nitrogen, 13; Carbonic Acid, 71.6; Oxygen, 15.3. Arterial blood: Nitrogen, 14.5; Carbonic Acid, 62.3; Oxygen, 23.2.

"Nitrogenous compounds in general, are extremely prone to decomposition; their decomposition often involving a sudden and great evolution of force. We see that substances classed as ferments. . . . are all nitrogenous . . . and we see that even in organisms and parts of organisms where the activities are least, such changes as do take place are initiated by a substance containing nitrogen. . . . We see that organic matter is so constituted that small incidental actions are capable of initiating great reaction and liberating large quantities of power. . . . The seed of a plant contains nitrogenous substances in a far higher ratio than the rest of the plant; and the seed differs from the rest of the plant in its ability to initiate . . . extensive vital changes—the changes constituting germination. Similarly in the bodies of animals . . . in every living vegetal cell there is a certain part that contains nitrogen. This part initiates these changes which constitute the development of the cell. . . . It is a curious and significant fact that, in technology, we not only utilize the same principle of initiating extensive changes among comparatively stable compounds by the help of compounds much less stable, but we employ for the purpose compounds of the same general class. Our modern method of firing a gun is to place in close proximity with the gunpowder which we choose to decompose or explode, a small portion of fulminating powder, which is decomposed or exploded with extreme facility, and which on decomposing, communicates the consequent molecular disturbances to the less easily decomposed gunpowder. When we ask what this fulminating powder is composed of, we find that it is a nitrogenous salt."—Spencer.

able for *direct* use; they have first to be mastered and directed by human brain. The same is true in regard to the getting of animal food, the creation of a water- or windmill, or a steam engine, or the art of using a team of horses, or a bushel of wheat; these are not available except by the use of the human "time-binding" power.

This short survey of facts, known to everybody, brings us to the conclusion that all problems of production come ultimately to the analysis of

(1) Natural resources of raw material and natural energy, freely supplied by nature, which, as we have seen, in the form as produced by nature alone, have very little or no value for humanity;

(2) The activity of the human brain (because human muscles are always directed by the brain) which gives value to the otherwise useless raw materials and energies.

Hence, to understand the processes of production, it is essential to realize that humanity is able to survive only by virtue of the capacity of humans to exploit natural resources—to convert the products of nature into forms available for human needs. If humanity had only the capacity of apes, depending exclusively on wild fruits and the like, they would be confined to those comparatively small regions of the globe where the climate and the fertility of the soil are specially favorable. But in the case supposed, humans would not be humans, they would not be time-binders—they would be animals—mere space-binders.

There are other facts which must be kept constantly in mind. One of them is that, in the world in which we live, there are natural laws of inorganic as well as organic phenomena. Another of the facts is, as before said, that the human class of life has the peculiar capacity of establishing the social laws and customs which regulate and influence its destinies, which help or hinder the processes of production upon which the lives and happiness of mankind essentially and fundamentally depend.

It must not be lost sight of in this connection that the human class of life is a part and a product of nature, and that, therefore, there must be *fundamental laws which are natural for this class of life*. A stone obeys the natural laws of stones; a liquid conforms to the natural law of liquids; a plant, to the natural laws of plants; an animal, to the natural laws of animals; it follows inevitably that there *must* be natural laws for humans.

But here the problem becomes more complicated; for the stone, the plant and the animal do not possess the intellectual power to create and initiate and so must *blindly* obey the laws that are natural for them; they are not free to determine their own destinies. Not so with man; man has the capacity and he can, through ignorance or neglect or mal-intent, deviate from, or misinterpret, the natural laws for the human class of life. Just therein lies the secret and the source of human chaos and woe—a fact of such tremendous importance that it cannot be over-emphasized and it seems impossible to evade it longer. To discover the nature of Man and the laws of that *nature,* marks the summit of human enterprises. For to solve this *problem is to open the way to everything which can be of importance to humanity*—to human welfare and happiness.

The great problem has been felt as a powerful impulse throughout the ages of human striving, for in all times it has been evident to thinkers that upon the right solution of the problem must forever depend the welfare of mankind. Many "solutions" have been offered; and, though they have differed widely, they agree in one respect—they have had a common fate—the fate of being false. What has been the trouble? The trouble has been, in every instance, a radical misconception of what a human being really is. The problem is to discover the natural laws of the human class of life. All the "solutions" offered in the course of history and those which are current to-day are of two and only two kinds—*zoological* and *mythological.* The zoological solutions are those which grow out of the false conception according to which human beings are animals; if humans are animals, the laws of human nature are the laws of animal nature; and so the social "sciences" of ethics, law, politics, economics, government become nothing but branches of zoology; as sciences, they are the studies of animal life; as arts, they are the arts of managing and controlling animals; according to this zoological philosophy, human wisdom about human beings is animal wisdom about animals.

The mythological "solutions" are those which start with the monstrous conception according to which human beings have no proper place in nature but are mixtures of natural and *super*natural—unions or combinations of animality and divinity. Such "solutions" contain no conception of *natural* law; scientifically judged, they are mythological absurdities—muddle-headed chattering of crude and irresponsible metaphysics—well-meaning no doubt, but silly, and deadly in their effects upon the interests of mankind, vitiating ethics, law, economics, politics and government.

Such have been and still are the regnant philosophies of human nature. What is the remedy? How are the laws of human nature to be discovered?

It is evident that the enterprise, like all other scientific enterprises, must be based upon and guided by realities. It is essential to realize that the great, central, dominant, all-embracing reality is the reality

of *human nature*. If we misconceive this fundamental matter, the enterprise must fail; that is both
logically clear and clear in the sad light of history;
but if we conceive it aright, we may confidently expect
the enterprise to prosper. That is why, in the chapter on "The Classes of Life," I have laid so much
stress on the absolute necessity of conceiving Man
as being what he really is, and not something else.
And we have discovered what man is: we have discovered that man is characterized by the capacity
or power to bind time, and so we have *defined*
humanity as the time-binding class of life. That concept is fundamental. It contains the germ of the
science and art of Human Engineering. The problem of discovering and applying the "laws of human
nature" is the problem of discovering and applying
to the conduct of life the laws of time-binding—of
time-binding activity—of time-binding *energy*. This
fact must be firmly seized and kept steadily in mind.

Energy, we have noted, is the capacity to do work.
In human economy work may be (1) *useful* or (2)
neutral or (3) *harmful*. These words have no significance except in human economy. The energy of
the human intellect is a time-binding energy, for it
is able to direct, to use, to transform other energies.
This time-binding energy is of higher rank—of
higher dimensionality—than the other natural
energies which it directs, controls, uses, and trans-

forms. This higher energy—which is commonly called the mental or spiritual power of man—*is* time-binding because it makes past achievements live in the present and present activities in time-to-come. It is an energy that initiates; it is an energy that creates; it is an energy that can understand the past and foretell the future—it is both historian and prophet; it is an energy that loads *abstract* time—the vehicle of events—with an ever-increasing burden of intellectual achievements, of spiritual wealth, destined for the civilization of posterity. And what is the natural law of the increase? What is the natural law of human advancements in all great matters of human concern?

The question is of utmost importance both theoretically and practically, for the law—whatever it be —is a *natural* law—a law of human nature—a law of the time-binding energy of man. What *is* the law? We have already noted the law of arithmetical progression and the law of geometric progression; we have seen the immense difference between them; and we have seen that the natural law of human progress in each and every cardinal matter is a law like that of a rapidly increasing geometric progression. In other words, the natural law of human progress—the natural law of amelioration in human affairs—the fundamental law of human nature—the basic law of the time-binding energy peculiar to man—is a Logarithmic law—a law of logarithmic increase. I beg the reader not to let the term bewilder him but to make it his own. It is easy to understand; and its significance is mighty and everlasting. Even its mathematical formulation can be understood by boys and girls. Let us see how the formulation looks.

Suppose PR to denote the amount of progress made in some important field by a given generation—which we may call the "first" generation; where R denotes the common ratio—the ratio of improvement—that is, the number by which the progress of one generation must be multiplied to give the amount of progress made by the next generation; then the amount of progress made by the second generation will be PR^2; that made by the third generation will be PR^3; and so on; now denote by T the number of generations, counting the first one and all that follow in endless succession. Then the following series will show the law of human progress in the chosen field:

$$PR, PR^2, PR^3, PR^4, PR^5, \ldots, PR^T, PR^{T+1}, \ldots;$$

notice how it goes; the first generation *ends* with PR; the second generation starts with PR, adds PR^2, and ends with $PR+PR^2$; the third generation starts with $PR+PR^2$, adds PR^3 and ends with $PR+PR^2+PR^3$; and so on and on; the *gain* made in the Tth generation is PR^T; *the total gain* made in T generations is

$$PR+PR^2+PR^3+ \ldots +PR^T;$$

this total gain is given by the formula,

$$\text{Total gain in } T \text{ generations} = \frac{R}{R-1}(PR^T - P).$$

If we take R to be 2 (which is a very small ratio, requiring the progress of each generation to be merely double that of the preceding one) and if we take T to be (say) 10, then we see that the progress made by the single 10*th* generation is $P \times 2^{10}$, which is 1024 times the progress made in the "first" generation; and we readily compute that the total gain in 10 generations is 2046 times the progress made in the "first" generation. Moreover, to gain a just sense of the impressiveness of this law, the reader must reflect upon the fact that it operates, not merely on one field, but in all fields of human interest. "Operates in all fields" I have just now said; as a matter of fact, as before pointed out, it does not so operate *now* in *all* fields nor has it ever done so. My point is that it *will* so operate when we once acquire sense enough to let it do so. That sense we shall have when and only when we discover that by nature we are time-binders and that the *effectiveness* of our time-binding capacity is not only a function of time but is, as I have explained, a logarithmic or exponential function of time—a function in which time (T) enters as an *exponent*, as in the expression PR^T, so that we humans are, unlike animals, naturally qualified not only to progress, but to progress more and more rapidly, with an always *accelerating acceleration*, as the generations pass.

This great fact is to be at once the basis, the regulator and guide in the science and art of Human Engineering. Whatever squares with that law of time-binding human energy, is right and makes foɪ human weal; whatever contravenes it, is wrong and makes for human woe.

And so I repeat that the world will have uninter-rupted, peaceful progress when and only when the so-called social "sciences"—the life-regulating "sciences" of ethics, law, philosophy, economics, religion, politics, and government—are technologized; when and only when they are made genuinely scientific in spirit and method; for then and only then will they advance, like the natural, mathematical and techno-logical sciences, in conformity to the fundamental exponential law of the time-binding nature of man; then and then only, by the equal pace of progress in all cardinal matters, the equilibrium of social insti-tutions will remain stable and social cataclysms cease.

CHAPTER V

WEALTH

I BEG the reader to allow me to begin this chapter with a word of warning. The reader is aware that Criticism—by which I mean Thought—may be any one of three kinds: it may be purely destructive; it may be purely constructive; or it may be both destructive and constructive at the same time. Purely destructive criticism is sometimes highly useful. If an old idea or a system of old ideas be false and therefore harmful, it is a genuine service to attack it and destroy it even if nothing be offered to take its place, just as it is good to destroy a rattlesnake lurking by a human pathway, even if one does not offer a substitute for the snake. But, however useful destructive criticism may be, it is not an easy service to render; for old ideas, however false and harmful, are protected alike by habit and by the inborn conservatism of many minds. Now, habit indeed is exceedingly useful—even indispensable to the effective conduct of life—for it enables us to do many useful things automatically and therefore easily, without conscious thinking, and thus to save our mental energy for other work; but for the same reason, habit is often very harmful; it makes us protect false ideas automatically, and so when the destructive critic endeavors to destroy such ideas by reasoning with us, he finds that he is trying to reason with automats—with machines. Such is the chief difficulty encountered by destructive criticism. On the other hand, purely constructive criticism—purely constructive thought—consists in introducing new ideas of a kind that do not clash, or do not seem to clash, with old ones. Is such criticism or thought easy? Far from it. It has difficulties of its own. These are of two varieties: the difficulty of showing people who are content with their present stock of old ideas that the new ones are interesting or important; and the great difficulty of making *new* ideas clear and intelligible, for the art of being clear and perfectly intelligible is very, very hard to acquire and to practise. The third kind of criticism—the third kind of thought—the kind that is at once both destructive and constructive—has a double aim—that of destroying old ideas that are false and that of replacing them with new ideas that are true; and so the third kind of criticism or thought is the most difficult of all, for it has to overcome both the difficulty of destructive criticism and that of constructive thought.

The reader, therefore, if he will be good enough to reflect a little upon the matter, can not fail to appreciate the tremendous difficulties which beset the writing of this little book, for he must perceive, not only that the work belongs to the third kind of critical thought, but—what is much more—the errors it aims to destroy are fundamental, world-wide and old, while the true ideas it seeks to substitute for them are fundamental and new. This great difficulty, felt at *every* stage of this writing, is, for a reason to be presently explained, greatly enhanced and felt with especial keenness in the present chapter. I therefore beg the reader to give me here very special cooperation—the cooperation of open-mindedness, candor and critical attention. It is essential to keep in mind the nature of our enterprise as a whole, which is that of pointing the way to the science and art of Human Engineering and laying the foundations thereof; we have seen Human Engineering, when developed, is to be the science and art of so directing human energies and capacities as to make them contribute most effectively to the advancement of human welfare; we have seen that this science and art must have its basis in a true conception of human nature—a just conception of what Man really is and of his natural place in the complex of the world; we have seen that the ages-old and still current conceptions of man—zoological and mythological conceptions, according to which human beings are either animals or else hybrids of animals and gods—are mainly responsible for the dismal things in human history; we have seen that man, far from being an animal or a compound of natural and supernatural, is a perfectly natural being characterized by a certain capacity or power—the capacity or power to bind time; we have seen that humanity is, therefore, to be rightly conceived and scientifically defined as the time-binding class of life; we have seen that, therefore, the laws of time-binding energies and time-binding phenomena are the laws of human nature; we have seen that this conception of man—which must be the basic concept, the fundamental principle and the perpetual guide and regulator of Human Engineering—is bound to work a profound transformation in all our views on human affairs and, in particular, must radically alter the so-called social "sciences"—the life-regulating "sciences" of ethics, sociology, economics, politics and government—advancing them from their present estate of pseudo sciences to the level of genuine sciences and technologizing them for the effective service of mankind. I call them "life-regulating," not because they play a more important part in human affairs than do the genuine sciences of mathematics, physics, chemistry, astronomy and biology, for they are not more important than these, but because they are, so to say, closer, more immediate and more obvious in their influence and effects. These life-regulating sciences

are, of course, not independent; they depend ultimately upon the genuine sciences for much of their
power and ought to go to them for light and guidance; but what I mean here by saying they are not
independent is that they are dependent upon each
other, interpenetrating and interlocking in innumerable ways. To show *in detail* how the so-called
sciences will have to be transformed to make them
accord with the right conception of man and qualify
them for their proper business will eventually require
a large volume or indeed volumes.

In this introductory work I cannot deal fully with
one of those "sciences" nor in suitable outline with
each of them separately. I must be content here to
deal, very briefly, with one of them by way of illustration and suggestion. Which one shall it be?

Now among these life-regulating "sciences" there
is one specially marked by the importance of its subject, by its central relation to the others and by its
prominence in the public mind. I mean Economics—
the "dismal science" of Political Economy. For that
reason I have chosen to deal with economics. In the
present chapter I shall discuss three of its principal
terms—Wealth, Capital and Money—with a view
to showing that the current meanings and interpretations of these familiar terms must be very greatly
deepened, enlarged and elevated if they are to accord
with facts and laws of human nature and if the so-

called "science" which employs them is to become a genuine science properly qualified to be a branch of Human Engineering. It is to be shown that the meanings currently attached by political economists and others to the terms in question belong to what I have called the period of humanity's childhood; and it is to be shown that the new meanings which the terms must receive belong to the period of humanity's manhood. It will be seen that the new meanings differ so radically from the old ones as to make it desirable for the sake of clarity to give the new meanings new names. But this, however scientifically desirable, is impracticable because the old terms—wealth, capital, money—are so deeply imbedded in the speech of the world. And here comes into view the very special difficulty alluded to above and which led me to request the reader's special cooperation in this chapter. The difficulty is not merely that of destroying old ideas that are false; it is not merely that of replacing them with true ideas that are new; it is that of causing people habitually to associate meanings that are new and true with terms associated so long, so universally, so uniformly with meanings that are false.

The secret of philosophy, said Leibnitz, is to treat familiar things as unfamiliar. By the secret of "philosophy" Leibnitz meant the secret of what we call science. Let us apply this wholesome maxim in our present study; let us, in so far as we can, regard the familiar terms—wealth, capital and money—as unfamiliar; let us deal with them afresh; let us examine openmindedly the facts—the phenomena— to which the terms relate and ascertain scientifically the significance the terms must have in a genuine science of human economy. Examine "the facts" I say—examine "the phenomena"—for bending facts to theories is a vital danger, while bending theories to facts is essential to science and the peaceful progress of society.

Human beings have always had some sense of values—some perception or cognition of values. In order to express or measure values, it was necessary to introduce units of measure, or units of exchange. People began to measure values by means of agricultural and other products, such as cattle, for example. The Latin word for cattle was *pecus,* and the word *pecunia,* which came to signify money, accounts for the meaning of our familiar word pecuniary. The earliest units for measuring became unsuited to the increasing needs of growing trade, "business," or traffic. Finally a unit called money was adopted in which the base was the value of some weight of gold. Thus we see that money came to mean simply the accepted unit for measuring, representing and expressing values of and in wealth.

But what is wealth? I have said that the old

conceptions of wealth, capital and money—the conceptions that are still current throughout the world —belong to the period of humanity's childhood— they are childish conceptions. I have said that they must be replaced by scientific conceptions—by conceptions fit for humanity's manhood. The change that must be made in our conceptions of the great terms is tremendous. It is necessary to analyse the current conceptions of wealth, capital, and money— the childish conceptions of them—in order to reveal their falseness, stupidity and folly. To do this we must enter the field of Political Economy—a field beset with peculiar difficulties and dangers. All the Furies of private interests are involved. One gains the impression that there is little or no real desire to gain a true conception—a scientific conception— of wealth. Everybody seems to prefer an emotional definition—a definition that suits his personal love of wealth or his hatred of it. Many definitions of wealth, capital and money are to be found in modern books of political economy—definitions and books belonging to humanity's childhood. For the purpose of this writing they all of them look alike—they sufficiently agree—they are all of them childish. Mill, for example, tells us that wealth consists of "useful or agreeable things which possess exchangeable value." Of capital one of the simplest definitions is this:

"Capital is that part of wealth which is devoted to obtaining further wealth." (Alfred Marshall, *Economics of Industry*.)

Walker (in his *Money, Trade and Industry*) defines money as follows:

"Money is that which passes freely from hand to hand throughout the community in final discharge of debts and full payment for commodities, being accepted equally without reference to the character or credit of the person who offers it, and without the intention of the person who receives it to consume it, or to enjoy it, or apply it to any other use than, in turn, to tender it to others in discharge of debts or full payment for commodities."

Political economy has many different schools of thought and methods of classification. Its reasonings are mainly speculative, metaphysical, and legalistic; its ethics is zoological ethics, based on the zoological conception of man as an animal. The elements of natural logic and natural ethics are absent. The sophisticated ideas about the subject of political economy, bluntly do not correspond to facts. Our primitive forefather in the jungle would have died from hunger, cold, heat, blood poisoning or the attacks of wild animals, if he had not used his brain and muscles to take some stone or a piece of wood to knock down fruit from trees, to kill an animal, so as to use his hide for clothes and his meat for food, or to break wood and trees for a shelter and to make some weapons for defense and hunting.

"In the first stone which he (the savage) flings at the wild animal he pursues, in the first stick that he seizes to strike down the fruit which hangs above his reach, we see the appropriation of one article for the purpose of aiding in the acquisition of another and thus we discover the origin of capital." (R. Torrens, *An Essay on the Production of Wealth.*)

Our primitive forefather's first acquaintance with fire was probably through lightning; he discovered, probably by chance, the possibility of making fire by rubbing together two pieces of wood and by striking together two pieces of stone; he established one of the first facts in technology; he felt the warm effect of fire and also the good effect of broiling his food by finding some roasted animals in a fire. Thus nature revealed to him one of its great gifts, the stored-up energy of the sun in vegetation and its primitive beneficial use. He was already a time-binding being; evolution had brought him to that level. Being a product of nature, he was reflecting those natural laws that belong to his class of life; he had ceased to be static—he had become dynamic —progressiveness had got into his blood—he was above the estate of animals.

We also observe that primitive man produced commodities, acquired experiences, made observations, and that some of the produced commodities had a use-value for other people and remained good for use, even after his death.

The produced commodities were composed of raw material, freely supplied by nature, combined with some mental work which gave him the conception of how to make and to use the object, and some work on his part which finally shaped the thing; all of this mental and manual work consumed an amount of time. It is obvious that all of these elements are indispensable to produce anything of any value, or of any use-value. His child not only directly received some of the use-values produced by him, but was initiated into all of his experiences and observations. (As we know, power, as defined in mechanics, means the ratio of work done to the time used in doing it.)

All those things are time-binding phenomena produced by the time-binding capacity of man; but man has *not* known that *this capacity* was his *defining mark*. We must notice the strange fact that, from the engineering point of view, humanity, though very developed in some ways, is childishly undeveloped in others. Humanity has some conceptions about dimensions and talks of the world in which we live as having three dimensions; yet even in its wildest imagination it can not picture tangibly a *fourth* dimension; nay, humanity has not learned to grasp the real meanings of things that are basic or fundamental. All of our conceptions are relative and comparative; all of them are based upon matters which we do not yet understand; for example, we talk of time, space, electricity, gravity, and so on, but no one has been able to define them in terms of the data of sensation; nevertheless—and it is a fact of the greatest importance—we learn how to use many things which we do not fully understand and are not yet able to define.

In political economy the meagreness of our understanding is especially remarkable; we have not yet grasped the obvious fact—a fact of immeasurable import for all of the social sciences—that with little exception the wealth and capital possessed by a given generation are not produced by its own toil but are the inherited fruit of dead men's toil—a free gift of the past. We have yet to learn and apply the lesson that not only our material wealth and capital but our science and art and learning and wisdom— all that goes to constitute our civilization—were produced, not by our own labor, but by the time-binding energies of past generations.

Primitive man used natural laws without knowing them or understanding them, but he was able to cause nature to express itself, by finding a way to release nature's stored up energy. Through the work of his brain and its direction in the use of his muscles, he found that some of his appliances were not good; he made better ones, and thus slowly at first, the progress of humanity went on. I will not enlarge upon the history of the evolution of civilization because it is told in many books.

In the earliest times the religious, philosophical, legal and ethical systems had not been invented. The morale at that time was a natural morale. Humans knew that they did not create nature. They did not feel it "proper" to "expropriate the creator" and legalistically appropriate the earth and its treasure for themselves. They felt, in their unsophisticated morale, that being called into existence they had a natural right to exist and to use freely the gifts of nature in the preservation of their life; and that is what they did.

After the death of a man, some of the objects produced by him still survived, such as weapons, fishing or hunting instruments, or the caves adapted for living; a baby had to be nourished for some years by its parents or it would have died. Those facts had important consequences; objects made by someone for some particular use could be used by someone else, even after the death of one or more successive users; again the experiences acquired by one member of a family or a group of people were taught by example or precept to others of the same generation and to the next generation. Such simple facts are the corner stones of our whole civilization and they are the direct result of the HUMAN CAPACITY OF TIME-BINDING.

The world to-day is full of controversy about wealth, capital, and money, and because humanity, through its peculiar time-binding power, binds this element "time" in an ever larger and larger degree, the controversy becomes more and more acute. Civilization as a process is the process of binding time; progress is made by the fact that each generation adds to the material and spiritual wealth which it inherits. Past achievements—the fruit of bygone time—thus live in the present, are augmented in the present, and transmitted to the future; the process goes on; time, the essential element, is so involved that, though it increases arithmetically, its fruit, civilization, advances geometrically.

But there is another peculiarity in wealth and money: If a wooden or iron "inch" be allowed to rot or rust quietly on some shelf, this "inch" does not represent anything besides this piece of wood or iron. But if we take the MENTAL value of an inch, this unit of one of the measures of space, and use it, with other quantities, in the contemplation of the skies for the solving of an astronomical problem, it gives a prophetic answer that, in a certain place there is a star; this star may be for years looked for in vain. Was it that the calculation was wrong? No, for after further search with telescopes of greater power, the star is found and the calculation thus verified.

It is obvious that the "unit"—inch—has no value by itself, but is very precious as a unit for measuring the phenomenon of length, which it perfectly represents, and that is why it was introduced.

It is exactly the same with money if the term be rightly understood. Understood aright, money, being the measure and representative of wealth, is in the main, the measure and the representative of dead men's toil; for, rightly understood, wealth is almost entirely the product of the labor of by-gone generations. This product, we have seen, involves the element of time as the chief factor. And so we discover how money, properly understood, is connected with time—the main function of money is to measure and represent the accumulated products of the labor of past generations. Hoarded money is like an iron "inch" upon a shelf—a useless lump; but when used as a measure and representative of wealth rightly understood, money renders invaluable service, for it then serves to measure and represent the living fruit of dead men's toil.

For this reason, it is useless to argue who is the more important, the capitalist who has legal possession of most of the material fruit of dead men's toil, or the laborer who has legal possession of but little of it. In the laborer, we do not now really look for his physical muscular labor ALONE; for this is replaced by mechanical or animal power as soon as it can be. What we do need from labor, and what we will always need, is his BRAIN—HIS TIME-BIND-ING POWER.

The population of the world may be divided into different classes; if the classes are not here enumerated in the customary way, it is because it is necessary to classify human beings, as nearly as possible, according to their "power-value." There is no assertion that this is an ideal classification, but if someone is moved to exclaim—"what a foolish, unscientific division!"—I will answer by saying: "I grant that the division is foolish and unscientific; but IT IS THE ONLY DIVISION WHICH *CORRESPONDS TO FACTS* IN LIFE, and it is not the writer's fault. By this 'foolishness' some good may be accomplished."

From an engineer's point of view humanity is apparently to be divided into three classes; (1) the intellectuals; (2) the rich; and (3) the poor. This division would seem to be contrary to all the rules of logic, but it corresponds to facts. Of course some individuals belong to two of the classes or even to all three of them, an after-war product, but essentially, they belong to the one class IN PROPORTION to the characteristic which is the most marked in their life; that is, in the sense of social classes— BASED ON MAGNITUDE OF VALUES.

(1) The intellectuals are the men and women

who possess the knowledge produced by the labor of by-gone generations but do not possess the material wealth thus produced. In mastering and using this inheritance of knowledge, they are exercising their time-binding energies and making the labor of the dead live in the present and for the future.

(2) The rich are those who have possession and control of most of the *material* wealth produced by the toil of bygone generations—wealth that is dead unless animated and transformed by the time-binding labor of the living.

(3) The poor are those who have neither the knowledge possessed by the intellectuals nor the material wealth possessed by the rich and who, moreover, because nearly all their efforts, under present conditions, are limited to the struggle for mere existence, have little or no opportunity to exercise their time-binding capacity.

Let us now try to ascertain the rôle of the time-binding class of life as a whole. We have by necessity, to go back to the beginning—back to the savage. We have seen what were the conditions of his work and progress; we saw that for each successful achievement he often had to wrestle with a very large number of unsuccessful achievements, and his lifetime being so limited, the total of his successful achievements was very limited, so that he was able to give to his child only a few useful objects and

the sum of his experience. Generally speaking, each
successor did not start his life at the point where
his father started; he started somewhere near where
his father left off. His father gave, say, fifty years
to discover two truths in nature and succeeded in
making two or three simple objects; but the son does
not need to give fifty years to discover and create the
same achievements, and so he has time to achieve
something *new*. He thus adds his own achievements
to those of his father in tools and experience; this is
the mathematical equivalent of adding his parent's
years of life to his own. His mother's work and
experience are of course included—the name father
and son being only used representatively.

This stupendous fact is the definitive mark of
humanity—the power to roll up continuously the
ever-increasing achievements of generation after
generation endlessly. We have seen that this time-
binding power is an exponential power or function
of time. Time flows on, increasing in arithmetical
progression, adding generation unto generation;
but the results of human energies working in time
do not go on arithmetically; they pile up or roll up
more and more rapidly, augmenting in accordance
with the law of a more and more rapidly increasing
geometric progression. The typical term of the
progression is PR^T where PR denotes the ending
progress made in the generation with which we

agree to start our reckoning, R denotes the ratio increase, and T denotes the number of generations after the chosen " start." The quantity, PR^T of progress made in the Tth generation contains T as an exponent, and so the quantity, varying as time T passes, is called an exponential function of the time.

Nature is the source of all energy. Plants, the lowest form of life, have a definite rôle to perform in the economy of nature. Their function is the forming of albuminoids and other substances for higher purposes. All of their nitrates are high-explosives, or low explosives, but explosives anyway. They are powerful sources of some new energy. Animal life uses these "explosives" as food and is correspondingly more dynamic, but in animal life time does not play the rôle it plays in human life. Animals are limited by death permanently. If animals make any progress from generation to generation, it is so small as to be negligible. A beaver, for example, is a remarkable builder of dams, but he does not progress in the way of inventions or further development. A beaver dam is always a beaver dam.

Finally humanity, the highest known class of life, has time-binding capacity as its characteristic, its discriminant, its peculiar and definitive mark. It is an unrealized fact that in this higher class of life, *the law of organic growth develops into the law of energy-growth—the mind—the time-binding energy— an increasing exponential function of time.* That fact is of basic importance for the science and art of Human Engineering. In mechanics we have the well-known formula

$$(1) \quad \frac{\text{Work}}{\text{Time}} = \text{Power}.$$

We have seen that, in accordance with the law of geometric progression, PR^T represents the progress made—the work done— in the Tth generation (T being counted from some generation taken as starting point of reckoning); this progress, achievement, or *work*, being done in *one* generation, we have by (1)

$$(2) \quad \frac{\text{Work} = PR^T}{\text{Time} = 1} = \text{Power},$$

that is, $PR^T = \text{Power}$; this means that the number PR^T, which measures the work done in a given generation, is also the measure of the power that does the work. Now, the total work, W, done in the T generations is

$$(3) \quad W = PR^1 + PR^2 + PR^3 + \ldots + PR^T;$$

that is,

$$(4) \quad W = \frac{R}{R-1} (PR^T - P)$$

It should be noticed that by (2) this expression for W may also be regarded as the sum of T different powers PR, PR^2, etc., each working during one and only one generation; if we divided this sum by T, the quotient would be a power that would have to act through T generations to produce W. The reader should not fail to notice very carefully that the expression (4) for W is an expression for the total progress made—the total work done—the total wealth produced— in the course of T generations and he should especially note how the expression involves the exponential function of time (T), namely PR^T.

The formula makes mathematically evident the time-binding capacity characteristic of the human class of life. Properly understood, *wealth* consists of the fruits or products of this time-binding capacity of man. Animals do not produce wealth; it is produced by Man and only Man. The foregoing basic formulation should lead to further similar developments throwing much light upon the process of civilization and serving to eliminate " private opinion " from the conduct of human affairs. (In this writing it is not important to look deeper into these proposed series. The fact remains that P, as well as R, are peculiarly increasing series of a geometrical character—the precise form will be developed in another writing.)

Human achievements and progress, because cumulative, are knocking out the barriers of time. This fact is the vital and dynamic difference between animal life and human life. As plants gather in and store up solar energy into sheaves for the use and growth of animal and man—so humans are gathering and binding the knowledge of past centuries into sheaves for the use and development of generations yet unborn.

We have seen that the term wealth, rightly understood, means the fruit of the time-binding work of humanity. Wealth is of two kinds: one is material; the other is knowledge. Both kinds have use-value. The first kind perishes—the commodities composing it deteriorate and become useless. The other is permanent in character; it is imperishable; it may be lost or forgotten but it does not wear out.

The one is limited in time; the other, unlimited in time; the former I call POTENTIAL USE-VALUE; the latter, KINETIC USE-VALUE. Analysis will justify the names. The energy of a body which is due to its position, is called potential energy. The energy of a body which is due to its motion, is called kinetic energy. Here the material use-value has value through its position, shape and so forth; it is immobile if not used, and has not the capacity to progress. Mental use-values are not static but permanently dynamic; one thought, one discovery, is the impulse to others; they follow the law of an increasing *potential* function of time. (See app. II.) This is why these names correspond to the two names of the two mentioned classes of energy.

Here I must return to the current conceptions of wealth and capital, before cited. "Wealth," we are told, "is any useful or agreeable thing which possesses *exchangeable value*." And we are told that "Capital is that part of wealth which is devoted to obtaining further wealth." I have said that such conceptions—such definitions—of wealth and capital are childish—they belong to the period of humanity's childhood. That they are indeed childish conceptions the reader can not fail to see if he will reflect upon them and especially if he will compare them with the scientific conception according to which wealth consists of those things—whether they be material commodities or forms of knowledge and understanding—that have been produced by the time-binding energies of humanity, and according to which *nearly all the wealth of the world at any given time* is the *accumulated fruit of the toil of past generations*—the living work of the dead. It seems unnecessary to warn the reader against confusing the "*making*" of money by hook or crook, by trick or trade, with the *creating* of wealth, by the product of labor. In calling the old conceptions childish, I do not mean that they contain no element of truth whatever; I mean that they are shallow, scientifically or spiritually meagre, narrow in their vision, wrong in their accent; I especially mean that they are dumb, bcause they are blind, regarding the central matter that wealth is the natural offspring of Time and Human Toil. The old conceptions do indeed imply that wealth and capital involve both potential and kinetic use-values, and in so far they are right. But how do such use-values arise?

The potential use-values in wealth are created by human work operating in time upon raw material given by nature. The use-values are produced by time-taking transformations of the raw materials; these transformations are wrought by human brain labor and human muscular labor directed by the human brain acting in time. The kinetic use-values of wealth are also created by human toil—mainly by the intellectual labor of observation, experimentation, imagination, deduction and invention, all consuming the precious time of short human lives. It is obvious that in the creation of use-values whether potential or kinetic, the element of *time* enters as an absolutely essential factor. The fundamental importance of time as a factor in the production of wealth—the fact that wealth and the use-values of wealth are literally the natural offspring of the spiritual union of time with toil—has been completely overlooked, not only by the economics, but by the ethics, the jurisprudence and the other branches of speculative reasoning, throughout the long period of humanity's childhood. In the course of the ages there has indeed been much "talk" about time, but there has been no recognition of the basic significance of time as essential in the conception and in the very constitution of human values.

It is often said that "Time is Money"; the statement is often false; but the proposition that Money is Time is always true. It is always true in the profound sense that Money is the measure and symbol of Wealth—the product of Time and Toil—the crystallization of the time-binding human capacity. IT IS THUS TRUE THAT MONEY IS A VERY PRECIOUS THING, THE MEASURE AND SYMBOL OF WORK—IN PART THE WORK OF THE LIVING BUT, IN THE MAIN, THE LIVING WORK OF THE DEAD.

Nature's laws are supreme; we cannot change them; we can deviate from them for a while, but the end is evil. That is the lesson we must learn from the history of Humanity's childhood. False conceptions of Man—ignorance of the laws of human nature—have given us unscientific economies, unscientific ethics, unscientific law, unscientific politics, unscientific government. These have made human history the history of social cataclysms—insurrections, wars, revolutions—sad tokens not so much of human lust as of human ignorance of the laws of

human nature. There is but one remedy, one hope
—a science and art of Human Engineering based
upon the just conception of humanity as the time-
binding class of life and conforming to the laws of
nature including the laws of human nature.

CHAPTER VI

CAPITALISTIC ERA

THE immortal work done by Descartes, Newton and Leibnitz was to discover powerful methods for mathematics—the only fit language for expressing the laws of nature.

Human Engineering will be the science by which the great social problems will be solved. For the first time since the first day of man, humanity will really understand its own nature and status; and will learn to direct scientifically the living and the non-living forces for construction, avoiding unnecessary destruction and waste.

It may seem strange but it is true that the time-binding exponential powers, called humans, do not die—their bodies die but their achievements live forever—a permanent source of power. All of our precious possessions—science, acquired by experience, accumulated wealth in all fields of life—are kinetic and potential use-values created and left by by-gone generations; they are humanity's treasures produced mainly in the past, and conserved for our use, by that peculiar function or power of man for the binding of time. That the natural trend of life and the progress of the development of this treasury is so often checked, turned from its natural course, or set back, is due to ignorance of human nature, to metaphysical speculation and sophistry. Those who, with or without intention, keep the rate of humanity's mental advancement down to that of an arithmetic progression are the real enemies of society; for they keep the life-regulating "sciences" and institutions far behind the gallop of life itself. The consequence is periodic social violence—wars and revolutions.

Let us carry the analysis of potential and kinetic use-values a little further. All potential use-values left to us by the dead are temporal and differ in utility. Many potential use-values are found in museums and have very limited value to-day in practical life. On the other hand some roads or waterways built by the ancients have use-value to-day; and an almost endless list of modern potential use-values have or will have use-values for a long time to come, such as buildings, improved lands, railroad tracks, certain machines or tools; the use-value of some such items of material wealth will last for more than one generation. Kinetic use-values are permanent in their character, for, though they may become antiquated, they yet serve as the foundation for the developments that supersede them, and so they continue to live in that to which they lead.

I would draw attention at this point to one of the

most important kinetic and potential use-values produced by humanity—the invention of the steam engine. Through this invention, humanity has been able to avail itself, not only of the living fruits of dead men's toil, but also of the inconceivably vast amounts of solar energy and time bound up in the growth of vegetable life and conserved for use in the form of coal and other fuels of vegetable origin. This invention has revolutionized our life in countless directions. To be brief, I will analyse only the most salient effects. Human Engineering has never existed except in the most embryonic form. In remote antiquity the conception and knowledge of natural law was wholly absent or exceedingly vague. Before the invention of the steam engine, people depended mainly upon human powers—that is, upon "living powers"—the powers of living men, and the living fruits of the labor of the dead. Even then there were manifold complications.

The invention of the steam engine released for human use a new power of tremendous magnitude— the stored-up power of solar energy and ages of time. But we must not fail to note carefully that we to-day are enabled to use this immense new power of bound-up solar energy and time by a human invention, a product of the dead.

The full significance of the last statement requires reflection. The now dead inventor of the steam engine could not have produced his ingenious invention except by using the living powers of other dead men—except by using the material and spiritual or mental wealth created by those who had gone before. In the inventor's intellectual equipment there was actively present the kinetic use-value of "bound-up-time," enabling him to discover the laws of heat, water, and steam; and he employed both the potential and kinetic use-values of mechanical instruments, methods of work, and scientific knowledge of his time and generation—use-values of wealth created by the genius and toil of by-gone generations. This invention was not produced, let us say 6000 years ago, because civilization was not then sufficiently advanced: mathematically considered, the production of this great use-value had to await all the accumulated work of six thousand years of human ingenuity and human labor. So, if we choose, the steam engine may be considered a kinetic use-value in which the factor of time is equal to something like 6000 years, or let us say roughly 200 generations.

It is obvious that, in one life time, even a genius of the highest order, could not, in aboriginal conditions, have invented and built a steam engine, when everything, even iron, was unknown. Of course if the same inventor could have had a life of several thousands of years and could have consecutively followed up all the processes, unhampered by the prejudices of those days, and been able to make all of these inventions by himself, he would represent in himself all the progress of civilization.

By this illustration we see the profound meaning of the words—the living powers of the dead; we see the grave importance in human life of the factor TIME; we behold the significance of the time-binding capacity of man. The steam engine is to be seen anew, as in the main the accumulated production of dead-men's work. The life of one generation is short, and were it not for our human capacity to inherit the material and spiritual fruit of dead men's toil, to augment it a little in the brief span of our own lives, and to transmit it to posterity, the process of civilization would not be possible and our present estate would be that of aboriginal man. Civilization is a creature, its creator is the time-binding power of man. Animals have it not, because they belong to a lower type or dimension of life.

Sophistry avails nothing here; a child, left in the woods, would be and remain a savage, matching his wits with gorillas. He becomes a civilized man only by the accumulation of, and acquaintance with dead men's work; for then and only then can he start where the preceding generation left off. This capacity is peculiar to men; the fact can not be repeated too often.

It is untrue to say that *A* started his life aided

exclusively by the achievements of (say) his father, for his father's achievements depended on the achievements of *his* immediate predecessors; and so on all the way back through the life of humanity. This fact, of supreme ethical importance, applies to *all* of us; none of us may speak or act as if the material or spiritual wealth we have were produced by us; for, if we be not stupid, we must see that what we call *our* wealth, *our* civilization, everything we use or enjoy, is in the main the product of the labor of men now dead, some of them slaves, some of them "owners" of slaves. The metal spoon or the knife which we use daily is a product of the work of many generations, including those who discovered the metal and the use of it, and the utility of the spoon.

And here arises a most important question: Since the wealth of the world is in the main the free gift of the past—the fruit of the labor of the dead— to whom does it of right belong? The question can not be evaded. Is the existing monopoly of the great inherited treasures produced by dead men's toil a normal and natural evolution?

Or is it an artificial status imposed by the few upon the many? Such is the crux of the modern controversy.

It is generally known that the invention of the steam engine and other combustion engines which re- lease sun-power for mechanical use, has revolution-

ized the economic system; for the building of engines
in the scale of modern needs, it is necessary to concentrate a great number of living men in one place,
to build factories, to set up machines used in producing the engines, and all this requires the use of
vast amounts of money. That is why this era is
called the capitalistic era. But it is necessary to stop
here and analyse the factors of value in the engine
to be made and in the money used for the purpose of
making use of the stored-up energies of the sun. We
have found that the major part of the engine and all
factors connected with its production are the combined power of dead men's labor. We have found
that wealth or capital and its symbol, money, are
also, in the main, the bound-up power of dead men's
labor; so that the only way to obtain the benefit in the
release of sun-power, is by using the product of the
toil of the dead. It is further obvious that only the
men or organizations that are able to concentrate the
largest amounts of money, representing the work of
the dead, can have the fullest use of the stored-up
energies of time and the ancient sun. Thus the
monopoly of the stored-up energies of the sun arises
from monopolizing the accumulated fruits of dead
men's toil. These problems will, in the future, be
the concern of the science and art of Human Engineering.

Let us glance briefly at the problems from another

angle. The power developed in the combustion of one pound of coal is theoretically equal to 11,580,000 foot pounds. But by our imperfect methods of utilization, not more than 1,500,000 foot pounds are made available. This is about the amount of physical power exerted by a man of ordinary strength during a day's work. Hence 300 pounds of coal will represent the labor of a man for a year. The current production of coal in the world is about 500,000,000 tons (1906). If we suppose that only half of this coal goes for mechanical use, this will give us approximately the number as 1,600,-000,000 man-powers that are producers but not consumers.

Let us take a still broader view of resources; we have approximately 1,600,000,000 living human beings (all censuses available between 1902 and 1906); a wealth of approximately $357,000,000,-000 (*Social Progress*, 1906, page 221) which in our analysis is dead men's work; and sun-power equal, in work, to the work of our whole living population, or equal to 1,600,000,000 sun man-powers. Taking, for simplicity's sake, $35.70 as the average living expenses per annum for each one of the *world's* population, we will have:

(1) 1,600,000,000 living men.

(2) 10,000,000,000 living man-powers of the dead.

(3) 1,600,000,000 sun man-powers.

Such classification needs a reflection: man is intrinsically an increasing exponential power and always produces two use-values—the potential and the kinetic. All living men have in some degree this type of power; they are *able to direct and use basic powers*.

So we see that this world is really populated today by three different populations, all of them dynamic and active: to wit, 1,600,000,000 living men; 10,000,000,000 living man-powers of the dead; 1,600,000,000 sun man-powers.

Thus it is obvious beyond any argument, *that this additional producing but not consuming* population, has been produced mainly by the work of all our past generations. It is said "mainly" because, if we were the first generation, we would be just aboriginal savages having nothing and progressing very slowly. The reason why we progress very rapidly, in this stage of civilization, is explained very clearly by the mathematical law of a geometrical progression, with an ever increasing number of terms, the magnitude of the terms increasing more rapidly all the time.*

* Of course, the geometric progression does not represent *precisely* the law of human progression; it is here employed because it is familiar and serves, better perhaps than any other simple mathematical means, to show *roughly* how human progress goes on. The essential elements of a progression are the first term P and the ratio R and the number of the terms T; in the human progression $PR^{1'}$ PR^2, PR^3, . . . PR^T, P is the

This fact is the reason why the old unscientific and artificial social system requires and must undergo profound transformation. Human progress, in many directions, is so far advanced that social institutions can not much longer continue to lag so far behind. Static ethics, static jurisprudence, static economics, and the rest must become dynamic; if they do not continue to progress peacefully in accordance with the law of the progress of science, they will be forced by violent readjustments, recurring with ever increasing frequency.

Here we have a problem of very high importance and enormous magnitude. To serve 1,600,000,000 living men, we have 11,600,000,000 dead man-powers and all the sun man-powers—SEVEN SER-VANTS TO EACH LIVING MAN, WOMAN AND CHILD

starting status of the first generation, R is the peculiar capacity of humans to bind time and is a *free gift* and *law* of *nature*, which it would be folly not to recognize and accept as such, T is time, or number of generations. It is obvious that the magnitude, PR^T, is entirely dependent on the magnitudes of PR, and T. The existence of R and T is independent of humans, R being a law of nature, T a gift of nature, P the starting status of the initial generation. With $P = O$ or $R = O$ THERE WOULD BE NO PROGRESS or progression at all; each term in the case of human progression is mainly dependent upon the time and the work done by the dead. The existence of R and T is entirely beyond human control. Humans can control only the MAGNI-TUDE of those elements by education. Here comes the tremendous responsibility of education. It is not necessary to use much imagination to see that if humanity had always been rightly educated, science would have long ago discovered the natural forces and laws essential to human welfare, and human misery would to-day be relatively small.

included. It looks like the millennium. It would be so if we but used all this power in a constructive way, eliminating waste and controversy and all those factors which hamper production and progress. The present economic system does not realize even the beginning of the magnitude of this truth and the tremendous results which are to be achieved through the adjustment of it. The problem will be solved by Human Engineering, for this will establish the right understanding of values and will show how to manage world problems scientifically; it will give a scientific foundation to Political Economy and transform so-called "scientific shop management" into genuine "scientific world management." *

There is a chasm between "Capital" and "Labor," but nature does not know "Capital" or "Labor" at all. Nature knows only matter, energy, "space," "time," potential and kinetic use-values, forces in all their direct and indirect expression, the energies of living men, living powers of dead men, and the bound-up powers of Time and the ancient Sun. Nature made man an increasing exponential function of time, a time-binder, a power able to transform and direct basic powers. Sometimes we hypocritically like to delude ourselves, if our delusions are agreeable— and profitable. We call human work "manual labor" and we pretend that we need the laborer for

* See Appendix III.

his muscular service, but when we thus speak, we are thoughtless, stupid, or insincere. What we look for in the worker is his *control* of his muscles; mechanical work is or can be replaced almost entirely by machinery. What we will never be able to replace by machinery is a Man, because man belongs to the level of a dimension above machinery. Engine-power, sun man-power, and capital—mainly the work of the dead—are inanimate; they become productive only when quickened by the time-binding energies of living men and women. Then only are the results proportional to the ever growing magnitude of exponential power. In nature's economy the time-binders are the intelligent forces. There is none else known to us, and from the engineer's point of view, Edison and the simplest laborer, Smith or Jones, are basically the same; their powers or capacities are exponential, and, though differing in degree, are the same in kind. This may seem optimistic but all engineers are optimists. They deal only with fact and truth. If they make mistakes, if their bridges break down, then, no matter how clever their sophistry, they are adjudged criminal. Like severity must be made the rule and practice toward all those who control the institutions and great affairs of human society. Periodical break-downs must be prevented. The engineers of human society must be held responsible, as the bridge engineer is held to-day.

Things are often simpler than they appear at the first glance. There may be fire and plenty of coal in a stove, yet no heat; the fire does not burn well; an engineer will remove the natural causes of obstruction of the natural process; even such a simple thing as the removal of ashes may solve the problem. It seems simple enough. The truth is often clear and simple, if only it be not obscured and complicated by sophistry.

"Capitalistic" reasoning and "Socialistic" reasoning—Nature does not know such things. Nature has only one "reasoning" in all its functions. Our falsifying of nature's laws makes the controversy. Socialism exists as an *ism* because Capitalism exists as an *ism;* the clash is only an expression of the eternal law of action and reaction.

We are living in a world of wealth, a world enriched by many generations of dead men's toil; between the lust of the one to *keep* and the lust of others to *get,* there is little to choose; such contentions of lust against lust are *sub*-human—animalistic; such ethics is zoological ethics—the righteousness of tooth and claw; below the human dimensions of life, utterly unworthy of the creative energy—the time-binding capacity—of humanity. Socialism feels keenly and sees dimly that human affairs are not conducted in conformity with natural laws. Capitalism neither sees it nor keenly feels it. Neither the one nor the other stops to investigate natural laws—nature's laws—laws of human nature—scientifically. They both of them use the same speculative methods in their arguments, and there can be no issue. Against one old-fashioned, speculative argument, there is always a speculative answer. They both speak about the truth, but their methods can not find the truth nor their language express it. They speak of "justice," "right" and so forth, not knowing that their conceptions of those terms are based on a wrong understanding of values. There is one and but one remedy, and that remedy consists in applying scientific method to the study of the subject. Sound reasoning, once introduced, will overrun humanity as the fields turn green in the spring; it will eliminate the waste of energy in controversies; it will attract all forces toward construction and the exploitation of nature for the common weal.

There are capitalists and capitalists; there are socialists and socialists. Among the capitalists there are those who want wealth—mainly the fruit of dead men's toil—for themselves. Among the socialists there are those—the orthodox socialists—who seek to disperse it. The former do not perceive that the product of the labor of the dead is itself dead if not quickened by the energies of living men. The orthodox socialists do not perceive the tremendous benefits that accrue to mankind from the accumulation of wealth, if *rightly used*.

Whether we be capitalists or socialists or neither, we must learn that to prey upon the treasury left by the dead is to live, not the life of a human being, but that of a *ghoul*. Legalistic title—documentary ownership—does not alter the fact. Neither does lust for the same.

When we have acquired the just conception of what a human being is we shall get away from the Roman conception according to which a human being is *instrumentum vocale;* an animal, *instrumentum semivocale:* and a tool, *instrumentum mutum*. To regard human beings as tools—as instruments—for the use of other human beings is not only unscientific but it is repugnant, stupid and short sighted. Tools are made by man but have not the autonomy of their maker—they have not man's time-binding capacity for initiation, for self-direction, and self-improvement. In their own nature, tools, instruments, machines belong to a dimension far lower than that of man.

Talk of dimensions or dimensionality is by no means theoretical rubbish. The right understanding of dimensions is of life-and-death importance in practical life. The intermixing of dimensions leads to wrong conclusions in our thought and wrong conclusions lead to disasters.

Consider the classes of life as representing three dimensions (as explained in an earlier chapter), then human production belongs essentially to the human or as I call it the third dimension. With the base of (say) 5, we produce in the third dimension a result of 125 units, and so when humans are paid but 25 units in accordance with the standards of the second dimension (that of animals), humanity is deprived of the benefit of 100 units of produced wealth. That is an illustration of what a part dimensions play in practical life. The reflective reader may analyse for himself what effect these same rules would have, if expressed and applied in the human "time-binding" dimension, time being the supreme test. The following table gives the visual shock:

1st Dimension	2nd Dimension	3rd Dimension
5	25	125
10	100	1,000
100	10,000	1,000,000
1,000	1,000,000	1,000,000,000

This explains why the intermixing of dimensions is the source of tremendous evil.

Who can now assert that the problem of dimensions is one only of theory? It is not even a question of limitation of mind, but it becomes a question of limitation of eyesight, not to be able to see the overwhelming differences between the laws of development of the first, second, and the third dimension.

Dollars, or pounds sterling, or other units of money follow the same rules: the strength and in fact the source of power of modern capitalism, is found in just this difference in dimensions—in the difference between what is given and what is taken, in the difference between what is earned and what is "made." The problem of dimensions is, therefore, a key which unlocks the secrets of the power of capitalism and opens the door to a new civilization where the understanding of dimensions will establish order out of the chaos.

We have seen that kinetic and potential use-values, produced mainly by the dead, are bound up in wealth, which is measured and symbolized by money. This being true, it is obvious that money is a measure and symbol of power, of work done, of bound-up time.

The *space*-binding *animal* standard of miscivilization has brought us to an impasse—a blind alley—for the simple physical reason that there is no more space to "bind." Practically all the habitable lands, and practically all the natural resources, are already divided among private legalistic owners. What hope is there for the ever increasing population?

But we have these 1,600,000,000 living men; 10,000,000,000 living man-powers of the dead; and 1,600,000,000 sun man-powers: that is indeed a tremendous power to PRODUCE WEALTH FOR ALL, IF WISELY DIRECTED, but to-day it is ignorantly and shamefully misdirected, because human beings are not treated in accordance with their nature as the time-binding class of life.

Much more is to be gained in exploiting nature aimfully, all the time, with a full mobilization of our living, dead, and sun-powers, than by exploiting man all the time and nature occasionally. Selfishness and ignorance—is it these that prevent full mobilization of the producing powers of the world?

Such as contribute most to human progress and human enlightenment—men like Gutenberg, Copernicus, Newton, Leibnitz, Watts, Franklin, Mendeleieff, Pasteur, Sklodowska-Curie, Edison, Steinmetz, Loeb, Dewey, Keyser, Whitehead, Russell, Poincaré, William Benjamin Smith, Gibbs, Einstein, and many others—consume no more bread than the simplest of their fellow mortals. Indeed such men are often in want. How many a genius has perished inarticulate because unable to stand the strain of social conditions where animal standards prevail and "survival of the fittest" means, not survival of the "fittest in time-binding capacity," but survival of the strongest in ruthlessness and guile—in space-binding competition!

Wealth is produced by those who work with hand or brain and by no others. The great mass of the wealth of the world has been thus produced by generations that have gone. We know that the greatest

wealth producers—immeasurably the greatest—have
been and are scientific men, discoverers and in-
ventors. If an invention, in the course of a few
years after it is made, must become public property,
then the wealth produced by the *use* of the invention should also become public property in the course
of a like period of years after it is thus produced.
Against this proposition no sophistry can avail.

One of the greatest powers of modern times is
the Press; it commands the resources of space and
time; it affects in a thousand subtle ways the form
of our thoughts. It controls the exchange of news
throughout the world. Unfortunately the press is
often controlled by exploiters of the "living powers
of the dead," and so what is presented as news is
frequently so limited, colored and distorted by selfish
interests as to be falsehood in the guise of truth.
Honest, independent papers are frequently starved
by selfish conspirators and forced to close down.
Thus the press, which is itself the product in the
main of dead men's toil, is made a means for the
deception and exploitation of the living. Indeed the
bitter words of Voltaire seem to be too true: "Since
God created man in his own image, how often has
man endeavored to render similar service to God."
Those who want to use such "God-like" powers to
rule the world are modern Neros, who in their
wickedness and folly fancy themselves divine. To

deceive, and through deception, to exploit, rob and subjugate living men and women, and to do it by prostituting the living powers created by the dead, is the work, I will not say of men, but of *mad* men, greedy, ignorant and blind. What is the remedy? Revolution? Revolution is also mad. The only remedy is enlightenment—knowledge, knowledge of nature, knowledge of human nature, scientific education, science applied to all the affairs of man—the science and art of Human Engineering.

CHAPTER VII

SURVIVAL OF THE FITTEST

HUMANITY is a dynamic affair, nay, the most dynamic known, because it is able to transform and direct basic powers. Where power is produced there must be an issue for it. Power must perforce express itself in some form. Electricity produced in the skies comes down in an often disastrous manner. Electricity, produced aimfully, runs our railroads; just so the enormous power produced by humanity must be used aimfully, in a constructive way or it will burst into insurrections, revolutions and wars.

Hitherto we have been guided by those bottomless sciences having only mythological ideas of power— by ideas moulded by personal ambitions, personal interests, or downright ignorance. Periodically we have had all the evils of the lack of a common aim and scientific guidance. Power has been held by the "God-given" or the "cleverest"; seldom has the power been given to the "fittest" in the sense of the most capable "to do." Those who speak of the "survival of the fittest," as in the Darwinian theory of animals, bark an animal language. This rule, being natural only in the life of plants and animals and appropriate only to the lower forms of physical life, cannot, except with profound change of meaning, be applied to the time-binding class of life, without disaster.

The modern vast accumulation of wealth for private purposes, justifies itself by using the argument of the "survival of the fittest." Very well, where there is a "survival," there must be victims; where there are victims, there has been fighting. Is this what the users of this argument mean? Like the Kaiser, they talk peace and make war. This method of doing things is not in any way new. The world has been accustomed to it for a very long while.

Personally I believe that most of the masters of speculative semi-sciences, such as economics, law, ethics, politics and government are honest in their beliefs and speculations. Simply the right man believes in the wrong thing; if shown the right way out of the mess he will cease to hamper progress; he will be of the greatest value to the new world built by Human Engineers, where human capacities, exponential functions of time, will operate naturally; where economy, law, ethics, politics and government will be *dynamic,* not *static.* There is a world of difference between these two words.

The immediate object of this writing is to show the way to directing the time-binding powers of mankind for the benefit of all. Human technology, as an art and science, does not yet exist; some basic principles were required as a foundation for such a science. Especially was it necessary to establish a *human* standard, and thus make it certain and clear that "space-binders"—the members of the *animal* world—are "outside of the human law"—outside the natural laws for the human class of life.

Present civilization is a very complicated affair; although many of our social problems are very badly managed, sudden changes could not be made without endangering the welfare and life of all classes of society. In the meantime, changes must be made because the world can not proceed much longer under pre-war conditions; they have been too well exposed by facts for humanity to allow itself to be blindly led again.

In the World War humanity passed through a tremendous trial and for those years was under the strain of an extensive mobilization campaign. The necessity of increasing power was manifest; the importance of a common base or aim became equally manifest. In this case the base, the common aim, was found in "war patriotism." This common base enabled all the states to add up individual powers and build maximum efficiency into a *collective* power. This expression is used, not only as a social truth, but as a known mathematical truth. Those high ideals, which were given "Urbi et orbi" in thou-

sands of speeches and in millions of propaganda
papers, had a much greater educational importance
and influence than most people are aware of. People
have been awakened and have acquired the taste for
those higher purposes which in the past were available only for the few.

Many old worn-out idols, ideas and ideals have
fallen; but what is going to take their place? We
witness an unrest which will not be eliminated until
something essential is done to adjust it. Calm often
betokens a coming storm. The coming storm is not
the work of any "bad man," but it is the inevitable
consequence of a "bad system." It is dangerous
to hide our heads in the sand, like an ostrich, and
fancy we are safe.

"Survival of the fittest" in the commonly used animal sense is not a theory or principle for a "time-
binding" being. This theory is only for the physical
bodies of animals; its effect upon humanity is sin-
ister and degrading (see App. II). We see the principle at work all about us in criminal exploitation and
profiteering. As a matter of fact, the ages-long application of this animal principle to human affairs
has degraded the whole human morale in an inconceivably far-reaching way. Personal greed and selfishness are brazenly owned as principles of conduct.
We shrug our shoulders in acquiescence and proclaim
greed and selfishness to be the very core of human

nature, take it all for granted, and let it pass at that. We have gone so far in our degradation that the prophet of capitalistic principles, Adam Smith, in his famous *Wealth of Nations,* arrives at the laws of wealth, not from the phenomena of wealth nor from statistical statements, but from the phenomena of selfishness—a fact which shows how far-reaching in its dire influence upon all humanity is the theory that human beings are "animals." Of course the effect is very disastrous. The preceding chapters have shown that the theory is false; it is false, not only because of its unhappy effects, but it belies the characteristic nature of man. Human nature, this time-binding power, not only has the peculiar capacity for perpetual progress, but it has, over and above all animal propensities, certain qualities constituting it a distinctive dimension or type of life. Not only our whole collective life proves a love for higher ideals, but even our dead *give* us the rich heritage, material and spiritual, of all their toils. There is nothing mystical about it; to call SUCH a class a *naturally* selfish class is not only nonsensical but monstrous.

This capacity for higher ideals does not originate in some *"super*natural" outside factor; it is *not* of extraneous origin, it is the expression of the time-binding element which we *inherently* possess, independently of our "will"; it is an inborn capacity—a *gift* of nature. We simply are made this way and not in any other. There is indeed a fine sense in which we can, if we choose, apply the expression—survival of the fittest—to the activity of the time-binding energies of man. Having the peculiar capacity to survive in our deeds, we have an inclination to use it and we survive in the deeds of our creation; and so there is brought about the "survival in time" of higher and higher ideals. The moment we consider Man in his proper dimension—active in TIME—these things become simple, stupendous, and beautiful.

"Note the radical character of the transformation to be effected. The world shall no longer be beheld as an alien thing, beheld by eyes that are not its own. Conception of the whole and by the whole shall embrace *us* as *part,* really, literally, consciously, as the latest term, it may be, of an advancing sequence of developments, as occupying the highest rank perhaps in the ever-ascending hierarchy of being, but, at all events, as emerged and still emerging *natura naturata* from some propensive source within. I grant that the change in point of view is hard to make—old habits, like walls of rock, tending to confine the tides of consciousness within their accustomed channels—but it can be made and, by assiduous effort, in the course of time, maintained. Suppose it done. By that reunion, the whole regains, while the part retains, the consciousness the latter purloined. . . . In the whole universe of events, none is more wonderful than the birth of wonder, none more curious than the nascence of curiosity itself, nothing to compare with the dawning of consciousness in the ancient dark and the gradual extension of psychic life and illumination throughout a cosmos that before had only *been*. An eternity of blindly acting, transforming, unconscious existence, assuming at length, through the birth of sense and intellect, without loss or break of continuity, the abiding form of fleeting time." (C. J. Keyser, loc. cit.)

It must be emphasized that the development of higher ideals is due to the *natural* capacity of humanity; the impulse is simply time-binding impulse. As we have seen, by analysing the functions of the different classes of life, every class of life has an impulse to exercise its peculiar capacity or function. Nitrogen resists compound combinations and if found in such combinations it breaks away as quickly as ever it can. Birds have wings—they fly. Animals have feet—they run. Man has the capacity of time-binding—he binds time. It does not matter whether we understand the very "essence" of the phenomenon or not, any more than we understand the "essence" of electricity or any other "essence." Life shows that man has time-binding capacity as a natural gift and is naturally impelled to use it. One of the best examples is procreation. Conception is a completely incomprehensible phenomenon in its "essence," nevertheless, having the capacity to procreate we use it without bothering about its "essence." Indeed neither life nor science bothers about "essences"—they leave "essences" to metaphysics, which is neither life nor science. It is sufficient for

our purpose that idealization is in fact a natural
process of time-binding human energy.   And however imperfect ethics has been owing to the prevalence of animal standards, such merits as our ethics
has had witness to the natural presence of "idealization" in time-binding human life.

"It is thus evident that ideals are not things to gush over
or to sigh and sentimentalize about; they are not what would
be left if that which is hard in reality were taken away;
ideals are themselves the very flint of reality, beautiful no
doubt and precious, without which there would be neither
dignity nor hope nor light; but their aspect is not sentimental
and soft; it is hard, cold, intellectual, logical, austere.   Idealization consists in the conception or the intuition of ideals and
in the pursuit of them.   And ideals, I have said, are of two
kinds.   Let us make the distinction clearer.   Every sort of
human activity—shoeing horses, abdominal surgery, or painting profiles—admits of a peculiar type of excellence.   No sort
of activity can escape from its own type but within its type
it admits of indefinite improvement.   For each type there is
an ideal—a dream of perfection—an unattainable limit of
an endless sequence of potential ameliorations within the type
and on its level.   The dreams of such unattainable perfections are as countless as the types of excellence to which they
respectively belong and they together constitute the familiar
world of our human ideals.   To share in it—to feel the lure
of perfection in one or more types of excellence, however
lowly—is to be human; not to feel it is to be sub-human.
But this common kind of idealization, though it is very important and very precious, does not produce the great events
in the life of mankind.   These are produced by the kind of
idealization that corresponds to what we have called in the
mathematical prototype, limit-begotten generalization—a kind

of idealization that is peculiar to creative genius and that, not content to pursue ideals within established types of excellences, creates new types thereof in science, in art, in philosophy, in letters, in ethics, in education, in social order, in all the fields and forms of the spiritual life of man." (Quoted from the manuscript of the forthcoming book, *Mathematical Philosophy,* by Cassius J. Keyser.)

"Survival of the fittest" has a different form for different classes of life. Applying animal standards to time-binding beings is like applying inches to measuring weight. As a matter or fact, we cannot raise one class to a higher class, unless we add an entirely new function to the former; we can only improve their lower status; but if we apply the reverse method, we can degrade human standards to animal standards.

Animal standards belong to a class of life whose capacity is *not* an *exponential* function of *Time.* There is nothing theological or sentimental in this fact; it is a purely mathematical truth.

It is fatal to apply the "survival of the fittest" theory in the same sense to two radically different classes of life. The "survival of the fittest" for animals—for *space*-binders—is survival *in space,* which means fighting and other brutal forms of struggle; on the other hand, "survival of the fittest" for human beings *as such*—that is, for *time-binders*—is survival *in time,* which means intellectual or spiritual competition, struggle for excellence, for making the *best* survive. The-fittest-in-time—those who make the best survive—are those who do the most in producing values for all mankind including *posterity*. This is the scientific base for natural ethics, and ethics from which there can be no side-stepping, or escape.

Therefore time-binders can not use *"animal"* logic without degrading themselves from their proper status as human beings—their status as established by nature. "Animal" logic leads to "animal" ethics and "animal" economics; it leads inevitably to a brutalized industrial system in which cunning contrives to rob the living of the fruit of the dead.

Human logic points to human ethics and human economics; it will lead to a humanized industrial system in which competition will be competition in science, in art, in justice: a competition and struggle for the attainment of excellence in human life. The time-binding capacity, which manifests itself in drawing from the PAST, through the PRESENT for the FUTURE gives human beings the means of attaining a precious kind of immortality; it enables them to fulfill the law of their own class of life and to survive everlastingly in the fruits of their toil, a perpetual blessing to endless generations of the children of men. This is the truth we instinctively recognize when we call a great man "immortal." We mean that he has done deeds that *survive in time* for the perpetual weal of mankind.

Human logic—mathematical logic, the logic *natural* for man—will thus show us that "good" and "just" and "right" are to have their significance defined and understood entirely in terms of human *nature*. Human nature—not animal nature—is to be the basis and guide of Human Engineering. Thus based and guided, Human Engineering will eliminate "wild-cat schemers," gamblers and "politicians." It will put an end to industrial violence, strikes, insurrections, war and revolutions.

The present system of social life is largely built upon misconceptions or misrepresentations. For all work we need the human brain, the human time-binding power, yet we continue to call it "hand-labor" and treat it as such. Even in mechanical science, in the use of the term "horse-power," we are incorrect in this expression. How does this "horse" look in reality? Let us analyse this "horse." All science, all mechanical appliances have been produced by "man" and man alone. Everything we possess is the production of either dead men's or living men's work. The enslavement of the solar man-power is purely a human invention in theory and practice. Everything we have is evidently therefore a time-binding product. What perfect nonsense to call a purely human achievement the equivalent of so much

"horse-power"! Of course it does not matter mathematically what name we give to a unit of power;
we may call it a Zeus or a Zebra; but there is a very
vicious implication in using the name of an animal
to denote a purely human product. Everything in
our civilization was produced by MAN; it seems only
reasonable that this unit of power which is the direct
product of Man's work, should be correctly named
after him. The educational effect would be wholesome and tremendous. The human value in work
would be thus emphasized again and again, and respect for human work would be taught, from the
beginning in the schools. This "horse-power" unit
causes us to forget the human part in it and it de-
grades human work to the level of a commodity.
This is an example of the degrading influence of
wrong conceptions and wrong language. I said
"educational" because even our subconscious mind is
affected by this. (See App. II.)

Human Engineering will not interfere with any
scientific research; on the contrary, it will promote
it in many ways. Grown-ups, it is to be hoped, will
stop the nonsense of intermixing dimensions, for
which we chastise children. It is the same kind of
blundering as when we intermix phenomena—measuring "God" by human standards, or human beings
by animal standards. The relationship, if any, between these phenomena or the overlapping of dif-

ferent classes, is interesting and important; but in studying such relationships of classes, it is fatal to mix the classes; for example, if we are studying the relations between surfaces and solids, it is fatal to mistake solids for surfaces; just so, too, if we stupidly confuse humans with animals.

In the reality of life, we are interested only in the values of the function of the phenomena by themselves and to arrive at right conclusions we have to use units appropriate to the phenomena. The intermixing of units gives us a wrong conception of the values of each phenomenon; the results of our calculations are wrong and the outcome is a misconception of the process of human life. The fact once realized, we will cease applying animal measures to man; even theology will abandon the monstrous habit.

Animal units and standards are to be applied to animals, human standards to man, "Divine" standards to "God."

In the dark ages, with the complete innocence or misunderstanding of science, the "why" of things was explained by the "who" of things; therein investigation culminated; man was regarded as *homo sapiens* and homo sapiens $=$ animal $\times$ spark of *super*natural; this monstrous formula was accepted as a final truth—as an answer to the question: What is Man? This type of answer became in the hands of church and state a powerful instrument for keeping the people in subjection.

The tendency of the masses to let others think for them is not really a *natural* characteristic—quite the opposite. The habit of not thinking for one's self is the result of thousands of years of subjection. Those in authority, in general, used their ingenuity to keep the people from thinking. The most vital reason why many humans appear to be, and are often called, "stupid," is that they have been spoken to in a language of speculation which they instinctively dislike and distrust; thus there arose the proverb that speech was made to conceal the truth. It is no wonder that they appear "stupid," the wonder is that they are not more "stupid." The truth is that they will be found to be far less stupid when addressed in the natural language of ascertainable fact. My whole theory is based upon, and is in harmony with, the natural feelings of man. The conceptions I introduce are based on human *nature*. Natural language—so different from the speech of metaphysical speculation—will lead to mutual understanding and the disappearance of warring factions.

"Discrimination, as the proverb rightly teaches, is the beginning of mind. The first psychic product of that initial psychic act is *numerical:* to discriminate is to produce *two,* the simplest possible example of multiplicity. The discovery, or better the invention, better still the production, best of all the creation, of multiplicity with its correlate of number, is, therefore, the most primitive achievement or manifestation of mind. . . . Let us, then, trust the arithmetic instinct as fundamental and, for instruments of thought that shall not fail, repair at once to the domain of number." (C. J. Keyser, Loc. Cit.)

The thinking few knew the power there is in "thinking"; they wanted to have it and to keep the advantage of it for themselves; witness the late introduction of public schools. Belief in the inferiority of the masses became the unwritten law of the "privileged classes"; it was forced upon, rubbed into, the subconscious mind of the masses by church and state alike, and was humbly and dumbly accepted by the "lower orders" as their "destiny." Ignorance was proclaimed as a bliss.

As time went on, this "coefficient of ignorance" became so useful to some people and some classes of people that no effort was spared to keep the world in ignorance. It gave a legalistic excuse to imprison, burn and hang people for expressing an opinion which the ruling classes did not like. The elimination from church, from school, from universities, of any teacher, any professor or any minister who dared to exemplify or encourage fearless investigation and freedom of speech became very common. It is less common in our generation, but there remains much to win in the way of freedom.

Freedom, rightly understood, is the aim of Human

Engineering. But freedom is not license, it is not licentiousness. Freedom consists in *lawful* living— in living in accord with the laws of human *nature*— in accord with the *natural* laws of Man. A plant is free when it is not prevented from living and growing according to the natural laws of plant life; an animal is free when it is not prevented from living according to the natural laws of animal life; human beings are free when and only when they are not prevented from living in accord with the natural laws of human life. I say "when not prevented," for human beings will live *naturally* and, therefore, in freedom, when they are not prevented from thus living by ignorance of what human nature is and by artificial social systems established, maintained, and protected by such ignorance. Human freedom consists in exercising the time-binding energies of man in accordance with the natural laws of such natural energies. Human freedom is thus the aim of Human Engineering because Human Engineering is to be the science of human nature and the art of conducting human affairs in accordance with the laws of human nature. Survival of the fittest, where *fittest* means *strongest,* is a *natural* law for brutes, for animals, for the class of mere *space*-binders. Survival of the fittest, where *fittest* means *best* in science and art and wisdom, is a *natural* law for mankind, the time-binding class of life.

CHAPTER VIII

ELEMENTS OF POWER

IN the World War Germany displayed tremendous *power*. Restraining our emotions as much as possible, let us endeavor to analyse that power with mathematical dispassionateness.

Why did Germany display more power than any other single nation? Because in the establishment of her "ethics," her political system, and her economic structure, Germany availed herself, in larger measure than any other nation, of scientific achievements and scientific methods. It is a very common, very erroneous, and very harmful belief that war was created solely by a "war-lord." Every idea or movement doubtless originates with somebody but back of such "originations" or initiations there are favoring conditions, forces and impulses. The stage is set by life and the ages; the actor enters and the show begins. In the instance in question, the stage was set by our whole modern system of civilization. The war lords were the "Deus ex machina"—the show was a real one—a tragedy.

The true origin of this war must be looked for

in the economic field. Our economic system is the
very complicated result of all our creeds, philosophies and social customs. It is therefore impossible
to understand the working of the economic forces
without understanding the foundation upon which
this system of forces is based. A short list of works
on the subject is given at the end of this book. A
plain statement here will be enough.

Germany was committed to a policy of indefinite
industrial expansion. This artificial expansion had
reached its limits. Germany was on the verge of
bankruptcy. Only a victorious war could avoid a
national catastrophe; she played her last card, and
lost despite her gigantic power, the greatest ever
displayed by any nation. The leading European
states were not able to overpower her for a long
time. This writing is not intended as an apology
for Germany, much less to praise her or her war
lords. German purposes were nationally narrow
and nationally selfish to the root; her methods were
inhuman but Germany displayed power; and without
the understanding of power, Human Engineering is
impossible.

It is possibly a fault of the writer's military training, but it seems to him that the "General Staff"
point of view has as much claim to consideration as
any other among the many different interpretations
of history—perhaps it has more. It is not the pri-

mary aim of the general staff to "fight," very far
from it. Their primary aim is "victory" and all the
better if victory be possible without a fight. Strategy,
brain-work, intelligence, knowledge of facts—these
are the chief weapons; brutal fighting is only a last
resort. It is highly important to bear that in mind.
Soldiers and engineers do not argue—they act. Germany affords the first example of a philosophy or a
society having for its main purpose the generating
of power to "do things." It seems only reasonable
and intelligent to analyse the history of the war
from the engineer's point of view, which, in this case,
happens to coincide with the military point of view.
It must be clearly understood that the modern general staff, or military, point of view has very little or
nothing to do with the romance or poetry of war.
War to-day is a grim business—but "business" before
all else. It has to mobilize all the resources of a
nation and generate power to the limit of its
capacity. The conduct of war to-day is a technological affair—its methods have to be engineering
methods. To crush an obstacle, there is need of a
giant hammer, and the more mass that can be given
it and the greater the force put behind it, the more
deadly will be the blow. Prior to the World War
technology had not been mobilized on so vast a scale
nor confronted with a task so gigantic. Mobilized
technology has revealed and demonstrated the fact

that it is possible to generate almost unlimited power
and has shown the way to do it; at the same time
it has demonstrated the measureless potency of engineering and our utter helplessness without it.   Technology is comparatively a new science; by some it is
called a "semi-science" because it deals primarily
with the application of science to practical issues.
But when it became necessary "to do things," an
engineer had to be called; the general staff had to
adopt his view, and all other practices and traditions
were bent to his ideas.

I have already repeatedly pointed out that the
progress of technology proceeds according to a law
like that of a rapidly increasing geometrical progression, and I have stressed the danger of inattention
to any phenomena, force or movement that conforms
to such a law.   We have only to recollect the story
of the simple but very greedy farmer who was very
happy to make a contract with a laborer for a
month's work, paying him only one cent the first day,
twice as much the second, twice for the third, and so
on to the end.   Behold!   The bill for the month ran
into millions of dollars and the farmer was ruined.
Such is the deadly secret of the geometrical progression.   Violent readjustments await any society whose
ethics, jurisprudence and the like do not keep pace
with the developments of engineering.

Engineers are the wizards who, using the results

of scientific research, can subjugate or release the concealed powers of nature. The supreme factor is the use of the mind—the exponential function of time —the time-binding energy of man. From that we have to take our start because that is the source of human power.

The German philosophy, as a whole, has its definite place in the history of philosophy; and the first thing to consider are those philosophic writers who directly and indirectly have contributed to the building up of German power. Hegel greatly affected the building up of the German mind—strange as it may seem; but Hegel was greatly under the influence of the work of Fichte, and Fichte in turn under that of Spinoza. All of them were, in a way, mathematicians in their methods and philosophy, as much as they could be in their time. I said "strange," because it is significant that the mathematical part of their philosophy was just the part which built up the German power. But if we look into it, it is not strange.

It had to be so, because mathematical and mechanical methods are the only ones by which power can be understood and built. Hegel in 1805 lectured on history of philosophy, pure mathematics and natural law. It would be hard to find a better combination for a philosophy of power. That is precisely what this philosophy was. It influenced not only German philosophy but even German theology, and through these channels it sank deep into the national consciousness. It affected every phase of life. An immense cult of disciples arose. Each one added something to that philosophy of power. One of the most brilliant representatives of this movement is Professor Oswald, who in his *Monist Sermons* gave the famous advice: "Do not waste energy but give it value." The German understanding of the great value of technology directly applied that principle to their philosophy, law, ethics, politics, and so on.

With increase of population, the problem of the State becomes more and more pressing. There are many theories about the state. For the purpose of the moment it is important to realize that a state is the governing center of an accumulation of human beings—of time-binding powers—increasing exponential functions of time. These powers, though the same in kind, differ in degree and in respect of individuality. If they are to be united so as to constitute a whole, they must be given a common aim; they must, so to speak, be reduced to a common base; if they be respectively X^m, Y^n, Z^p, and so on, we can not unite them and compute the whole by adding the exponents; but if we give them a common base—a common aim or purpose—then we can readily represent the magnitudes of the whole constituted by them; if we take X to be their common aim or base, then, if $Y = aX$, $Z = bX$, and so on, we shall have:

$$X^m \cdot Y^n \cdot Z^p \ldots = X^m \cdot a^n \cdot X^n \cdot b^p \cdot X^p \ldots$$
$$= (a^n \cdot b^p \ldots) X^{m+n+p} \ldots$$

The last expression, where the parenthetical coefficient is the product of individualities, serves to represent the united powers of all in terms of X, the common base, purpose or aim.

Let us look at the matter in another way. One mechanical "horse-power" is less than the power of one living horse. One living horse can do more work than one mechanical horse-power, but in using more than one living horse at one time we get less work than by using the same number of mechanical horse-powers; the reason is very obvious. The mechanical horse-powers are the same in kind, equal, and constant, but living horses differ in character, they are not equal, and each one is a variable. Hence mechanical horse-powers can be added or multiplied arithmetically, but the powers of living horses can not, except very roughly; the living horses of a team interfere with each other; they do not pull together, as we say, and energy is lost.

The German mathematical philosophy or theory of the state did not express itself in just this way, but the foregoing gives a clue to it. Germany united the powers of living men and women and children:

it gave them a common base; it gave them one common "social" mood and aim; they all became con-
solidated in service of that which is called the State;
they studied and taught for the State; they worked,
lived and died for the State: the State was their idol,
King and God.

Such was the aim of German philosophy, theology,
law and science. The establishment of ONE AIM for
all was the decisive factor. It is obvious that if we
want to inspire 60 Millions of individuals with one
aim, this aim can not be private or personal. It
must be a higher aim, collective, general, impersonal,
in some way uniting and including all personal aims.
I shall call it simply a *collective* aim. But collective
aims may differ profoundly in kind; out of personal
or egoistic aims there grows a series of collective
aims, increasing in generality, such as: (1) Family
aims; (2) association, congregation, club aims; (3)
class or professional aims; (4) national or race aims;
and finally (5) HUMAN AIMS—the natural aims for
the time-binding class of life. The fatal error of
German political philosophy was an error of aim—
her aim was too low—too narrow—the welfare of
a state instead of the welfare of Humanity.

In the case of Germany, the national aim was
equivalent to the state aim. German philosophy
made the "state" equivalent to the "good" and equivalent to "power." Of course such philosophy influ-

enced the whole national life in every detail; in consequence Germany proclaimed herself the first nation of the world, and this soon evolved into a plan for the conquest of the world. The German General Staff as an institution had, par excellence, as its aim and first object, "power," "concentration of power" and "efficiency." It took the leadership in all branches of life and industry. Militarism and industrialism are almost synonymous from the mechanical point of view; they are both of them power. They both have to use the same scientific methods and in the *present* conditions of the world they are dependent upon each other, for war cannot be waged without strong industries. Here we have to face the fact that geometrically progressing industry can not live without new markets, which under present conditions have been largely acquired, directly or indirectly, by the power of the army; and this has been the case with Germany. If we curse Germany for being a "military nation" we can, with no less justice, curse her for being a *completely* "industrialized nation." If we add to that her nationally selfish and narrow national aim, we will readily understand this "world peach." Those who have tasted it know something of its sweetness.

There is no need to go into further details. Special books give us all the data. That which is of interest is the impersonal fact that what was the *strength*

and *power* of Germany is the best possible illustration we have had of what science and a sort of mathematical philosophy are able to accomplish, even
when directed, not to the welfare of Humanity, but
to that of a relatively small group of people. The
above-cited political philosophies had a very pro-
nounced effect upon Marx. One of the branches of
socialism is the so-called state socialism. State socialists, as the name indicates, believe that the state should
assume the most important functions in society. It
is obvious that in monarchical countries where "god-
given" rulers represent the state, such a theory is not
unwelcome, as it gives the rulers an opportunity to
show a sort of "advanced liberalism," which serves
to strengthen their power. The astute Bismarck can
not be suspected of being a progressionist in the
modern sense but, being a product of German culture
and philosophy, all his ideals were those of a strong
state. He was a proclaimed advocate of state socialism. Since 1879 at least, Bismarck was considered
almost the leading spirit of paternal state socialism.
He was a believer and promoter of the close relation of the state and the railways, keeping always
in view a thorough nationalization which he finally
accomplished. This fact eliminated from German
public life all that phase of corruption which private
ownership of railroads brings in any country, the
railroad being the very life of any country.

To sum up: Germany applied the most scientific methods to build up her national power; she understood the elements of "power," for they were disclosed to her by her science and her philosophy. She applied technological methods in every part of her civil life, and thus built her gigantic power. Her industrial life followed the military way; her military strength was built on industrial power. And so the vicious circle. Germany adopted a *collective* aim instead of a personal individualistic aim, and because of this broader aim, she was able to mobilize and to keep mobilized all her moral, political and industrial forces for long years before the war. The direct effect of this system of continuous mobilization was over-production. For this she desperately needed new markets. The cheapest and quickest way to acquire them, if they were not to be grabbed otherwise, was to conquer them by a victorious war. Her plans progressed according to the program, all except the victory in the battle fields.

This war was a calamity of unprecedented magnitude for the world and it is our duty to study it dispassionately and learn the lesson of it, if we do not want to be moral accomplices of this great modern crime, by letting the world drift into an even worse catastrophe. We have to arouse ourselves from our inertia and go to the bottom of this problem and analyse it ruthlessly, no matter whether the analysis be pleasant or not. We must value every-one of our "ten sacred dead" at least as much as we value one rabbit killed in scientific laboratories, and take the lesson to heart or be prepared for a repetition of world slaughter.

If Human Engineering had been established long ago our social system would have been different, our civilization would have been much higher, this war would have been avoided. We do not need to delude ourselves. The World War was the result of badly balanced social and economic forces. The world needs other "balances of power" than such as are devised by lawyers and politicians, by single-selfish or group-selfish interests. Humanity is reaching out for a science and art of human guidance based upon a right understanding of human nature.

CHAPTER IX

MANHOOD OF HUMANITY

IN a previous chapter I have said that the World War marks the end of one vast period in the life of humankind and marks the beginning of another. It marks the end of Humanity's Childhood and the beginning of Humanity's Manhood.

Our human Past is a mighty fact of our world. Many facts are unstable, impermanent, and evanescent—they are here to-day, and to-morrow they are gone. Not so with the great fact of our human Past. Our past abides.

"It is permanent. It can be counted on. It is nearly eternal as the race of man. Out of that past we have come. Into it we are constantly returning. Meanwhile, it is of the utmost importance to our lives. It contains the *roots* of all we are, and of all we have of wisdom, of science, of philosophy, of art, of jurisprudence, of customs and institutions. It contains the record or ruins of all the experiments that man has made during a quarter or a half million years in the art of living in this world." (Keyser, *Human Worth of Rigorous Thinking.*)

In our relation to the past there are three wide-open ways in which one may be a fool. Cne of the ways is the way of ignoring the past—the way of remaining blankly ignorant of the human past as the animals are blankly ignorant of *their* past and so of drifting through life as animals do, without reference to the experience of bygone generations. Fools of this type may be called drifting fools or Drifters. Another way to be a fool—a very alluring way—is that of falsifying the past by *idealizing* it—by stupidly disregarding its vices, misery, ignorance, slothfulness, and folly, and stupidly magnifying its virtues, happiness, knowledge, achievements and wisdom; it is the way of the self-complacent—the way of those who, being comfortably situated and prosperous, are opposed to change; the past, they say, was wise for it produced the present and the present is good—let us alone. Fools of this type may be called idolatrous fools, worshiping the Past; or static fools, contented with the Present; or cowardly fools, opposed to change, fearful of the Future. A third way to be a fool—which is also alluring—is the opposite of the foregoing; it is the way of those who falsify the past by stupidly and contemptuously disregarding its virtues, its happiness, its knowledge, its great achievements, and its wisdom, and by stupidly or dishonestly magnifying its vices, its misery, its ignorance, its great slothfulness, and its folly; it is apt to be the way of the woeful, the unprosperous, the desperate—especially the way of such as find escape from the bore of routine life in the excitements of unrest, turbulence, and change; the past, they say, was all wrong, for it produced the present and the present is thoroughly bad—let us destroy it, root and branch. Fools of this type may be called scorning fools, Scorners of the Past; or destroying fools, Destroyers of the Present; or dynamic fools, Revelers in the excitements of Change.

Such are the children of folly: (1) Drifting fools —ignorers of the past—disregarders of race experience—thoughtless floaters on the shifting currents of human affairs; (2) Static fools—idealizers of the past—complacent lovers of the present—enemies of change—fearful of the future; (3) Dynamic fools —scorners of the past—haters of the present—destroyers of the works of the dead—most *modest* of fools, each of them saying: "What ought to be begins with *Me;* I will make the world a paradise; but my genius must be free; *now* it is hampered by the existing 'order'—the bungling work of the past; I will destroy it; I will start with chaos; we need light— the Sun casts shadows—I will begin by blotting out the Sun; then the world will be full of glory—the light of my genius."

In striking contrast with that three-fold division of Folly, the counsel of Wisdom is one, and it is one with the sober counsel of Common Sense. What is that counsel? What is the united counsel of wisdom and common sense respecting the past? The answer is easy and easy to understand. The counsel is this: Do not ignore the past but study it—study it diligently as being the mightiest factor among the great factors of our human world; endeavor to view the past justly, to contemplate it as it was and is, to see it *whole*—to see it in true perspective—magnifying neither its good nor its evil, neither its knowledge nor its ignorance, neither its enterprise nor its slothfulness, neither its achievements nor its failures; as the salient facts are ascertained, endeavor to account for them, to find their causes, their favoring conditions, to explain the facts to understand them, applying always the question *Why?* Centuries of centuries of cruel superstition—Why? Centuries of centuries of almost complete ignorance of natural law—Why? Centuries of centuries of monstrous misconceptions of human nature—Why? Measureless creations, wastings and destructions of wealth—Why? Endless rolling cycles of enterprise, stagnation, and decay—Why? Interminable alterations of peace and war, enslavements and emancipations—Why? Age after age of world-wide worship of man-made gods, silly, savage, enthroned by myth and magic, celebrated and supported by poetry and the wayward speculations of ignorant "sages"— Why? Age upon age of world-wide slow developments of useful inventions, craftsmanship, commerce, and art—Why? Ages of dark impulsive groping before the slow discovery of reason, followed by centuries of belief in the sufficiency of ratiocination unaided by systematic observation and experiment— Why? At length the dawn of scientific method and science, the growth of natural knowledge, immeasurable expansion of the universe *in Time* and *in Space*, belief in the lawfulness of Nature, rapidly increasing subjugation of natural forces to human control, growing faith in the limitless progressibility of human knowledge and in the limitless perfectibility of human welfare—Why? The widely diverse peoples of the world constrained by scientific progress to live together as in one community upon a greatly shrunken and rapidly shrinking planet, the unpreparedness of existing ethics, law, philosophy, economics, politics and government to meet the exigencies thus arising—Why?

Such I take to be the counsel of wisdom—the simple wisdom of sober common sense. To ascertain the salient facts of our immense human past and then to explain them in terms of their causes and conditions is not an easy task. It is an exceedingly difficult one, requiring the labor of many men, of many generations; but it must be performed; for it is only in proportion as we learn to know the great facts of our human past and their causes that we are enabled to understand our human present, for the present is the child of the past; and it is only in proportion as we thus learn to understand the present that we can face the future with confidence and competence. Past, Present, Future—these can not be understood singly and separately—they are welded together indissolubly as *one*.

The period of humanity's childhood has been long —300,000 to 500,000 years, according to the witness of human relics, ruins and records of the caves and the rocks—a stretch of time too vast for our imaginations to grasp. Of that immense succession of ages, except a minute fraction of it including our own time, we have, properly speaking, no history; we have only a rude, dim, broken outline. Herodotus, whom we call "the father of history" proper, lived less than 2500 years ago. What is 2500 years compared with the whole backward stretch of human time? We have to say that the father of human history lived but yesterday—a virtual contemporary of those now living. Our humankind groped upon this globe for probably 400,000 years before the writing of what we call history had even begun. If we regard history as a kind of *racial memory,* what must we say of our race's memory? It is like that of a man of 20 years whose recollection extends back less than 3 months or like that of a man of 60 years whose recollection fails to reach any event of the first 59 years of his life. Owing to the work of geologists, paleontologists, ethnologists and their

co-workers, the history of prehistoric man will grow,
just as we know to-day more about the life of mankind in the time of Herodotus than Herodotus himself knew.   Meanwhile we must try to make the best
use of such historical knowledge of man as we now
possess.

Even if the story of humanity's childhood were
fully recorded in the libraries of the world, it would
not be possible in this brief writing to recount the
story in even the most summary fashion.   Except the
tale of recent years, the story is known as I have
said, only in outline, rude, dim and broken, but for
the present purpose this will suffice.   Countless mul-
titudes of details are lost—most of them doubtless
forever.   But we need not despair.   The really great
facts of our racial childhood—the massive, dominant, outstanding facts—are sufficiently clear for our
guidance in the present enterprise.   And what do we
know?

We know that the period of our human childhood has been inconceivably long; we know that in
the far distant time, the first specimens of humankind—the initial members of the time-binding race
of man—were absolutely without human knowledge
of the hostile world in which they found themselves;
we know that they had no conception of what they
themselves were; we know that they had neither
speech nor art nor philosophy nor religion nor sci-

ence nor tools nor human history nor human tradition; we know, though we to-day can hardly imagine
it, that their *sole* equipment for *initiating* the career
of the human race was that peculiar faculty which
made them human—the capacity of man for binding
time; we know that they actually did that work of
initiation, without any guidance or example, maxim
or precedent; and we know that they were able to do
it just because the power of initiation—the power to
originate—is a time-binding power.

What else do we know of the earliest part of
humanity's childhood? We know that in that far-
distant age, our ancestors—being, not animals, but
human creatures—not only *began* to live in the
human dimension of life—forever above the level of
animals—but *continued* therein, taking not only the
first step, but the second, the third, and so on indefinitely; we know, in other words, that they were
progressive creatures, that they made advancement;
we know that their progress was *natural* to them—
as natural as swimming is to fishes or as flying is to
birds—for both the impulse and the ability to progress—to make improvement—to do greater things
by help of things already done—are of the very
nature of the time-binding capacity which makes
humans human.

We know that time-binding capacity—the capacity for accumulating racial experience, enlarging it,

and transmitting it for future expansion—is the peculiar power, the characteristic energy, the definitive nature, the defining mark, of man; we know that the mental power, the time-binding capacity, of our pre-historic ancestors, was the same in *kind* as our own, if not in degree; we know that it is natural for this capacity, the highest known agency of Nature, to produce ideas, inventions, insights, doctrines, knowledge and other forms of wealth; we know that progress in what we call civilization, which is nothing but progress in the production and right use of material and spiritual wealth, has been possible and actual simply and solely because the products of time-binding work not only *survive*, but naturally tend to propagate their kind—ideas begetting ideas, inventions leading to other inventions, knowledge breeding knowledge; we therefore, know that the amount of progress which a single generation can make, if it have an adequate supply of raw material and be unhampered by hostile circumstances, depends, not only upon its native capacity for binding time, but also—and this is of the utmost importance—upon the total progress made by preceding generations—upon the inherited fruit, that is, of the time-binding toil of the dead; accordingly we know that the amount of progress a single generation can thus make is what mathematicians call an increasing function of time, and not only an increasing function but an increasing *exponential* function of time—a function like PR^T, as already explained; we know, too, that the *total* progress which T successive generations can thus make is:

$$\frac{R}{R-1}(PR^T - P)$$

which is also an increasing exponential function of time; we know from the differential calculus that these functions—which represent natural laws, laws of human *nature,* laws of the time-binding energies of man—are very remarkable functions—not only do they increase with time but their *rates* of increase are also exponential functions of time and so the rates of increase themselves increase at rates which are, again, exponential functions, and so on and on without limit; that, I say, is a marvelous fact, and it is for us a fact of immeasurable significance; for it means that the time-binding power of man is such that, if it be allowed to operate naturally, civilization —the production and right use of material and spiritual wealth—will not only grow towards infinity (as mathematicians say), but will thus grow with a *swiftness* which is not constant but which itself grows towards infinity with a swiftness which, again, is not constant but increases according to the same law, and so on indefinitely. We thus see, if we will

only retire to our cloisters and contemplate it, that
the proper life of man *as man* is not life-in-space
like that of animals, but is life-in-time; we thus see
that in distinctively human life, in the life of man
as man, the past is present and the dead survive
destined to greet and to bless the unborn generations: time, bound-up time, is literally of the core
and substance of civilization.   So it has been since
the beginning of man.

We know that the total progress made in the long
course of humanity's childhood, though it is absolutely great, is relatively small; we know that, compared with no-civilization, our present civilization is
vast and rich in many ways; we know, however, that,
if the time-binding energies of humanity had been
always permitted to operate unhampered by hostile
circumstances, they would long ere now have produced a state of civilization compared with which
our present estate would seem mean, meagre, savage.
For we know that those peculiar energies—the civilization-producing energies of man—far from being
always permitted to operate according to the laws
of their nature, have *never* been permitted so to
operate, but have always been hampered and are
hampered to-day by hostile circumstances.   And, if
we reflect, we may know well enough what the
enemies—the hostile circumstances—have been and
are.   We know that in the beginning of humanity's

childhood—in its babyhood, so to speak—there was,
as already said, no *capital* whatever to start with—
no material wealth—no spiritual wealth in the form
of knowledge of the world or the nature of man—
no existing fruit of dead men's toil—no bound-up
time—nothing but wild and raw material, whose
very location, properties and potencies had all to be
discovered; even now, because we have inherited so
much bound-up time and because our imaginations
have been so little disciplined to understand realities,
we can scarcely picture to ourselves the actual conditions of that far-off time of humanity's babyhood;
still less do we realize that present civilization has
hardly begun to be that of enlightened men. We
know, moreover, that the time-binding energies of
our remote ancestors were hampered and baulked,
in a measure too vast for our imaginations, by immense geologic and climatic changes, both sudden
and secular, unforeseen and irresistible—by earthquake and storm, by age-long seasons of flood and
frost and heat and drought, not only destroying both
natural resources and the slowly accumulated products of by-gone generations but often extinguishing
the people themselves with the centers and abodes of
struggling civilization.

Of all the hostile circumstances, of all the causes
which throughout the long period of humanity's
childhood have operated to keep civilization and

human welfare from progressing in full accord with
the natural laws of the time-binding energies of man,
the most potent cause and most disastrous, a cause
still everywhere in operation, remains to be mentioned. I mean human ignorance. I do not mean
ignorance of physical facts and the laws of physical
nature for this latter ignorance is in large measure
the effect of the cause I have in mind. The ignorance I mean is far more fundamental and far more
potent. I mean human ignorance of *Human Nature*
—I mean man's ignorance of what Man is—I mean
false conceptions of the rightful place of man in the
scheme of life and the order of the world. What
the false conceptions are I have already pointed out.
They are two. One of them is the conception according to which human beings are animals. The other
one is the conception according to which human
beings have no place in Nature but are hybrids of
natural and *super*natural, animals combined with
something "divine." Both of them are characteristic
of humanity's childhood; both of them are erroneous, and both of them have done infinite harm in
a thousand ways. Whose is the fault? In a deep
sense, it is the fault of none. Man started with no
capital—on knowledge—with nothing but his physical strength and the natural stirring within of the
capacity for binding time; and so he had to grope.
It is not strange that he was puzzled by himself. It

is not strange that he thought himself an animal; for he has animal propensities as a cube has surfaces, and his animal propensities were so obtrusive, so very evident to physical sense—he was born, grew, had legs and hair, ate, ran, slept, died—all just like animals—while his distinctive mark, his time-binding capacity, was subtle; it was spiritual; it was not a *visible organ* but an *invisible function;* it was the energy called intellect or mind, which the physical senses do not perceive; and so I say it is not strange —it is indeed very sad and very pathetic—but it is not to be wondered at that human beings have falsely believed themselves to be animals. So, too, of the rival belief—the belief that humans are neither natural nor supernatural but are both at once, at once brutal and divine, hybrid offspring of beast and god. The belief is monstrous, it is very pathetic and very sad, but its origin is easy to understand; once invented, it became a powerful instrument for evil men, for impostors, but it was not invented by them; it was only an erroneous result of an honest effort to understand and to explain. For the obvious facts created a real puzzle to be explained: On the one hand, men, women and children—animal-hunting and animal-hunted human beings—certainly resembled animals physically in a hundred unmistakable ways; on the other hand, it became more and more evident that the same animal-resembling human beings could do many things which animals never did and could not do. Here was a puzzle, a mystery. Time-binding curiosity demanded an explanation. What was it to be? Natural science had not yet arisen; critical conception—conception that avoids the mixing of dimensions—was in the state of feeble infancy. It is easy to understand what the answer had to be—childish and mythical; and so it was—humans are neither animals nor gods, neither natural nor *super*natural, they are both at once, a mixture, a mysterious union of animal with something "divine."

Such, then, are the two rival answers which, in the long dark, groping course of humanity's childhood, human beings have given to the most important of all questions—the question: What is Man? I have said that the answers, no matter how sincere, no matter how honestly arrived at, are erroneous, false to fact, and monstrous. I have said, and I repeat, that the misconceptions involved in them have done more throughout the by-gone centuries, and are doing more to-day, than all other hindering causes, to hamper and thwart the *natural* activity of the time-binding energies of man and thus to retard the *natural* progress of civilization. It is not merely our privilege, it is our high and solemn duty, to examine them. To perform the great duty is not an easy task. The misconceptions in question have come down to us from remote antiquity; they have not come down singly, separately, clean-cut, clear and well-defined; they have come *entangled* in the complicated mesh of traditional opinions and creeds that constitute the vulgar "philosophy"—the mental fog —of our time.   If we are to perform the duty of examining them we have first of all to draw them forth, to disengage them from our inherited tangle of beliefs and frame them in suitable words; we have next to bring ourselves to realize vividly and keenly that the conceptions, thus disentangled and framed, are in fact, whether they be true or false, at the very heart of the social philosophy of the world; we have in the third place to detect the fundamental character of the blunder involved in them—to see clearly and coldly wherein they are wrong and why they are ruinous; we have, finally, to trace, if we can, their deadly effects both in the course of human history and in the present status of our human world.

The task of disengaging the two monstrous misconceptions from the tangled skein of inherited beliefs and framing them in words, I have already repeatedly performed.   Let us keep the results in mind.   Here they are in their nakedness: (1) Human beings—men, women, and children—are animals (and so they are natural): (2) human beings are neither natural nor *super*natural, neither wholly animal nor wholly "divine," but are *both* natural and *super*natural *at once*—a sort of mysterious hybrid compound of brute and gods.

The second part of our task—which is the reader's task as much as mine—is not so easy; and the reason is evident. It is this: The false creeds in question—the fatal misconceptions they involve—are so *familiar* to us—they have been so long and so deeply imbedded in our thought and speech and ways of life—we have been so thoroughly *bred* in them by home and school and church and state—that we *habitually* and *unconsciously* take them for granted and have to be virtually *stung* into an awareness of the fact that we do actually hold them and that they do actually reign to-day throughout the world and have so reigned from time immemorial. We have, therefore, to shake ourselves awake, to *prick* ourselves into a realization of the truth.

I assume that the reader is at once hard-headed, rational, I mean, and interested in the welfare of mankind. If he is not, he will not be a "reader" of this book. He, therefore, knows that the third task—the task of detecting and exposing the fundamental error of the misconceptions in question—is a task of the utmost importance. What is that error? It is, I have said, an error in logic. But logical errors are not all alike—they are of many kinds. What is the "kind" of *this* one? It is the kind that consists in what mathematicians call "confusion of types," or "mixing of dimensions." The answer can not be made too clear nor too emphatic, for its importance in the criticism of *all* our thinking is great beyond measure. There are millions of examples that help to make the matter clear. I will again employ the simplest of them—one so simple that a child can understand it. It is a mathematical example, as it ought to be, for the whole question of logical types, or dimensions, is a mathematical one. I beg the reader not to shy at, or run away from, the mere word mathematical, for, although most of us have but little mathematical *knowledge,* we all of us have the mathematical *spirit,* for else we should not be human—we are all of us mathematicians *at heart.* Let us, then, proceed confidently and at once to our simple example. Here is a *surface,* say a *plane* surface. It has length and breadth—and so it has, we say, *two* dimensions; next consider a *solid,* say a *cube.* It has length, breadth and thickness— and so *it* has, we say, *three* dimensions. Now we notice that the cube *has* surfaces and so *has certain surface properties.* Do we, therefore, say that a solid *is* a surface? That the cube is a member of the class of surfaces? If we did, we should be fools —type-confusing fools—dimension-mixing fools. That is evident. Or suppose we notice that solids have certain *surface* properties and certain properties that surfaces do *not* have; and suppose we say the *surface* properties of solids are *natural* but the other properties are so mysterious that they must be "*super*natural" or somehow "divine"; and suppose we then say that solids are unions, mixtures, compounds or hybrids of surfaces and something divine or *super*natural; is it not evident that, if we did that, we should be again blundering like fools? Type-confusing fools? Dimension-mixing fools? That such would be the case any one can see. Let us now consider animals and human beings, and let us look squarely and candidly at the facts. To get a start, think for a moment of plants. Plants are living things; they take, transform and appropriate the energies of sun, soil, and air, but they have *not* the *autonomous* power to move about in space; we may say that plants constitute the lowest order or class or type or dimension of life—the dimension *one;* plants, we see are binders of the *basic* energies of the world. What of animals? Like the plants, animals, too, take in, transform and appropriate the energies of sun, soil and air, though in large part they take them in forms already prepared by the plants themselves; but, *unlike* the plants, animals possess the *autonomous* power to move about in space—to creep or crawl or run or swim or fly—it is thus evident that, compared with plants, animals belong to a higher order, or higher class, or higher type, or higher dimension of life; we may therefore say that the type of animal life is a type of *two* dimensions—a two-dimensional type; I have called them space-binders because they are distinguished, or marked, by their autonomous power to move about in space, to abandon one place and occupy another and so to appropriate the natural fruits of many localities; the life of animals is thus a life-in-space in a sense evidently not applicable to plants. And now what shall we say of *Man?* Like the animals, human beings have indeed the power of mobility— the autonomous power to move—the capacity for binding space, and it is obvious that, if they possessed no capacity of higher order, men, women and children would indeed be animals. But what are the facts? The facts, if we will but note them and reflect upon them, are such as to show us that the chasm separating human nature from animal nature is even wider and deeper than the chasm between animal life and the life of plants. For man improves, animals do not; man progresses, animals do not; man invents more and more complicated tools, animals do not; man is a creator of material and spiritual wealth, animals are not; man is a builder of civilization, animals are not; man makes the *past live in the present and the present in the future,* animals do not; man is thus a *binder* of *time,* animals are not. In the light of such considerations, if only we will attend to their mighty significance, it

is as clear as anything can be or can become, that
the life of man—the time-binder—is as radically distinct from that of animals—mere space-binders—as
animal life is distinct from that of plants or
as the nature of a solid is distinct from that of
a surface, or that of a surface from that of a line.
It is, therefore, perfectly manifest that, when we regard human beings as animals or as mixtures of animal nature with something mysteriously *super*natural,
we are guilty of the same *kind* of blunder as if we
regarded animals as plants or as plants touched by
"divinity"—the same *kind* of blunder as that of regarding a solid as a surface or as a surface miraculously transfigured by some mysterious influence from
outside the universe of space. It is thus evident that
our guilt in the matter is the guilt of a blunder that
is *fundamental*—a confusing of types, a mixing of
dimensions.

Nothing can be more disastrous. For what are
the consequences of that kind of error? Let the
reader reflect. He knows that, if our ancestors had
committed that kind of error regarding lines and
surfaces and solids, there would to-day be no science
of geometry; and he knows that, if there were no
geometry, there would be no architecture in the
world, no surveying, no railroads, no astronomy, no
charting of the seas, no steamships, no engineering,
nothing whatever of the now familiar world-wide

affairs made possible by the scientific conquest of space. I say again, let the reader reflect; for if he does not, he will here miss the gravity of a most momentous truth. He readily sees, in the case supposed, how very appalling the consequences would have been if, throughout the period of humanity's childhood, there had occurred a certain confusion of types, a certain mixing of dimensions, and he is *enabled* to see it just because, happily, the blunder was *not* made or, if made, was not persisted in, for, if it had been made and persisted in, then the great and now familiar things of which it would have deprived the world would not be here; we should not now be able even to imagine them, and so we could not now compute even roughly the tremendous magnitude of the blunder's disastrous consequences. Let the reader not deviate nor falter nor stagger here; let him shoulder the burden of the mighty argument and bear it to the goal. He easily perceives the truly appalling consequences that *would* have inevitably followed from the error of confusing types—the error of mixing dimensions—in the matter of lines and surfaces and solids, *if* that error had been committed and persisted in throughout the centuries; he *can* perceive those consequences just because the error was *not* made and hence the great things of which (had the blunder been made) it would have deprived the world are here, so that

he can say: "Behold those splendid things—the
science of geometry and its manifold applications
everywhere shining in human affairs—imagine all of
them gone, imagine the world if they had never been,
and you will have a measure of the consequences that
would have followed violation of the law of types,
the law of dimensions, in the matter of lines, surfaces
and solids." But, now, in regard to the exactly similar error respecting the nature of man, the situation
is reversed; for this blunder, unlike the other one,
is not merely hypothetical; we have seen that it was
actually committed and has been actually persisted in
from time immemorial; not merely for years or for
decades or for centuries but for *centuries* of *centuries*
including our own day, it has lain athwart the course
of human progress; age after age it has hampered
and baulked the natural activity of the time-binding
energies—the civilization-producing energies—of
humanity. How are we to estimate its consequences?
Let the reader keep in mind that the error is fundamental—a type-confusing blunder (like that supposed regarding geometric entities) ; let him reflect,
moreover, that it affects, not merely one of our human
concerns, but *all* of them, since it is an error regarding the *center* of them all—regarding the very *nature*
of man himself; and he will know, as well as anything can be known, that the consequences of the
ages-old blunder have been and are very momentous

and very terrible. Their measure is indeed beyond
our power; we cannot describe them adequately, we
cannot delineate their proportions, for we cannot
truly imagine them; and the reason is plain: it is that
those advancements of civilization, those augmenta-
tions of material and spiritual wealth, all of the
glorious achievements of which the tragic blunder
has deprived the world, are none of them here; they
have not been produced; and so we cannot say, as in
the other case: "Look upon these splendid treasures
of bound-up time, imagine them taken away, and
your sense of the appalling loss will give you the
measure required." It is evident that the glories of
which the misconceptions of human nature have deprived manhood must long remain, perhaps forever,
in the sad realm of dreams regarding great and noble
things that might have been.

I have said that the duty of examining the misconceptions imposes upon us four obligations. Three
of these we have performed: we have disengaged the
beliefs in question from the complicated tangle of
opinions in which they have come down to us from
remote antiquity; we have recognized the necessity
and the duty of virtually stinging ourselves into an
awareness of the fact that we have actually held
them for true and that from time immemorial they
have poured their virus into the heart of ethics, economics, politics and government throughout the

world; we have seen not only that the beliefs are
false but that their falseness is due to a blunder of
the most fundamental kind—the blunder of mixing
dimensions or confusing types. As already said, the
fourth one of the mentioned tasks is that of tracing,
if we can, the blunder's deadly effects both in human
history and in the present status of the world. We
have just reached the conclusion that this task cannot be *fully* performed; for there can be no doubt,
as we have seen, that, if the blunder had not been
committed and persisted in, the world would now
possess a civilization so far advanced, so rich in the
spiritual fruits of time and toil, as to be utterly
beyond our present power to conceive or imagine it.

But, though we cannot perform the task fully, our
plight is far from hopeless. The World War has
goaded us into thinking as we never thought before.
It has constrained us to think of realities and especially to think of the supreme reality—the reality
of Man. That is why the great Catastrophe marks
the close of humanity's childhood. The period has
been long and the manner of its end is memorable
forever—a sudden, flaming, world-wide cataclysmic
demonstration of fundamental ignorance—human
ignorance of human nature. It is just that tragic
demonstration, brutal as an earthquake, pitiless as
fate or famine, that gives us ground for future hope.
It has forced us to think of realities and it is thought

of reality that will heal the world. And so I say
that these days, despite their fear and gloom, are the
beginning of a new order in human affairs—the order
of permanent peace and swift advancement of human
weal. For we know at length what human beings
are, and the knowledge can be taught to men and
women and children by home and school and church
and press throughout the world; we know at length,
and we can teach the world, that man is neither an
animal nor a miraculous mixture of angel and beast;
we know at length, and we can teach, that, throughout the centuries, these monstrous misconceptions
have made countless millions mourn and that they
are doing so to-day, for, though we cannot compute the *good* of which they have *deprived* mankind,
we can trace the dark ramifications of their positive
evil in a thousand ways; we know at length, and we
can teach, that man, though he is not an animal,
is a natural being, having a definite place, a rank
of his own, in the hierarchy of natural life; we know
at length, and we can teach the world, that what
is *characteristic* of the human class of life—that
which makes us *human*—is the power to create
material and spiritual wealth—to beget the light of
reasoned understanding—to produce civilization—it
is the unique capacity of man for binding time, uniting past, present and future in a *single growing
reality* charged at once with the surviving creations

of the dead, with the productive labor of the living, with the rights and hopes of the yet unborn; we know at length, and we can teach, that the *natural* rate of human progress is the rate of a swiftly increasing exponential function of time; we know, and we can teach, that what is good in *present* civilization—all that is precious in it, sacred and holy—is the fruit of the time-binding toil struggling blindly through the ages against the perpetual barrier of human ignorance of human nature; we know at length, we can teach, and the world will understand, that in proportion as we rid our ethics and social philosophy of monstrous misrepresentations of human nature, the time-binding energies of humanity will advance civilization in accordance with their natural law PR^T, the forward-leaping function of time.

Such knowledge and such teaching will inaugurate the period of humanity's manhood. It can be made an endless period of rapid developments in True civilization. All the developments must grow out of the true conception of human beings as constituting the time-binding class of life, and so the work must begin with a campaign of education wide enough to embrace the world. The cooperation of all educational agencies—the home, the school, the church, the press—must be enlisted to make known the fundamental truth concerning the nature of man so that it shall become the guiding *light* and *habit* of men, women, and children everywhere. Gradual indeed but profound will be the transformations wrought in all the affairs of mankind, but especially and first of all in the so-called arts and sciences of ethics, economics, politics and government.

The ethics of humanity's manhood will be neither "animal" ethics nor "*super*natural" ethics. It will be a natural ethics based upon a knowledge of the laws of human nature. It will not be a branch of zoology, the ethics of tooth and claw, the ethics of profiteering, the ethics of space-binding beasts fighting for "a place in the sun." It will be a branch of humanology, a branch of Human Engineering; it will be a time-binding ethics, the ethics of the entirely natural civilization-producing energies of humanity. Whatever accords with the natural activity of those energies will be *right* and *good;* whatever does not, will be *wrong* and *bad.* "Survival of the fittest" in the sense of the *strongest* is a space-binding standard, the ethical standard of beasts; in the ethics of humanity's manhood survival of the fittest will mean survival of the *best* in competitions for excellence, and excellence will mean time-binding excellence— excellence in the production and right use of material and spiritual wealth—excellence in science, in art, in wisdom, in justice, in promoting the weal and protecting the rights both of the living and of the unborn. The ethics that arose in the dark period of humanity's childhood from the conception of human beings as mysterious unions of animality and divinity gave birth to two repulsive species of traffic—traffic in men regarded as animals, fit to be slaves, and traffic in the "supernatural," in the sale of indulgences in one form or another and the "divine wisdom" of ignorant priests. It is needless to say that in the natural ethics of humanity's manhood those species of commerce will not be found.

And what shall we say in particular of economics, of "industry," "business as usual," and the "finance" of "normalcy"? There lies before me an established handbook of *Corporation Finance*, by Mr. E. S. Mead, Ph.D. (Appleton, N. Y.), whose purpose is not that of adverse criticism but is that of showing the generally accepted "sound" bases for prosperous business. I can hardly do better than to ask the reader to ponder a few extracts from that work, showing the established, and amazing theories, for then I have only to say that in the period of humanity's manhood the moral blindness of such "principles," their space-binding spirit of calculating selfishness and greed, will be regarded with utter loathing as slavery is regarded to-day. Behold the picture:

"Since the bondholder is solely interested in the security of his principal, and regular payment of his interest, and since both security and interest depend upon the permanence of income, other things being equal the companies with the most stable earnings or a market . . . furnish the best security for bonds. Stability of earnings depends upon (1) the possession of a monopoly. . . . *Monopoly is exclusive or dominant control over a market. The more complete this control, the more valuable is the monopoly.* The advantage of monopoly lies in the fact that the prices of services or commodities are controlled by the producers (*meaning owners—Author*), rather than by the consumer. . . . Monopolies are of various origins. The most familiar are (1) franchises, the right to use *public property* for *private purposes,* for example, the furnishing of light, water and transportation, (2) *control of sources of raw material* . . ., (3) patents, . . ., (4) high cost of duplicating plant. . . . In manufacturing industries, for example, those enterprises which *produce raw materials* and the *necessities of life* have a more stable demand. . . . Railroads furnish perhaps the best basis of bond issue because of the stability of the demand for the transportation service . . . the high cost of duplicating the railroad plant, . . . enables them to fix their rates on freight and passenger traffic. . . . The security of the creditors is here the profitableness of the business *which is carried on in the factory.* Furthermore, a business is not an aggregate of physical property but consists of physical property—buildings, boilers, machine tools—plus an industrial opportunity, plus the organization and ability to operate business." (Italics indicated by the author.)

There we see the animal standards in their studied perfection. Comment would be superfluous.

In the period of humanity's manhood, the so-called "science" of economics, the "dismal science" of political economy, will become a genuine science based upon the laws of the time-binding energies of

humanity; it will become the light of Human Engineering—promoter, guardian, and guide of human
weal.   For it will discover, and will teach that a
human life, a time-binding life, is not merely a *civilized* life but a *civilizing* life; it will know and will
teach that a civilizing life is a life devoted to the
production of potential and kinetic use-values—to the
creation, that is, of material and spiritual wealth;
it will know and will teach that wealth—both material and spiritual wealth—is a natural phenomenon
—offspring of the marriage of Time and human
Toil; it will know and will teach that the wealth in
the world at any given moment is almost wholly the
inherited fruit of time and the labor of the dead;
and so it will ask: To whom does the inheritance
rightly belong?   Does it of right belong to Smith
and Brown? If so, *why?* Or does it of right belong
to man—to humanity? If so, *why?* And what does
"humanity" include? Only the living, who are relatively few? Or both the living and unborn? The
Economics of humanity's manhood will not only ask
these questions but it will answer them and answer
them aright. In seeking the answers, it will discover
some obvious truths and many old words will acquire
new meanings consistent with the time-binding nature
of man.   It will discover and will teach that the
time-binders of a given generation are *posterity* and
ancestry at once—posterity of the dead, ancestry of

all the generations to come; it will discover and will teach that in this time-binding double relationship uniting past and future in a single living growing Reality, are to be found the obligations of time-binding ethics and the seat of its authority; economics will know and will teach that *human* posterity—time-binding posterity—can not inherit the fruits of time and dead men's toil *as animals inherit the wild fruits of the earth, to fight about them and to devour them*, but only as *trustees* for the generations to come; it will know and will teach that "capitalistic" lust to *keep* for SELF and "proletarian" lust to *get* for SELF are both of them *space-binding* lust—animal lust—beneath the level of time-binding life. The economics of humanity's manhood will know and will teach that the characteristic energies of man as man are by *nature* civilizing energies, wealth-producing energies, time-binding energies, the peaceful energies of inventive mind, of growing knowledge and understanding and skill and light; it will know and will teach that these energies of existing men united with one billion six hundred million available "sun-man" powers united with the ten billion living "man-powers of the dead," if they be not wasted by ignorance and selfishness, by conflict and competition characteristic of beasts, are more than sufficient to produce a high order of increasing pros-

perity everywhere throughout the world; in the
period of its manhood economics will discover and
will teach that to produce world prosperity, cooperation—not the fighting of man against man—but
the peaceful cooperation of all is both *necessary* and
'sufficient; it will know and will teach that such cooperation demands *scientific* leadership and a common
aim; it will know, however, and will teach, for the
lesson of Germany is plain, that scientific knowledge
and a common aim are not alone sufficient; it will
know and teach and all will understand that the
common aim, the unifying principle, the basis of cooperation, cannot be the welfare of a family nor that
of a province or a state or a race, but must be the
welfare of *all* mankind, the prosperity of humanity,
the weal of the world—the peaceful production of
Wealth without the destruction of War.

In humanity's manhood, patriotism—the love of
country—will not perish—far from it—it will grow
to embrace the world, for your country and mine
will be the world. Your "state" and mine will be
the Human State—a Cooperative Commonwealth
of Man—a democracy in fact and not merely in
name. It will be a natural organic embodiment of
the civilizing energies—the wealth-producing energies—characteristic of the human class of life. Its
larger affairs will be guided by the science and art

of Human Engineering—not by ignorant and graft-
ing "politicians"—but by scientific men, by honest
men who *know*.

Is it a dream? It *is* a dream, but the dream will
come true. It is a scientific dream and science will
make it a living reality.

How is the thing to be done? No one can foresee
all the details, but in general outline the process is
clear. Violence is to be avoided. There must be a
period of transition—a period of adjustment. A
natural first step would probably be the establishment of a new institution which might be called a
Dynamic Department—Department of Coordination or a Department of Cooperation—the name is
of little importance, but it would be the *nucleus* of
the new civilization. Its functions would be those
of encouraging, helping and protecting the people
in such cooperative enterprises as agriculture, manu-
factures, finance, and distribution.

The Department of Cooperation should include
various sections, which might be as follows:

(1) *The Section of Mathematical Sociology* or
Humanology: composed of at least one sociologist,
one biologist, one mechanical engineer, and one mathematician. Their work would be the development
of human engineering and mathematical sociology
or humanology; promoting the progress of science;
providing and supervising instruction in the theory

of values and the rudiments of humanology for elementary schools and the public at large. *The members of the section would be selected by the appropriate scientific societies for a term fixed by the selectors.*

(2) *The Section of Mathematical Legislation:* composed of (say) one lawyer, one mathematician, one mechanical engineer, selected as above. Their task would be to recommend legislation, to provide means for eliminating "Legalism" from the theory and practice of law, and to bring jurisprudence into accord with the laws of time-binding human nature and the changing needs of human society. Their legislative proposals, if ratified in a joint session of sections (1) and (2), would then be recommended to the appropriate legislative bodies.

(3) *The Educational Section:* composed of two or three teachers, one sociologist, one mechanical engineer, one mathematician, selected as above. They would elaborate educational projects and revise school methods and books; their decisions being subject to the approval of the joint session of sections (1), (2), and (3).

(4) *The Cooperative Section:* composed of mechanical engineers, chemical engineers, production engineers, expert bookkeepers, accountants, business managers, lawyers and other specialists in their respective lines. This section would be an "In-

dustrial Red Cross" (Charles Ferguson) giving expert advice when asked for by any cooperative society.

(5) *The Cooperative Banking Section:* composed of financial experts, sociologists, and mathematicians; its task being to help with expert advice new cooperative people's banks.

(6) *The Promoters' Section:* composed of engineers whose duty would be to study all of the latest scientific facts, collect data, and elaborate plans. Those plans would be published, and no private person, but only cooperative societies, would be permitted by law to use them. The department would also study and give advice respecting the general conditions of the market and the needs in the various lines of production. This section would regulate the duplication of production.

(7) *The Farming Section:* composed of specialists in scientific and cooperative agriculture.

(8) *The Foreign Section:* for inter-cooperative foreign relations.

(9) *The Commercial Section.*

(10) *The News Section:* to edit a large daily paper giving *true, uncolored* news with a special supplement relating to progress in the work of Human Engineering. This paper would give daily news about the whole cooperative movement, markets, etc., etc.

All men selected to the places for this work should be the very best men in the nation. They should be well paid to enable them to give their full energy and time to their duties. All the selections for this work should be made in the same manner as mentioned above—through proven merits not clever oratory. Such appointments should be considered the highest honor that a country can offer to its citizens. Every selection should be a demonstration that the person selected was a person of the highest attainments in the field of his work.

The outline of this plan is vague; it aims merely at being suggestive. Its principal purpose is to accentuate the imperative necessity of establishing a national time-binding agency—a Dynamic Department for stimulating, guiding and guarding the civilizing energies, the wealth producing energies, the time-binding energies, in virtue of which human beings are human. For then and only then human welfare, unretarded by monstrous misconceptions of human nature, by vicious ethics, vicious economics and vicious politics, will advance peacefully, continuously, and rapidly, under the leadership of human engineering, happily and without fear, in accord with the exponential law—the *natural* law—of the time-binding energies of Man.

CHAPTER X

CONCLUSION

"In Europe we know that an age is dying. Here it would be easy to miss the signs of coming changes, but I have little doubt that it will come. A realization of the *aimlessness* of life lived to labor and to die, having achieved nothing but avoidance of starvation, and the birth of children also doomed to the weary treadmill, has seized the minds of millions."

Sir Auckland Geddes, British Ambassador to the U. S. 1920.

IN conclusion let me say very briefly, as I said in the beginning, that this little book has aimed to be only a sketch. The Problem of Life is old. I have endeavored to approach it afresh, with a new method, in a new spirit, from a new point of view. The literature of the subject is vast. It displays great knowledge and skill. Much of it is fitted to inform and to inspire such as really read with a genuine desire to understand. Its weakness is due to the absence of a true conception of what human beings are. That is what I miss in it and it is that lack of fundamental and central thought that I have striven to supply. If I have succeeded in that, I have no fear—all else will follow quickly, inevitably, as a matter of course. For a fundamental conception, once it is formed and expressed, has a strange power—the power of enlisting the thought and cooperation of many minds. And no conception can have greater power in our human world than a *true* conception of the nature of Man. For that most important of truths the times are ripe; the world is filled with the saddest of memories, with gloom, forebodings and fear. Without the truth in this matter, there can be no rational hope—history must go on in its dismal course; but *with* the truth, there is not only hope but certitude that the old order has passed and that humanity's manhood dates from the present day. That I have here presented the truth in this matter—the true conception of the human class of life—I have personally no doubt; and I have no doubt that that conception is to be the base, the guide, the source of light, of a new civilization. Whether I am mistaken or not, time will decide. I feel as Buckle felt in writing his *History of Civilization:*

"Whether or not I have effected anything of real value ... is a question for competent judges to decide. Of this, at least, I feel certain, that whatever imperfections may be observed, the fault consists, not in the method proposed, but in the extreme difficulty of any single man putting into full operation all the parts of so vast a scheme. It is on this point, and on this alone, that I feel the need of great indulgence. But, as to the plan itself, I have no misgivings. Of defects in its execution I am not unconscious. I can only plead the immensity of the subject, the shortness of a single life and the imperfection of every single enterprise. I, therefore, wish this work to be estimated, not according to the finish of its separate parts, but according to the way in which those parts have been fused into a complete and symmetrical whole. This, in an undertaking of such novelty and magnitude, I have a right to expect, and I would moreover, add, that if the reader has met with opinions adverse to his own, he should remember, that his views are, perhaps, the same as those which I too once held, and which I have abandoned, because, after a wider range of study, I found them unsupported by solid proof, subversive of the interest of Man, and fatal to the progress of his knowledge. To examine the notions in which we have been educated, and to turn aside from those which will not bear the test, is a task so painful, that they who shrink from the sufferings should pause before they reproach those by whom the suffering is undergone. . . . Conclusions arrived at in this way are not to be overturned by stating that they endanger some other conclusions; nor can they be even affected by allegation against their supposed tendency. The principles which I advocate are based upon distinct arguments supported by well ascertained facts. The only points, therefore, to be ascertained, are, whether the arguments are fair, and whether the facts are certain. If these two conditions have been obeyed, the principles follow by an inevitable inference."

And why have I sought throughout to follow the spirit of mathematics? Because I have been dealing with ideas and have desired, above all things else, to be right and clear. Ideas have a character of their own—they are right or wrong independently of our hopes and passions and will. In the connection of ideas there is an unbreakable thread of destiny. That is why in his *Mathematical Philosophy* Professor Keyser has truly said:

"Mathematics is the study of Fate—not fate in a physical sense, but in the sense of the binding thread that connects thought with thought and conclusions with their premises. Where, then, is our freedom? What do you love? Painting? Poetry? Music? The muses are *their* fates. Whoso loves them is free. Logic is the muse of Thought."

No doubt mathematics is truly impersonal in method; too impersonal maybe to please the sentimentalists before they take the time to think; mathematical analysis of life phenomena elevates our point of view above passion, above selfishness in any form, and, therefore, it is the only method which can tell us genuine truths about ourselves. Spinoza even in the 17th Century had well realized this fact and although imperfect in many ways, his was an effort in the right direction and this quoted conclusion may well be a conclusion for ourselves in the 20th century:

"The truth might forever have remained hid from the human race, if mathematics, which looks not to the final cause of figures, but to their essential nature and the properties involved in it, had not set another type of knowledge before them. . . . When I turned my mind to this subject, I did not propose to myself any novel or strange aim, but simply to demonstrate by certain and indubitable reason, those things which agree best with practice. And in order that I might enquire into the matters of the science with the same freedom of mind with which we are wont to treat lines and surfaces in mathematics; I determined not to laugh or to weep over the actions of men, but simply to understand them; and to contemplate their affections and passions, such as love, hate, anger, envy, arrogance, pity and all other disturbances of soul not as vices of human nature, but as properties pertaining to it in the same way as heat, cold, storm, thunder pertain to the nature of the atmosphere. For these, though troublesome, are yet necessary, and have certain causes through which we may come to understand them, and thus, by contemplating them in their truth, gain for our minds much joy as by the knowledge of things that are pleasing to the senses."

If only this little book will *initiate* the scientific study of Man, I shall be happy; for then we may confidently expect a science and art that will know how to direct the energies of man to the advancement of human weal.

What else? Many topics have not even been broached. Time-binding energy—what may it not achieve in course of the aeons to come? What light may it not yet throw upon such fundamental phenomena as *Space, Time, Infinity*, and so on? What, if any, are the limits of Time-binding? In it are somehow involved all the higher functions of mind. Is Time identical with Intelligence? Is either of them the other's cause? Is Time *in* the Cosmos or is the latter in the former? Is the Cosmos intelligent? Many no doubt and marvelous are the fields which the scientific study of man will open for research.

APPENDIX I

MATHEMATICS AND TIME-BINDING

THE purpose of this appendix is to give an expression of some new ideas which evolve directly out of the fact that humans are time-binders and which may serve as suggestions for the foundation of *scientific psychology*. The problem is of exceeding difficulty to give expression to in any form and therefore much more difficult to express in any exact or correct form, and so I beg the reader's patience in regard to the language because some of the ideas are in themselves correct and sometimes very suggestive in spite of the language used. I am particularly interested that mathematicians, physicists and metaphysicians should read it carefully, forgive me the form, and look into the suggestions, because scientific psychology if such a science is to exist, would by necessity have to be a branch of physics. I particularly beg the mathematicians and physicists not to discard this appendix with too hasty a judgment of "Oh! metaphysics," and also the metaphysicians not to do the same with an equally hasty judgment "Oh! mathematics." I hope that if this appendix is sympathetically understood, mathematicians and physicists will be moved to investigate the problem. If mathematicians and physicists would be more tolerant toward metaphysics and if metaphysicians would be moved to study mathematics, both would find tremendous fields to work in.

Some scientists are very pedantic and therefore intolerant in their pedantry and they may say "the fellow should learn first how to express himself and then ask our attention." My answer is that the problems involved are too pressing, too vital, too fundamental for humankind, to permit me to delay for perhaps long years before I shall be able to present the subject in a correct and satisfactory form, and also that the problems involved cover too vast a field for a single man to work it conclusively. It seems best to give the new ideas to the public in a suggestive form so that many people may be led to work on them more fully.

The old word "metaphysics" is an illegitimate child of ignorance and an unnecessary word in the scientific study of nature. Every phenomenon of nature can be classed and studied in physics or chemistry or mathematics; the problem, therefore, is not in any way *super*natural or *super*physical, but belongs rather to an unknown or an undeveloped branch of physics. The problem, therefore, may be not that of some *new* science, but rather that of a new branch of mathematics, or physics, or chemistry, etc., or all combined.

It is pathetic that only after many aeons of human existence the dimensionality of man has been discovered and his proper status in *nature* has been given by the definition of "time-binder." The old metaphysics, in spite of its being far from exact, accomplished a great deal. What prevented metaphysics from achieving more was its use of unmathematical method, or, to be more explicit, its failure to understand the importance of dimensions. Metaphysics used words and conceptions of multi-dimensional meanings which of necessity resulted in hopeless confusion, in "a talking" about words, in mere verbalism. An example will serve to make this clear. If we were to speak of a cow, a man, an automobile, and a locomotive as "pullers," and if we were not to use any other names in connection with them, what would happen? If we characterized these things or beings, by one common characteristic, namely, "to pull," havoc would be introduced into our conceptions and in practical life; we would try to milk an automobile or we would try to extract gasoline from a cow, or look for a screw in a man, or we would speculate about any or all of these things. Too obviously nonsensical—but exactly the same thing happens, in a much more subtle way, when we use such words as "life in a crystal" or "memory in animals"; we are thus mentally making a mistake no less nonsensical than the talk of "milking an automobile" would be. Laymen are baffled by the word dimension. They imagine that dimensions are applicable only to space, which is three dimensional, but they are mistaken; a moving object is four-dimensional—that is, it has three dimensions as any object at rest, but, when the object is moving, a fourth dimension is necessary to give its *position* at any one instant. We see, therefore, that a moving body has four dimensions, and so on. As a matter of fact, scientific psychology will very much need mathematics, but a special *humanized* mathematics. Can this be produced? It seems to me that it can.

It is a well known fact that experimental sciences bring us to face facts which require further theoretical elaboration; in this way experimental sciences are a permanent source of inspiration to mathematicians because new facts bring about the need of new methods of analysis.

In this book a new and experimental fact has been disclosed and analysed. It is the fact that humanity is a time-binding class of life where the time-binding capacity or the time-binding ENERGY is the highest function of humanity, including all the so-called mental, spiritual, will, etc., powers. In using the words mental, spiritual, and will powers, I deliberately accept and use them in the popular, ordinary sense without further analysing them.

Once the word and concept *Time* enters, the ground for analysis and reasoning at once becomes very slippery. Mathematicians, physicists, etc., may feel that the expression is just a "well adapted one," and they may not be very much inclined to look closer into it or attentively to analyse it. Theologians and metaphysicians probably will speculate a great deal about it vaguely, with undefined terms and incoherent ideas with incoherent results; which will not lead us toward a scientific or true solution, but will keep us away from the discovery of truth.

In the meantime two facts remain facts: namely, mathematicians and physicists have almost all agreed with Minkowski "that space by itself and time by itself, are mere shadows, and only a kind of blend of the two exists in its own right." The other fact—psychological fact—is that *time* exists psychologically by itself, undefined and not understood. One chief difficulty is always that humans have to sit in judgment upon their own case. The psychological time as such, is our own human time; scientific time as such, is also our own human time. Which one of them is the best concept—which one more nearly corresponds to the truth about "time"? What is time (if any) anyway? Until now we have gone from "Cosmos" to "Bios," from "Bios" to "Logos," now we are confronted with the fact that "Logos" —Intelligence—and Time-binding are dangerously near to akin to each other, or may be identical. Do we in this way approach or go back to "Cosmos"? Such are the crucial questions which arise out of this new concept of Man. One fact must be borne in mind, that "the principles of dynamics appeared first to us, as experimental truths; but we have been obliged to use them as definitions. It is by definition that force is equal to the product of mass by acceleration, or that action is equal to reaction." (*The Foundation of Science,* by Henri Poincaré); and mathematics also has its whole foundation in a few axioms, "self evident," but *psychological facts*. It must be noted that the time-binding energy—the higher or highest energies of man (one of its branches anyway, for sake of discrimination let us call it *"M"*) when it works properly, that is, mathematically, does *not* work *psychologically* but works ABSTRACTLY: the higher the abstraction the less there is of the psychological element and the more there is, so to say, of the pure, impersonal time-binding energy (M). The definition of a man as a time-binder—a definition based on facts—suggests many reflections. One of them is the possibility that one of the functions of the time-binding energy in its pure form, in the highest abstraction (M), works automatically—machine-like, as it were, shaping *correctly* the product of its activity, but whether *truly* is another matter. Mathematics does not presume that its conclusions are true, but it does assert that its conclusions are correct; that is the inestimable value of mathematics. This becomes a very comprehensive fact if we approach and analyse the mathematical processes as some branch (M) of the time-binding process, which they are; then this process at once becomes impersonal and cosmic, because of the time-binding involved in it, no matter what *time* is (if there is such a thing as time).

Is the succession of cosmos, bios, logos, time-binding taking us right back to cosmos again? Now if we put *psychological* axioms into the time-binding apparatus, it will thrash out the results *correctly,* but whether the results are *true* is another question.

To be able to talk about these problems I have to introduce three new definitions, which are introduced only for practical purposes. It may happen that after some rewording these definitions may become scientific.

I will try to define "truth" and for this purpose I will divide the concept "truth" into three types:

(1) Psychological, or private, or relative truth, by which I will mean such conceptions of the truth as any one person possesses, but different from other types of truth $(\alpha_1, \alpha_2, \ldots \alpha_n)$.

(2) Scientific truth (α_S), by which I will mean a psychological truth when it is approved by the time-binding faculties or apparatus in the present stage of our development. This scientific truth represents the "bound-up-time" in our present knowledge; and finally,

(3) The absolute truth, which will be the *final definition* of a phenomenon based upon the final knowledge of *primal causation valid in infinity* (α_∞).

For simplicity's sake I will use the signs $\alpha_{1,\,2}\ldots\,_n$ for the "psychological," "private," or "relative" truths, between which, for the moment, I will not discriminate. $\alpha_{s1,\,s2}\ldots\,_{sn}$ will be used for scientific truths, and finally α_∞ for the absolute truth valid in infinity.

To make it easier to explain, I will illustrate the suggestions by an example. Let us suppose that the human time-binding capacities or energies in the *organic* chemistry correspond to radium in the *inorganic* chemistry; being of course of different dimensions and of absolutely different character. It may happen, for it probably is so, that the complex time-binding energy has many different stages of development and different kinds of "rays" $A,\ B,\ C,\ \ldots M\ldots$

Let us suppose that the so-called mental capacities are the M rays of the time-binding energy; the "spiritual" capacities, the A rays; the "will" powers, the B rays; and so on. Psychological truths will then be a function of all rays together, namely $A\ B\ C\ \ldots M\ \ldots$ or $f\ (A\ B\ C\ \ldots M\ \ldots)$, the character of any "truth" in question will largely depend upon which of these elements prevail.

If it were possible to isolate completely from the other rays the "mental" process—the "logos"—the M rays—and have a complete abstraction (which in the present could only be in mathematics), then the work of M could be compared to the work of an impersonal machine which always gives the same *correctly* shaped product *no matter what is* the material put into it.

It is a fact that mathematics is correct—impersonal—passionless. Again, as a matter of fact, all the basic axioms which underlie mathematics are "psychological axioms"; therefore it may happen that these "axioms" are not of the α_∞ type but are of the $f\ (A\ B\ C\ \ldots)$ personal type and this may be why mathematics cannot account for psychological facts. If psychology is to be an *exact science* it must be mathematical in principle. And, therefore, mathematics must find a way to embrace psychology. Here I will endeavor to outline a way in which this can be done. To express it correctly is more than difficult: I beg the mathematical reader to tolerate the form and look for the sense or even the feelings in what I attempt to express. To make it less shocking to the ear of the pure mathematician, I will use for the "infinitesimals" the words "very small numbers," for the "finite" the words "normal numbers" and for the "transfinite" the words "very great numbers." Instead of using the word "number" I will sometimes use the word "magnitude" and under the word "infinity" I will understand the meaning as "limitless." The base of the whole of mathematics or rather the starting point of mathematics was "psychological truths," axioms concerning normal numbers, and magnitudes that were tangible for the senses. Here to my mind is to be found the kernel of the whole trouble. The *base* of mathematics was f $(A \ B \ C \ldots M \ldots)$; the *work,* or the development, of mathematics is f (M); this is the reason for the "ghosts" in the background of mathematics. The f (M) evolved from this f $(A \ B \ C \ldots M \ldots)$ *base* a wonderful abstract theory absolutely correct for the normal, the very small, and for the very great numbers. But the rules which govern the small numbers, the normal, or psychological numbers, and the great numbers, are not the same. As a matter of fact, in the meantime, the physical world, the psychological world, is composed exclusively of very great numbers and of very small magnitudes (atoms, electrons, etc.). It seems to me that, if we want really to understand the world and man, we shall have to start from the beginning, from O, then take the next very small number as the first *finite* or "normal number"; then the old finites or the normal numbers would become very great numbers and the old very great numbers would become the very great of the second order and so on. Such transposed mathematics would become psychological and philosophic mathematics and mathematical philosophy would become philosophic mathematics. The immediate and most vital effect would be, that the *start* would be made not somewhere in the middle of the magnitudes but from the beginning, or from the limit "zero," from the "O"—from the intrinsic "to be or not to be"— and the next to it would be the very first small magnitude, the physical and therefore psychological continuum (I use the words physical continuum in the way Poincaré used them) would become a mathematical continuum in this new philosophic mathematics. This new branch of philosophic, psychological mathematics would be absolutely rigorous, correct and *true* in addition to which, maybe, it would change or enlarge and make humanly tangible for the layman, the concept of numbers, continuum, infinity, space, time and so on. Such a mathematics would be the mathematics for the time-binding psychology. Mathematical philosophy is the highest philosophy in existence; nevertheless, it could be changed to a still higher order in the way indicated here and become philosophic or psychological mathematics. This new science, of course, would not change the ordinary mathematics for ordinary purposes. It would be a special mathematics for the study of Man dealing only with the "natural finites" (the old infinitesimals) and great numbers of different orders (including the normal numbers), but starting from a real, common base—from O, and next to it very small number, which is a common *tangible* base for *psychological* as well as *analytical* truths.

This new philosophic mathematics would eliminate the concept of "infinitesimals" as such, which is an *artificial* concept and is not as a *concept* an element of *Nature*. The socalled *infinitesimals are Nature's real, natural finites.* In mathematics the infinitesimals were an analytical—an "M"—

time-binding—necessity, because of our starting point. I repeat once again that this transposition of our starting point would not affect the normal mathematics for normal purposes; it would build rather a new philosophic mathematics rigorously correct where analytical facts would be also psychological facts. This new mathematics would not only give correct results but also *true* results. Keeping in mind *both* conceptions of time, the scientific time and the psychological time, we may see that the human capacity of "Time-binding" is a very practical one and that this time-binding faculty is a *functional* name and definition for what we broadly mean by human "intelligence"; which makes it obvious that time (in any understanding of the term) is somehow very closely related to intelligence—the mental and spiritual activities of man. *All we know about "time" will explain to us a great deal about Man, and all we know about Man will explain to us a great deal about time,* if we consider *facts* alone. The "ghosts" in the background will rapidly vanish and become intelligible facts for philosophic mathematics. The most vital importance, nevertheless, is that taking zero as the limit and the next to it very small magnitude for the real starting point, it will give us a mathematical science from a natural base where *correct* formulas will be also true formulas and will correspond to psychological truths.

We have found that man is an exponential function where time enters as an exponent. If we compare the formula for organic growth $y = e^{kt}$, with the formula "$P\ R^T$," we see that they are of the same type and the *law of organic growth* applies to the human *time-binding energy*. We see, too, that the time-binding energy is also "*alive*" and multiplying in larger and larger families. The formula for the decomposing of radium is the same—only the exponent is negative instead of positive. This fact is indeed very curious and suggestive. Procreation, the organic growth, is also some function of time. I call it "time-linking" for the sake of difference. Whether the energy of procreation or that of "time-linking" can be accounted for in units of chemical energy taken up in food, I do not know. Not so with the mind—this "time-binding," higher exponential energy, "able to direct basic powers." If we analyse this energy, free from any speculation, we will find that this higher energy which is somehow directly connected with "time"—no matter what time is—is able to *produce,* by transformation or by drawing on other sources of energy, new energies unknown to nature. Thus the solar energy transformed into coal is, for instance, transformed into the energy of the drive of a piston, or the rotary energy in a steam engine, and so on. It is obvious that no amount of *chemical* energy in food can account for such an energy as the time-binding energy. There is only one supposition left, namely, that the time-binding apparatus has a source for its tremendous energy in the *transformation of organic atoms,* and—what is very characteristic—the results are *time*-binding energies.

This supposition is almost a certainty because it seems to be the only possible supposition to account for that energy. This supposition, which seems to be the only supposition, would bring us to face striking facts, namely, the transformation of organic atoms, which means a direct drawing upon the cosmic energy; and this cosmic energy—time—and intelligence are somehow connected—if not indeed equivalent. Happily these things can be verified in scientific laboratories. Radium was discovered only a few years ago and is still very scarce, but the results for science and life are already tremendous because scientific methods were applied in the understanding and use of it. We did not use any zoological or theological methods, but just direct, correct and scientific methods. There is no scarcity in "human radium," but, to my knowledge, physicists have never attempted to study this energy from that point of view. I am confident that, if once they start, there will be results in which all the so-called "supernatural, spiritual, psychic" phenomena, such as are not fakes, will become scientifically understood and will be consciously utilized. Now they are mostly wasted or only played with. It may happen that the science of Man—as the science of time-binding—will disclose to us the inner and final secrets—the final truth—of nature, valid in infinity.

It is very difficult to give in such a book as this an adequate list of the literature which may help to orient the reader in a general way in the great advance science has made in the last few years. This book is a pioneer book in its own way, and so there are no books dealing directly with its subject. There are two branches of science and one art which are fundamental for the further development of the subject; these two sciences are (1) Mathematical philosophy and (2) Scientific biology, the art is the art of creative engineering.

In mathematical philosophy there are to my knowledge only four great mathematical writers who treat the subject as a distinct science. They are two English scientists, Bertrand Russell and A. N. Whitehead; one Frenchman, Henri Poincaré (deceased); and one American, Professor C. J. Keyser. Messrs. Russell and Whitehead approach the problems from a purely logical point of view and therein lies the peculiar value of their work. Henri Poincaré was a physicist (as well as a mathematician) and, therefore, approaches the problems somewhat from a physicist's point of view, a circumstance giving his philosophy its particular value. Professor Keyser approaches the problems from both the logical and the warmly human points of view; in this is the great human and practical value of his work.

These four scientists are unique in their respective elaborations and elucidations of mathematical philosophy. It is not for me to advise the reader what selections to make, for if a thorough knowledge of the subject is desired the reader should read all these books, but not all readers are willing to make that effort toward clear thinking (which in the meantime will remain of the *highest* importance in science). Some readers will wish to select for themselves and to facilitate their selection I will lay out a "Menu" of this intellectual feast by giving in some cases the chapter heads.

For many temporary reasons I was not able, before going into print, to give a fuller list of the writings of those four unique men; but there is no stroke of their pen but which should be read with great attention—besides which there is a very valuable literature about their work.

(1) The purely mathematical foundation:

RUSSELL, BERTRAND.
> "The Principles of Mathematics." Cambridge University, 1903.
>
> > (I am not giving any selections from the contents of this book because this book should, without doubt, be read by every one interested in mathematical philosophy.)
>
> "The Problems of Philosophy." H. Holt & Co., N. Y., 1912.
>
> "Our Knowledge of the External World, as a Field for Scientific Method in Philosophy." Chicago, 1914.
>
> "Introduction to Mathematical Philosophy." Macmillan, N. Y.
> Selection from contents:
> Definition of number. The Definition of order. Kinds of relations. Infinite cardinal numbers. Infinite series and ordinals. Limits and continuity. The axiom of infinity and logical types. Classes. Mathematics and logic.
>
> "Mysticism and Logic." Longmans Green & Co. 1919. N. Y.
> Selection from contents:
> Mathematics and the metaphysicians. On scientific method in philosophy. The ultimate constituents of matter. On the notion of cause.

WHITEHEAD, ALFRED N.
"An Introduction to Mathematics."   Henry Holt & Co.
1911.   N. Y.

"The Organization of Thought Educational and Scientific."   London, 1917.
Selections from contents:
The principles of mathematics in relation to elementary teaching.   The organization of thought.   The
anatomy of some scientific ideas.   Space, time, and
relativity.

"An Enquiry Concerning the Principles of Natural
Knowledge."   Cambridge, 1919.
Selection from contents:
The traditions of science.   The data of science.   The
method of extensive abstraction.   The theory of
objects.

"The Concept of Nature."   Cambridge, 1920.
Selection from contents:
Nature and thought.   Time.   The method of extensive abstraction.   Space and motion.   Objects.   The
ultimate physical concepts.

"Principia Mathematica."   By A. N. Whitehead and
Bertrand Russell.   Cambridge, 1910–1913.
This monumental work stands alone.   "As a work
of constructive criticism it has never been surpassed.
To every one and especially to philosophers and men
of natural science, it is an amazing revelation of how
the familiar terms with which they deal plunge their
roots far into the darkness beneath the surface of
common sense.   It is a noble monument to the critical spirit of science and to the idealism of our time."

"Human Worth of Rigorous Thinking."   C. J. Keyser.

(2)   The physicist's point of view:

POINCARÉ, HENRI.
"The Foundations of Science."   The Science Press,
N. Y., 1913.
Selection from contents:
I. Science and hypothesis.   Number and magnitude.

Space. Force. Nature. II. The value of science.
The mathematical sciences. The physical sciences.
The objective value of science. III. Science and
method. Science and the scientist. Mathematical reasoning. The new mechanics. Astronomic science.

(3) The human, civilizing, practical life, point of view:

KEYSER, CASSIUS J.
"Science and Religion: The Rational and the Super-
rational." The Yale University Press.

"The New Infinity and the Old Theology." The Yale
University Press.

"The Human Worth of Rigorous Thinking." Essays
and Addresses. Columbia University Press, 1916.
Selection from contents:
The human worth of rigorous thinking. The human
significance of mathematics. The walls of the world;
or concerning the figure and the dimensions of the
Universe of space. The universe and beyond. The
existence of the hypercosmic. The axiom of infinity:
A new presupposition of thought. Research in American Universities. Mathematical productivity in the
United States.

"Mathematical Philosophy, the Study of Fate and Freedom. Lectures for Educated Laymen." Forthcoming Book.
Selection from contents of general interest.
The mathematical obligations of philosophy. Human-
istic and industrial education. Logic the muse of
thought. Radiant aspects of an over-world.—Veri-
fiers and falsifiers. Significance and nonsense.—
Distinction of logical and psychological. A diamond
test of harmony.—Distinction of doctrine and method.
—Theoretical and practical doubt.—Mathematical
philosophy in the rôle of critic. A world uncriticised—
the garden of the devil. "Supersimian" Wisdom.
Autonomous truth and autonomous falsehood. Other
Varieties of truth and untruth. Mathematics as the
study of fate and freedom. The prototype of reasoned discourse often disguised as in the Declaration
of Independence, the Constitution of the United

States, the Origin of Species, the Sermon on the Mount.
—Nature of mathematical transformation. No transformation, no thinking. Transformation law essentially psychological, Relation function and transformation as three aspects of one thing. Its study,
the common enterprise of science. The static and
the dynamic worlds. The problem of time and
kindred problems. Importation of time and sup-
pression of time as the classic devices of sciences.—
The nature of invariance. The ages-old problem of
permanence and change. The quest of what abides
in a fluctuant world as the binding thread of human
history. The tie of comradeship among the enterprises of human spirit.—The concept of a group.
The notion simply exemplified in many fields, is
"Mind" a group. The philosophy of the cosmic
year.—Limits and limit processes omnipresent as
ideals and idealization, in all thought and human
aspiration. Ideals the flint of reality.—Mathematical infinity, its dynamic and static aspects. Need of
history of the Imperious concept. The rôle of infinity
in a mighty poem.—Meaning of dimensionality.
Distinction of imagination and conception. Logical
existence and sensuous existence. Open avenues to
unimaginable worlds.—The theory of logical types.
A supreme application of it to definition of man, and
the science of human welfare.—The psychology of
mathematics and the mathematics of psychology.
Both of them in their infancy. Consequent retard-
ation of science. The symmetry of thought. The
asymmetry of imagination.—Science and engineering.
Science as engineering in preparation. Engineering
as science in action. Mathematics the guide of the
engineer. Engineering the guide of humanity. Humanity the civilizing or Time-Binding class of life.
Qualities essential to engineering leadership. The
ethics of the art. The engineer as educator, as
scientist, as philosopher, as psychologist, as economist,
as statesman, as mathematical thinker—as a Man.

APPENDIX II

BIOLOGY AND TIME-BINDING

THE life of one man is short, and to very few is it given to achieve much in their lifetime. Extensive achievements are made almost entirely by many men taking up the work done by a discoverer. In such a case, we arrive at a *complete* "truth," not by the production of one man but by a chain of men, but the initial discovery not only has to be produced but correctly defined before it can be used and that is the important point to be made. What we do not realize is the tremendous amount of mental work that is lost by an incorrect use of words.

Human thought—that unique, subtle and yet most energetic phenomenon of nature—is in the main wantonly wasted, because we do not use, or take pains to use, suitable language; at the same time, false definitions lead to consequences not merely wasteful but positively harmful. When ideas and facts are falsely defined, they tend to bring us to false conclusions, and false conclusions lead us in wrong directions, and life and knowledge greatly suffer in consequence. Our progress is not a well ordered pursuit after truth, as pure chance plays too large a part in it.

Until lately, logic was supposed to be the science of correct thinking, but modern thought has progressed so far that the old logic is not able to handle the great accumulated volume —the great complicated mass of existing ideas and facts—and so we are forced to look for another instrument much more expedient and powerful. There is no need to establish a new science to replace logic; we simply have to look closer into the sciences at hand and realize the fact, which was with us all the time, namely, that mathematics and mathematical reasoning is nothing else than the true logic of nature —nature's universal tongue—the one means of expression that is the same for all peoples. This is not a play on words, it is a fact which, after investigation, everybody must admit. Everybody who wants to think logically must think mathematically or give up any pretense of correct thinking—there is no escape and all who refuse to investigate the justice of this statement put themselves outside the pale of logically thinking people. The application of rigorous thinking to life will even revolutionize scientific methods by the introduction of right definitions, correct classifications, just language, and so will lead to trustworthy results. Very probably all our doctrines and creeds will have to be revised; some rejected, some rectified, some broadened; bringing about unanimity of all sciences and thus greatly increasing their effectiveness in the pursuit of truth. This application of mathematics to life will even revolutionize mathematics itself. In App. I it is suggested tentatively how this may be accomplished.

As the seemingly ultimate and highest experimentally known energy is the human time-binding energy, this new concept may lead to a change in our present concepts of matter, space and time, in much the same way as the discovery of radium has affected them. This problem can be solved only by *scientific* experiments with the *time*-binding energy.

In many, even in most, of the cases, the analysis of these phenomena presents great technical difficulty, but why confuse our minds by being afraid of, or being a slave of words? If instead of calling wine *wine,* we called it by its chemical formula, would this, in any way, change the quality of wine? Of course not. All the "qualities" will remain because they are facts, and cannot be altered by words.

A most pathetic picture of the havoc and chaos which

wrong use of words brings into life and science is exhibited in all fields of thought by the endless and bitter fighting over words not well defined. Mathematics has been able to make its most stupendous achievements because of its method of exact analysis of the continuum, dimensions, classes, relations, functions, transfinite numbers, etc., and also of space and time. Hitherto, not all of these conceptions in their sharply defined form have had direct application to our daily life or to our world conception. The thoughts expressed in App. I may suggest this "missing link"—connecting mathematics more intimately with life.

Modern science knows that all energies can be somehow transformed from one kind to another and that all of them represent one type of energetic phenomena, no matter what is the origin of each. For example, a galvanic or chemical battery produces the same kind of electricity as the mechanical process of friction or the interaction of cosmic laws as in the dynamo. In some instances, when our systems are suitably adjusted, the transformations are reversible, that is, the energy results in a chemical process—an accumulator; the chemical process results in electricity—the galvanic battery; motion results in electricity—the dynamo; electricity results in motion—the electric motor; etc. We know all energies are somehow related to each other, in that their transformation is possible. The effects produced by the same type of energy are absolutely the same—no matter what its origin. The marvel of an electric lamp is the same marvel, whether the origin of the electricity be chemical, mechanical or cosmic as in the dynamo. The experiments in scientific biology have proved this to be true in living organisms and just this is the tremendous importance of the discoveries in scientific biology. Light and other energies react on organisms in the same way as the chemical reactions and these phenomena are reversible. More than that, living complex organisms have been produced which grew to maturity through a chemical or mechanical treatment of the egg, and this has been accomplished in the infancy of scientific biology! (See *The Organisms as a Whole,* by Jacques Loeb.)

All phenomena *in nature* are *natural* and should be approached as *such.* The human mind is at least an energy which can direct other energies; it is incorrect and misleading to call it *super*natural. It is of course true that we do not fully understand the nature of the human mind and we shall learn to understand it when and only when we acquire sense enough to recognize it as *natural.* If we persist in saying and believing that the "spiritual evidences cannot be explained on a material base," this statement should be equally applicable to electricity or radium. If this statement is false for these phenomena, it is equally false for the mind or the so-called spiritual and will powers. The scientific understanding of these phenomena will not "degrade" these phenomena, *because that cannot be done. Facts remain facts and no scientific explanation of a phenomenon can lower or degrade that which is a fact.* Electricity is electricity and nothing else, no matter what its origin; human time-binding energies (embracing all faculties) are the highest of the known energies—equally magnificent and astonishing—no matter what the base; and the scientific understanding of them will only *add* to our respect for them and for ourselves; it will unmistakably help us to develop them indefinitely by mathematical analysis. The *base* is not the phenomenon—sulphuric acid and zinc *are not* electricity; time-binding energies *are not* a pound of beefsteak, although a pound of beefsteak may help to save life and be therefore *instrumental* in the production of a poem or of a sonata; but by no means can a beefsteak be taken for either of them.

I have attempted, with some measure of success I trust, to solve these problems in science and life; the results are astonishing, as they lead us to a much higher and more embracing ethics than society has ever had. By this analysis

I prove that the understanding of this most stupendous but
NATURAL phenomenon of human life brings us to the scien-
tifical source of ethics and I prove that the so-called "highest
ideals of humanity" have nothing of "sentimentalism" or of
the "*super*natural" in them, but are exclusively the *fulfilment*
of the *natural laws* for the *human class of life*. The recognition of the fact that the phenomena of the human mind
are natural and as such conform to natural law has the further advantage over the "supernatural" attitude in that we
can no more evade a law of human nature than the law of
gravity; in other words, human ethics will have the validity
of natural law. With the supernatural attitude, it was simple
enough to avoid the issues of life, by a simple statement—"I
do not believe"—and that was enough to break all bonds and
be free from the "supernatural morale"—but to get away
from the "natural morale" and *remain* HUMAN is IMPOS-
SIBLE. Whereas, with an artificially formulated morale it
was easy enough to break away by a simple mental speculation, and feel perfectly satisfied as long as one escaped the
jail; with a morale made clear that it is a NATURAL LAW for
the human class of life, the curtain of sophistry and speculation is removed and everyone who breaks away from the
NATURAL LAWS FOR HUMANS, WILL KNOW BY HIMSELF,
THAT HE IS OUTSIDE THE LAW—FOR HUMANS.

Engineers are not metaphysicians, their field is not one of
clever argument but one of proved facts; their work is not
to befog the air with cloudy expressions or sophistry, but to
create; their method is scientific and their tool is mathematics. It is known that in remote antiquity, in some temples
electrical phenomena were known and were used to keep
the ignorant masses in awe and obedience. Shall we follow
the methods used by those magicians or shall we squarely
face facts? Shall we look upon life, and the usually so-called
mental, spiritual phenomena, etc., as *super*natural, simply
because we do not understand them? It seems evident that

everything which *exists in nature, is natural,* no matter how simple or complicated a phenomenon it is; and on no occasion can the so-called *"super*natural" be anything else than a completely natural law, though it may, at the moment, be above or beyond our present understanding. The attitude of mind which admits the *super*natural blinds and frustrates any analysis or any attempt at analysis. The unprejudiced analysis of the so-called "supernatural" does not *alter* any part of the strange and high functions of it. The phenomena of the human time-binding energy are and will remain the most precious, subtle and highest of known functions, no matter what the origin. *Facts* may not be *denied* or *falsified* if analysis is to arrive at correct conclusions. The high dimensionality of the human mind, the so-called spiritual and will powers, *are facts* and must be *accepted* as such. It is about time to establish an exact science to deal with them. The problems of animal life were approached without prejudice, no supernatural "spark" was bothering us in our analysis —an animal was an animal and nothing else—we did not intermix dimensions, therefore we see that the "social structure" of the animals on a farm never breaks down as they are managed on a scientific base with an understanding of *their* proper standards. Animals to-day live more happily than man. We don't allow animals to practice the "survival of the fittest," or "competition," which is far too destructive. Our present social system imposes these disastrous methods upon man alone, and the result is that the hideous proverb "Homo homini lupus" has become true.

In modern science facts are not wanting, we have first but to know them. If we take, for example, sulphuric acid and zinc and make what we call a galvanic battery, we see that from two chemical substances a third—a salt—is made in addition to which we have a peculiar energy produced called electricity. Who does not know the marvelous properties of this phenomenon?

Scientific biology has made tremendous progress lately; engineers cannot afford to ignore the facts established in laboratory researches. The problem of "life" and of other energies, hitherto considered "*super*natural," is well in hand, and proves to be none the less astonishing though entirely natural. A number of scientists all over the world are working at this problem and the scientific facts which they have established, and which cannot now be denied, belong to-day to the realm of practical life. Engineers, of course, have to know these facts; mathematicians have to establish correct dimensions in the study of all the sciences and people will have to study mathematical philosophy; only then can the process of integration in any phase of thought be made without mistakes. There is no escape from that, if *truth* is what we really want. But here one objection may be raised, an objection which for some is a serious one indeed; namely, what will take the place of the old philosophy, law and ethics, if human life is nothing else than a physico-chemical process? To quote Doctor Jacques Loeb from his *Mechanistic Conception of Life:* "If on the basis of a serious survey, this question (*that all life phenomena can be unequivocally explained in physico-chemical terms*—Author) can be answered in the affirmative, our social and ethical life will have to be put on a scientific basis and our rules of conduct must be brought into harmony with the results of scientific biology. Not only is the mechanistic conception of life compatible with ethics, it seems the only conception of life which can lead to an understanding of the source of ethics."

I hope to have proved in this book that *scientific* ethics is based on natural laws for the human class of life; that it is based on the experimentally proved fact that Man is a Time-binder, naturally active as such in time; and that this concept or definition of Man is rigorously scientific and accounts for the highest functions of man—the highest of the mental and spiritual perfections—without the need of any *"super-natural"* hypothesis.

Scientific biology proves the fact that life and all of its phenomena are the results of some special physico-chemical processes, which manifest themselves in some peculiar energies, of which the human mind is the highest known form. These processes are known to be reversible, in that some of these peculiar energies cause physico-chemical changes in their own base; the process involved I propose to call biolysis, as I propose to call biolyte the substances produced. These phenomena have a parallel analogy in inorganic chemistry—in electricity—the difference being only in the scale or dimension. When an electric current is passed through a special battery called an accumulator or reversible battery, chemical changes occur, in that new compounds are formed which possess a reversible capacity; namely, in reproducing the former materials—that is, electricity is generated. This process of forming chemical substances by the passing of an electrical current is called electrolysis and the product so produced is called electrolyte. At the same time it is a known fact that organic chemistry is infinitely more complicated and variable than inorganic chemistry. The energy produced by the reactions of some organic chemical groups are, therefore, of a more complicated character and of another dimension. One of these energies of organic chemistry which lately has come into the scope of scientific analysis is called life—its physico-chemical base is the protoplasm, which *result* I call the "time-linking" capacity or energy. This name is important for the consequences it will bring about later on. The time-binding capacity or energy of man (no matter what time is—if it is), which is unique to man, is a most subtle complex; it is the highest known energy and probably has many subdivisions. Ears are sensitive to the vibration of the air. Eyes are sensitive to the more subtle vibrations of light; in a similar way, the time-binding apparatus is sensitive to the most subtle energies; besides which it has the capacity to register not only all of our sensations but also the time-binding energies of other people; and it apparently has the capacity to register the energies of the universe.

Here again we see the same continuity of phenomena; the protoplasm as a complex organic physico-chemical unit which has the peculiarity to "live," to grow and multiply "autonomously" and this same autonomous peculiarity *applies* to the *time-binding energy;* it grows and multiplies "autonomously" in its own dimension. The time-binding energy is a complex radiating energy somewhat like the emanations of radium and it probably also has many different subdivisions. *Note that the transformation of the atom* or the transformation of *radio-active substances after passing different stages, is not complete but probably ends in lead, whereas the transformation which occurs in the production of the time-binding energy probably is complete or nearly complete and is that which I call the time-binding energy..* (*See App. I.*) All the higher characteristics of man which it is customary to call the "mental, spiritual and will powers," etc., are embraced in this exact definition of energy—in the capacity of time-binding. A diagram will better explain the continuity, evolution and mechanism of this time-binding energy.

C_1 is the physico-chemical base (for simplicity I represent the whole complex as one base) of the human time-binding energy. T_1 is the thought produced by a physico-chemical process (corresponding, for illustration's sake only, to electricity produced by a galvanic battery). The thought T_1 in turn produces a physico-chemical effect E_1 on the base C_1 (corresponding for the same reason to electrolysis and electrolyte in electricity). C_1 and E_1 combined, or C_2 produces T_2 which again in turn affects the base and produces a physico-chemical effect E_2, this new combination produces the energy T_3, and so on . . . theoretically without limits,

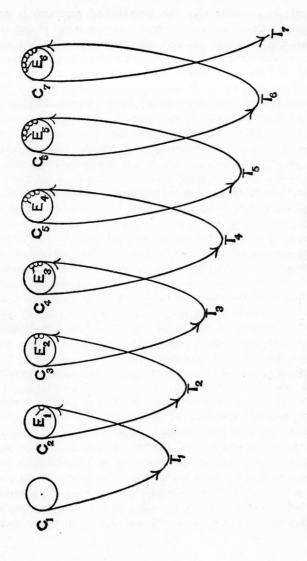

as long as there is *any source* of energy upon which this special energy can draw. This theory which I call the "spiral theory" represents a suggestive working mechanism of the time-binding energy and is in accord with the latest scientific discoveries. It explains the processes of all the mental and so-called spiritual energies which have been such a puzzle to humanity, and it also explains other phenomena which, until now, have had no scientific explanation whatever.

The animals are *not* time-binding, they have *not* the capacity of the "spiral"; therefore, they have not autonomous progress. At the same time, it will be obvious that if we teach humans false ideas, we affect their time-binding capacities and energies very seriously, by affecting in a wrong way the physico-chemical base. This energy is so peculiar that it embraces, if I may use the old expression, the highest ideals (when the time-binding energy is unobstructed and is allowed to work normally), and also the most criminal ideas (when the time-binding energy is obstructed by false teachings and in consequence works abnormally). We cannot make animals moral or immoral because they have not this time-binding capacity. Whereas human progress can be very seriously affected by false ideas; in other words, the biolyte of false teachings in the animal dimension must be very different from the biolyte of true ideas in the human dimension. Nature or nature's laws happily cannot be completely deviated from or violated—the time-binding energy cannot be completely suppressed in the time-binding class of life. The false teachings that we are animals and essentially brutal and selfish can, of course, degrade human nature not only down to the animal level but lower still. Happily now science can explain and prove how fundamentally fiendish in effect are these teachings in the life and progress of human beings. It will be a shock to those who teach, preach and practice animal standards and in the same breath contradict themselves in any talking about "immortality" and "salvation";

a little thought makes it perfectly clear that "animal standards" and "salvation" or "immortality" simply exclude each other. With the natural law of time-binding realized, the way is open to entering scientifically upon the problem of immortality. The time-binding energies as well as "life" follow the same type of exponential function. "The constant synthesis then of specific material from simple compounds of a non-specific character is the chief feature by which living matter differs from non-living matter. . . . This problem of synthesis leads to the assumption of immortality of the living cell, since there is no *a priori* reason why this synthesis should ever come to a standstill of its own accord as long as enough food is available and the proper outside physical conditions are guaranteed. . . . The idea that the body cells are naturally immortal and die only if exposed to extreme injuries such as prolonged lack of oxygen or too high a temperature helps to make one problem more intelligible. The medical student, who for the first time realizes that life depends upon that one organ, the heart, doing its duty incessantly for the seventy years or so allotted to man, is amazed at the precariousness of our existence. It seems indeed uncanny that so delicate a mechanism should function so regularly for so many years. The mysticism connected with this and other phenomena of adaptation would disappear if we would be certain that all cells are really immortal and that the fact which demands an explanation is not the continued activity but the cessation of activity in death. Thus we see that the idea of the immortality of the body cell if it can be generalized may be destined to become one of the main supports for a complete physico-chemical analysis of life phenomena since it makes the durability of organisms intelligible. . . ." (*The Organism as a Whole,* by Jacques Loeb.)

The outlook for those who live and profess selfish, greedy, "space-binding animal standards" is not very promising as disclosed by the "spiral," but unhappily we cannot help them;

only time-binding—only fulfilling the natural laws for humans—can give them the full benefit of their natural capacities by which they will be able to raise themselves above animals and their fate.

The results obtained in scientific biological researches are growing very rapidly and every advance in their knowledge proves this theory to be true. If they differ in a few instances it is not because the principles of this theory are wrong, but because they intermix dimensions and use words not sufficiently defined which always results in confusion and the checking of the progress of science.

Most of the problems touched upon in this appendix from a mathematical point of view are based upon laboratory facts. We have only to collect them and there is little need of imagination to see their general bearing. Since we have discovered the fact that Man is a time-binder (no matter what time is) and have introduced the sense of dimensionality into the study of life phenomena in general, a great many facts which were not clear before become very clear now.

I wrote this book on a farm without any books at hand and I had been out of touch with the progress of science for the five years spent in the war service and war duties. My friend Dr. Grove-Korski, formerly at Berkeley University, drew my attention particularly to the books of Dr. Jacques Loeb. I found there a treasury of laboratory facts which illustrate as nothing better could, the correctness of my theory. I found with deep satisfaction that the new "scientific biology" is scientific because it has used mathematical methods with notable regard to dimensionality—they do not "milk an automobile."

For the mathematician and the engineer, the "tropism theory of animal conduct," founded by Dr. J. Loeb, is of the greatest interest, because this is a theory which analyses the functions and reactions of an organism *as a whole* and therefore there is no chance for confusion of ideas or the intermixing of dimensions.

"Physiologists have long been in the habit of studying not the reactions of the whole organism but the reactions of isolated segments; the so-called reflexes. While it may seem justifiable to construct the reactions of the organism as a whole from the individual reflexes, such an attempt is in reality doomed to failure, since the reactions produced in an isolated element cannot be counted upon to occur when the same element is part of the whole, on account of the mutual inhibitions which the different parts of the organism produce upon each other when in organic connection; and it is, therefore, impossible to express the conduct of a whole animal as the algebraic sum of the reflexes of its isolated segments. . . . It would, therefore, be a misconception to speak of tropism as of reflexes, since tropisms are reactions of the organism as a whole, while reflexes are reactions of isolated segments. Reflexes and tropisms agree, however, in one respect, inasmuch as both are obviously of a purely physicochemical character." *Forced Movements—Tropism and Animal Conduct.* By Jacques Loeb.

I will quote here only a very few passages, but these books are of such importance that every mathematician and engineer should read them. They are, if I may say so, a "mathematical biology"—the survey of a life long study of "tropisms," which is the name given to express "forced movements" in organisms. They give the quintessence of laboratory experiments as to what are the effects of different energies such as light (heliotropism), electricity (galvanotropism), gravity (geotropism), etc., in their reaction and influence upon the movements and actions of living organisms. These experiments are conclusive and the conclusions arrived at cannot be overlooked or evaded. The tremendous practical results of such scientific methods are based upon two principles, namely: that, (1) the scientists must think mathematically, their studies of the phenomena must be in "systems" as a complex whole, and they must not intermix dimensions; (2)

they must see the danger and not be afraid of old words with wrong meanings, but must use clear and rigorous thinking to eliminate the prejudices in science—the poison of metaphysical speculating with words, or verbalism. These books give ample proofs of how misleading and obscuring are the words used and how basically wrong are the conclusions arrived at by such scientists as still persist in using the anthropomorphic or teleological methods of analysis. If a sceptical or doubtful reader is interested to see an ample proof of how deadly is the effect which an incorrect or unmathematical manner of thinking brings into science and life—he also may be referred to these books. The following quotations prove biologically that man is of a totally different dimension—a totally different being than an animal. From Dr. Conklin I quote only from his *Heredity and Environment* and to save a repetition of the title of the book, I will indicate the quotations by using only his name. (All italics are indicated by A. K.)

"It would be of the greatest importance to show directly that the *homologous proteins of different species are different. This has been done* for hemoglobins of the blood by Reichert and Brown, who have shown by crystallographic measurements that the hemoglobins of any species are definite substances for that species. . . . The following sentences by Reichert and Brown seem to indicate that this may be true for the crystals of hemoglobin. '*The hemoglobins of any species are different substances for that species.* But upon comparing the corresponding substances hemoglobins in different species of a genus it is generally found that they differ the one from the other to a greater or less degree; the differences being such that when complete crystallographic data are available the different *species can be distinguished* by these *differences in their hemoglobins'.* . . . The facts thus far reported imply the suggestion that heredity of the genus is determined by the proteins of a definite constitution differing from the proteins of other genera. This constitution of the proteins would therefore be responsible for the genus heredity. The different species of a genus have all the same genus proteins, but the proteins of each species of the same genus are apparently different again in chemical constitution and hence they may give rise to the specific biological or immunity reactions." *The Organism as a Whole*,   by Jacques Loeb.

"*All pecularities which are characteristic of a race, species, genus, order, class and phylum are of course inherited*, otherwise there would be no constant characteristics of these groups and no possibility of classifying organisms.   The chief characters of every living thing are unalterably fixed by heredity.   Men do not gather grapes of thorns nor figs of thistles.   Every living thing produces off-spring after its own kind, Men, horses, cattle; birds, reptiles, fishes; insects, mollusks, worms; polyps, sponges, micro-organisms,—all of the million known species of animals and plants differ from one another because of inherited peculiarities, *because they have come from different kinds of germ cells.*"   Conklin.

"The entire organism consisting of structures and functions, body and mind, develops out of the germ, and the organization of the germ determines all the possibilities of development of the mind no less than of the body, though the actual realization of any possibility is dependent also upon environmental stimuli." . . . Conklin.

"The development of the *mind parallels that of the body*; whatever the ultimate relation of the *mind* and body may be, there can be *no* reasonable *doubt* that the two develop together from the germ.   It is a curious fact that many people who are seriously disturbed by scientific teaching as to the evolution or gradual development of the human race accept with equanimity the universal observation as to the development of the human individual,—mind as well as body.   The animal ancestry of the race is surely no more disturbing to philosophical or religious beliefs than the germinal origin of the individual, and yet the latter is a fact of universal observation which cannot be relegated to the domain of hypothesis or theory, and which can not be successfully denied. . . . Now we know that the child comes from the germ cells which are not made by the bodies of the parents but have arisen by the division of the antecedent germ cell.   *Every cell comes from a pre-existing cell* by a process of division, and *every germ cell comes from a pre-existing germ cell.* Consequently it is not possible to hold, that the body generates germ cells, nor that the soul generates souls.   The only possible scientific position is that the *mind* or soul as well as the body develops from the *germ.*

" No fact in human experience is more certain than that the mind develops by gradual and natural processes from a simple condition which can scarcely be called mind at all; no fact in human experience is fraught with greater practical and philosophical significance than this, and yet no fact is more generally disregarded." Conklin.

"Doubtless the elements of which *consciousness* develops are *present in the germ cells*, in the same sense that the elements of the other psychic processes or of the organs of the body are there present; not as a miniature of the adult condition, but rather in the form of elements or factors, which by long series of combinations and transformations, due to interactions with one another and with the environment, give rise to the fully developed condition. . . . It is an interesting fact that in man, and in several other animals which may be assumed to have a sense of identity, the nerve cells, especially those of the *brain, cease dividing* at an early age, and these identical cells persist throughout the remainder of life." . . .

"The hen does not produce the egg, but the egg produces the hen and also other eggs. Individual traits are not transmitted from the hen to the egg, but they develop out of germinal factors which are carried along from *cell to cell, and from generation to generation*. . . . "

"The germ is the undeveloped organism which forms the bond between successive generations; the person is the developed organism which arises from the germ under the influence of environmental conditions, the person develops and dies in each generation; the germ-plasm is the continuous stream of living substance which connects all generations. The person nourishes and protects the germ, and in this sense the person is merely the carrier of the germ-plasm, the *mortal trustee* of an immortal substance." Conklin.

This is what I call "time-linking." (Author.)

"Through intelligence and social cooperation he is able to control environment for particular ends, in a manner quite impossible in other organisms. . . . Other animals develop much more rapidly than man but that development sooner comes to an end. The children of lower races of man develop more rapidly than those of higher races but in such cases they also cease to develop at an earlier age. The prolongation of the period of infancy and of immaturity in the human race greatly increases the importance of environment and training as *factors of development*." Conklin.

Another sidelight given on the "Spiral theory." (Author.)

"In education also we are strangely blind to proper aims and methods. Any education is bad which leads to the formation of habits of idleness, carelessness, failure, instead of habits of industry, thoroughness and success. Any religious or social institution is bad which leads to habits of pious make-believe, insincerity, slavish regard for authority and disregard for evidence, instead of habits of sincerity, open-mindedness and independence. . . ."

"All that man now is he has come to be without conscious human guidance. If evolution has progressed from the amœba to man without human interference, if the great progress from ape-like men to the most highly civilized races has taken place without conscious human control, the question may well be asked: Is it possible to improve on the natural method of evolution? It may not be possible to improve on the method of evolution and yet by intelligent action it may be possible to facilitate that method. *Man can not change a single law of nature but he can put himself into such relations to natural laws that he can profit by them.*" Conklin.

This proves the great importance of KNOWING THE NATURAL LAWS for the human class of life, and making natural time-binding impulses conscious, for then only will the spiral give a logarithmical accumulation of the right kind, otherwise the biolyte will be "animal" in substance as well as in effect. Here it is immaterial how the first "time-binder" was produced; the fact that he is of another dimension is of the greatest importance.

"From sands to stars, from the immensity of the universe to the minuteness of the electron, in living things no less than in lifeless ones, science recognizes everywhere the inevitable sequence of cause and effect, the universality of natural processes, the reign of natural law. *Man also is a part of Nature, a part of the great mechanism of the* universe, and all that he is and *does is limited and prescribed by laws of nature.* Every human being comes into existence by a process of development, every step of which is determined by antecedent causes. . . . Our anatomical, physiological, psychological possibilities were predetermined in the *germ cells* from which we came. . . ." Conklin.

This shows the importance of keeping the study of humans in their own dimensionality, and also the importance of finding the IMPERSONAL NATURAL LAWS for the human class of life. Now it can be realized that all the so-called human ideals are none else than the ever growing fulfillment of the NATURAL "TIME-BINDING" LAWS. This understanding will enable man to discover new "time-binding" laws for their conduct, their business relations, their state, which will not be a contradiction of the real, NATURAL LAWS but will be in accord with them; then and only then human progress will have a chance to develop peacefully.

"Adult characteristics are potential and not actual in the germ, and their actual appearance depends upon many complicated reactions of the germinal units with one another and with the environment. In short, our actual personalities are not predetermined in the germ cells, but our possible personalities are. . . . The influence of environment upon the minds and morals of men is especially great. To a large extent our habits, words, thoughts; our aspirations, ideals, satisfactions; our responsibility, morality, religion are the results of the environment and education of our early years. . . . "
"Owing to this vastly greater power of memory, reflection and inhibition man is much freer than any other animal. Animals which learn little from experience have little freedom and the more they learn the freer they become. . . . "   Conklin.

It may be added here that the "spiral theory" explains how our reactions can be accelerated and elaborated by ourselves, and how truly we are the masters of our destinies.

"Because we can find no place in our philosophy and logic for self determination shall we cease to be scientists and close our eyes to the evidence? The first duty of science is to appeal to fact and to settle later with logic and philosophy. . . . " Conklin.

There will be no difficulty in the settlement of facts with the new philosophy of "Human Engineering."

"The analysis of instinct from a purely physiological point of view ultimately furnishes the data for a scientific ethics. Human happiness is based upon the possibility of a natural and harmonious satisfaction of the instincts. . . . It is rather remarkable that we should still be under the influence of an ethics which considers the human instincts in themselves low and their gratification vicious. That such an ethics must have had a comforting effect upon the orientals, whose instincts were inhibited or warped through the combined effects of an enervating climate, despotism and miserable economic conditions is intelligible, and it is perhaps due to a continuation of the unsatisfactory economic conditions that this ethics still prevails to some extent. . . . Lawyers, criminologists and philosophers frequently imagine that only want makes man work. This is an erroneous view. We are instinctively forced to be active in the same way as ants or bees. The instinct of workmanship would be the greatest source of happiness if it were not for the fact that our present social and economic organization allows only a few to satisfy this instinct. Robert Mayer has pointed out that any successful display or setting free of energy is a source of pleasure to us. This is the reason why the satisfaction of the instinct of workmanship is of such importance in the economy of life, for the play and learning of the child, as well as for the scientists or commercial work of the man. . . . We can vary at will the instincts of animals. A number of marine animals . . . go away from the light, can be forced to go to light in two ways, first by lowering the temperature and second by increasing the concentration of the sea water, whereby the cells of the animals lose water. This instinct can be again reversed by raising the temperature or by lowering the concentration of the sea water. I have found repeatedly that by the same conditions by which phenomena of growth and organization can be controlled the instincts are controlled also. This indicates that there is a common basis for both classes of life phenomena. This common base is the physical and chemical character of the mixture of substances which we call protoplasm. . . . *The greatest happiness in life* can be obtained only if *all instincts*, that of workmanship included, can be maintained at a certain *optimal intensity*. But while it is certain that the individual can ruin or diminish the value of its life by a onesided development of its instincts, e.g., dissipation, it is at the same time true that the *economic and social conditions can ruin or diminish the value of life for a great number of individuals*. It is no doubt true that in our present social and economic conditions more than ninety per cent of human beings lead an existence whose value is far below what it should be. They are compelled by want to sacrifice a number of instincts especially the most valuable among them, that of workmanship, in order to save the lowest and most imperative, that of eating. If those who amass immense fortunes could possibly intensify their lives with their abundance, it might perhaps be rational to let many suffer in order to have a few cases of true happiness. But for an increase of happiness only that amount of money is of service which can be used for the harmonious development and satisfaction of inherited instincts. For this, comparatively little is necessary. The rest is of no more use to a man than the surplus of oxygen in the atmosphere. As a matter of fact, the only true satisfaction a multimillionaire can possibly get from increasing his fortunes, is the satisfaction of the instinct of workmanship or the pleasure that is connected with a successful display of energy. The scientist gets this satisfaction without diminishing the value of life of his fellow being, and the same should be true for the business man. . . . Although we recognize no metaphysical free-will, we do not deny personal responsibility. We can fill the memory of the young generation with such associations as will prevent wrong doing or dissipation. . . . Cruelty in the penal code and the tendency to exaggerate punishment are sure signs of a low civilization and of an imperfect educational system. . . . It seems to me that we can no more expect to unravel the mechanism of associative memory by histological or morphological methods than we can expect to unravel the dynamics of electrical phenomena by microscopic study of cross-sections through a telegraph wire or by counting and locating the telephone connections in a big city. If we are anxious to develop a dynamic of the various life-phenomena, we must remember that the colloidal substances are the machines which produce the life phenomena, but the physics of these substances is still a science of the future. . . . Physiology gives us no answer to the latter question. The idea of specific energy has always been regarded as the terminus for the investigation of the sense organs. Mach expressed the opinion that chemical conditions lie at the foundation of sensation in general. . . . " *Comparative Physiology of the Brain,* by Jacques Loeb.

Here it may be added that the "Instinct of Workmanship" in the animal class, becomes in the time-binding class of life the instinct of *creation,* and is nothing else than the expression of the natural impulse of the "Time-binding" energy. In the present social and economic system very few have a possibility to satisfy this instinct; scientific management is or may be satisfying the animal instinct of workmanship, but it is not satisfactory to the instinct of creation. "Time-binding" in its last analysis is creation and only such a social and economic system as will satisfy this want—this natural impulse—will satisfy Humans—the "Time-binders"—and will bring about their fullest growth in work and happiness.

"LAWS OF GROWTH" (from *Unified Mathematics,* by Louis C. Karpinski, Ph.D.). "*Compound interest function.* —The function $S=P(1+i)^n$ is of fundamental importance in other fields than in finance. Thus the growth of timber of a large forest tract may be expressed as a function of this kind, the assumption being that in a large tract the rate of growth may be taken as uniform from year to year. In the case of bacteria growing under ideal conditions in a culture, *i.e.* with unlimited food supplied, the increase in the number of bacteria per second is proportional to the number of bacteria present at the beginning of that second. Any function in which the rate of change or rate of growth at any instant t is directly proportional to the value of the function at the instant t obeys what has been termed the 'law of organic growth,' and may be expressed by the equation,

$$y=ce^{kt},$$

wherein c and k are constants determined by the physical facts involved, and e is a constant of nature analogous to π. The constant k is the proportionality constant and is negative when the quantity in question decreases; c is commonly positive;

$$e=2.7182\ldots.$$

"The values of the function of x, ce^{kx}, *increase according to the terms of a geometrical progression as the variable x increases in arithmetical progression. . . .*

"The most immediate application of a function in which the

growth is proportional to the function itself is to the air. The decrease in the pressure of the air at the distance h above the earth's surface is proportional to h.

"The expression $P = 760\ e^{-\frac{h}{7990}}$ gives the numerical value of the pressure in millimeters of mercury for h measured in meters. The negative exponent indicates that the pressure decreases as h increases. In inches as units of length of the mercury column, h in feet,

$$P = 29.92e^{-\frac{h}{26200}}$$

This is known as Halley's law.

"The growth of bean plants within limited intervals and the growth of children, again between quite restricted limits, follow approximately the law of organic growth. Radium in decomposing follows the same law; the rate of decrease at any instant being proportional to the quantity. In the case of vibrating bodies, like a pendulum, the rate of decrease of the amplitude follows this law; similarly in the case of a noise dying down and in certain electrical phenomena, the rate of decrease is proportional at any instant to the value of the function at the instant. . . .

"*The Curve of Healing of a Wound.*—Closely allied to the formulas expressing the law of organic growth, $y = e^{kt}$, and the law of 'organic decay,' $y = e^{-kt}$, is a recently discovered law which connects algebraically by an equation and graphically by a curve, the surface-area of a wound, with time expressed in days, measured from the time when the wound is aseptic or sterile. When this aseptic condition is reached, by washing and flushing continually with antiseptic solutions, two observations at an interval commonly of four days give the 'index of the individual,' and this index, and the two measurements of area of the wound-surface, enable the physician-scientist to determine the normal progress of the wound-surface, the expected decrease in area, for this wound-surface of this individual. The area of the wound is traced carefully on transparent paper, and then computed by using a mathematical machine, called a planimeter, which measures areas.

"The areas of the wound are plotted as ordinates with the respective times of observation measured in days as abscissas. After each observation and computation of area the point so obtained is plotted to the same axes as the graph which gives the ideal or prophetic curve of healing.

"When the observed area is found markedly greater than that determined by the ideal curve, the indication is that there is still infection in the wound. . . . A rather surprising and unexplained situation occurs frequently when the wound-surface heals more rapidly than the ideal curve would indicate; in this event secondary ulcers develop which bring the curve back to normal. . . . .

"This application of mathematics to medicine is largely due to Dr. Alexis Carrel of the Rockefeller Institute of Medical Research. He noted that the larger the wound-surface, the more rapidly it healed, and that the rate of healing seemed to be proportional to the area. This proportionality constant is not the same for all values of the surface or we would have an equation of the form,

$$S = S_1 e^{-kt}$$

in which S, is the area at the time that the wound is rendered sterile and observations to be plotted really begin. . . .

"The data given are taken from the Journal of Experimental Medicine, reprints kindly furnished by Major George A. Stewart of the Rockefeller Institute. The diagrams are reproduced from the issue of Feb. 1, 1918, pp. 171 and 172, article by Dr. T. Tuffier and R. Desmarres, Auxiliary Hospital 75, Paris. . . .

"WAVE MOTION. General.—In nature there are two types of recurrent motion, somewhat closely connected mathemat-

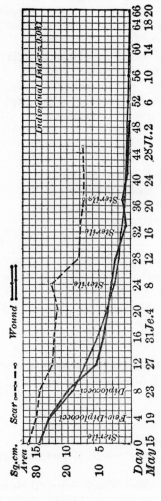

Progress of healing of a surface wound of the right leg, patient's age 31 years. The observed curve oscillates about the smoother calculated curve.

ically, in which repetition of motion occurs at regular intervals.

"One type of this motion, in cycles as we may say, repeats the motion in one place, and is in a sense stationary. The tuning fork in motion moves through the same space again and again; a similar movement is the motion of a vibrating string. Of this stationary type may be mentioned the heartbeats, the pulse, the respiration, the tides, and the rotation of a wheel about its axis.

"The second type of recurrent motion transmits or carries the vibratory impulse over an extent of space as well as time. The waves of the sea are of this character. Sound waves, electrical vibrations or waves, and radiant energy vibrations are transmitted by a process similar to that by which the waves of the sea are carried.

"Both of these types of motion are representable mathematically by equations involving a sequence of trigonometric functions. To the fundamental and basic function involved, $y = \sin x$, we will direct our attention in the next section and to simple applications in other sections of this chapter. . . .

"Sound Waves.—If a tuning fork for note lower C is set to vibrating, the free bar makes 129 complete, back-and-forth, vibrations in one second. By attaching a fine point to the end of the bar and moving under this bar at a uniform rate, as it vibrates, a smoke-blackened paper, a sinusoidal curve is traced on the paper. Our curve is traced by a bar vibrating 50 times in 1 second.

The curve $y = \sin (50 \times 2\pi t)$.
Tuning fork vibrations recorded on smoked paper. . . .

"Corresponding to each movement of the vibrating rod there is a movement of the air. As the bar moves to the right it compresses the layer of air to its right and that *compression* is immediately communicated to the layer of air to the right; as the bar moves back and to the left, the pressure on the adjacent air is released and a *rarefaction* takes place. In $\frac{1}{50}$ of 1 second you have the air adjacent to the rod *compressed,* back to normal, and *rarefied;* during this time the neighboring air is affected and the compression is communicated a distance which is the *wave length* of this given sound wave. In 1 second this disturbance is transmitted 1100 feet at 44° Fahrenheit. The wave length for this sound wave then is $\frac{1100}{50} = 22$ feet.

"The wave length is commonly designated by λ. If V is the velocity, and t the time of one vibration, $\lambda = Vt$.

ā

ou

r

Ē

ä

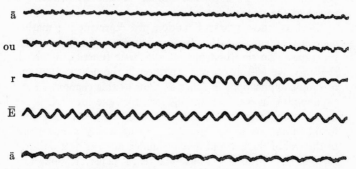

"Vibration records produced by the voice: 'ā' as in 'āte'; 'ou' as in 'about'; 'r' in 'relay'; 'ē' in 'bē'; and 'ä' in 'fäther.' The tuning fork record, frequency 50 per second, gives the vibration frequencies. . . . "

This last drawing may help to visualize the fact in what manner wrong expressions and untrue teachings hamper the true progress of humanity. Every word has its energy and produces some physico-chemical effects in the time-binding apparatus in accord with the idea which we associate with the sound of the word. If we teach ideas which are untrue, then the physico-chemical effects produced are not proper—in other words the human mind does NOT WORK PROPERLY, that is, it does not work *naturally* or *normally* or true to the human dimension. There is every reason why the standards in our civilization are so low, because we have "poisoned," in a literal sense of the word, our minds with the physico-chemical effects of wrong ideas. This correct NATURAL APPROACH to the "Time-binding" energies will make it obvious how unmeasured is the importance of the manner in which we handle this subtle mechanism, as the poisoning with wrong ideas or with careless or incorrect words does not in any way differ in consequences from poisoning with any other stupor-producing or wrongly stimulating poison.

MONOGRAPHS ON EXPERIMENTAL BIOLOGY AND PHYSIOLOGY

LOEB, J.: "Comparative Physiology of the Brain and Comparative Psychology." New York, 1900.
LOEB, J.: "Studies in General Physiology." Chicago, 1905.
LOEB, J.: "The Dynamics of Living Matter." New York, 1906.
LOEB, J.: "The Mechanistic Conception of Life." Chicago, 1912.

CONTENTS

LOEB, J.: The Organism as a Whole. G. P. Putnam's Sons. New York, 1916.

CONTENTS

LOEB, J.: "Forced Movements, Tropisms, and Animal Conduct." J. B. Lippincott, Philadelphia, 1918.

CONTENTS

1. General Facts.
2. Direct Proof of the Muscle Tension Theory of Heliotropism in Motile Animals.
3. Heliotropism of Unicellular Organisms.
4. Heliotropism of Sessile Animals.
  VI. An Artificial Heliotropic Machine.
 VII. Asymmetrical Animals.
VIII. Two Sources of Light of Different Intensity.
  IX. The Validity of the Bunsen-Roscoe Law for the Heliotropic Reactions of Animals and Plants.
   X. The Effect of Rapid Changes in Intensity of Light.
  XI. The Relative Heliotropic Efficiency of Light of Different Wave Lengths.
 XII. Change in the Sense of Heliotropism.
XIII. Geotropism.
 XIV. Forced Movements Caused by Moving Retina Images: Rheotropism: Anemotropism.
  XV. Stereotropism.
 XVI. Chemotropism.
XVII. Thermotropism.
XVIII. Instincts.
 XIX. Memory Images and Tropisms.

> A list of *554 books on this subject*, in which any reader interested will find a vast storehouse of exact knowledge in this line.   Author.

CONKLIN, EDWIN GRANT: "Heredity and Environment in the Development of Men."   Princeton University Press, 1915.

CONTENTS

   I. Facts and Factors of Development.
      Introduction.
      A. Phenomena of Development.
      B. Factors of Development.
  II. Cellular Basis of Heredity and Development.
      A. Introductory.
      B. The Germ Cells.
      C. The Mechanism of Heredity.
      D. The Mechanism of Development.
 III. Phenomena of Inheritance.
      A. Observations on Inheritance.
      B. Statistical Study of Inheritance.
      C. Experimental Study of Inheritance.

IV. Influence of Environment.
    A. Relative Importance of Heredity and Environment.
    B. Experimental Modifications of Development.
    C. Functional Activity as a Factor of Development.
    D. Inheritance or Non-inheritance of Acquired Characters.
    E. Applications to Human Development: Euthenics.
V. Control of Heredity: Eugenics.
    A. Domesticated Animals and Cultivated Plants.
    B. Control of Human Heredity.
VI. Genetics and Ethics.
    Glossary of books on this subject; for those who desire to be more fully acquainted with the subjects of heredity and development. Author.

MORGAN, T. H., "Physical Basis of Heredity."

EAST, E. M., and JONES, D. F., "Inbreeding and Outbreeding," etc.

PARKER, G. H., "The Elementary Nervous System."

HARVEY, E. N., "The Nature of Animal Light."

APPENDIX III

ENGINEERING AND TIME-BINDING

THE Arts of Engineering, by their very nature, are derived from the work of dead men and destined to serve not only the present but the future. They are freer than any other human activity from the errors of intermixing dimensions and from the fallacy of belief in individualistic accomplishment and pride. The simple steel structure of a bridge, familiar to us in every day life, is a clear reminder to us all of the arts of Hephæstus and the bound-up knowledge of countless generations of smiths and mechanics, metallurgists and chemists, mathematicians and builders, teachers and engineers who toiled for many thousands of years to make possible the riveted steel beams which are the elements of modern structure. These structures do not collapse unless the natural laws for their construction are transgressed; which seldom happens—for no one is entrusted with the work unless he has bound up in his knowledge the accumulated experience of the past; yet the transgressors of these natural laws are punished with all the severity of the common law. When a bridge is opened and tested, the written laws in some countries and the unwritten in others, and the pride and the sense of responsibility of the designer and builder of the bridge demand that he, the creator of the bridge, be the first to enter it and the last to leave it; and should the bridge collapse, he has to take the immediate consequences of his neglect of the time-binding laws.

Rarely are the affairs of engineering done with the entirely selfish motive of merely acquiring immediate selfish gain, for even when this could be traced—this unworthy thought disappears in the halo of the glory of the accomplishment. Mr. Eiffel did not erect his tower to haunt Paris with the sight of a steel skeleton towering over the city of daring thoughts. His tower stands to-day as a mechanical proof of mathematical formulas proving the possibility of erecting tall, self-supporting structures and thereby serving future humanity. The Time-binding capacity of humans creates and formulates new values for the service of mankind. Again, no student of the Arts of Engineering could ever forget himself to the point of claiming his accomplishments, no matter how marvelous, all to himself. No wondrous discovery of modern electricity, not even the talking from one hemisphere to another, is rightly the accomplishment of any one man, for the origin of the discovery can be traced at least as far back as the days of that barefooted shepherd boy Magnus, who first observed the phenomena of magnetism.

In an attempt to trace and evaluate the time-binding faculties manifested in the Arts of Engineering, one is at once astonished, and bewildered, at the confusion and contradictions unrealized in the mass of evidence, and how pathetic and deplorable is the sight of hundreds of thousands of workers in the field of engineering toil and creation who unconsciously submit to the degradation, in silent consent, of seeing their marvelous collective achievements chained to spacebinding aims.

Upon the completion of this book I was astonished that there are such a small number of engineers who have the intuitive feeling of the greatness of the assets at their command and of the gravity of their liabilities concerning affairs of humanity. I was eager to have my book read and analysed by a few leading engineers. The late H. L. Gantt being no more with us, I then turned to Walter N. Polakov, Doctor of Engineering; Industrial Counselor; Chairman of Committee on Service and Information, Fuels Section, A.S.M.E., and Robert B. Wolf, Vice-President of A.S.M.E. In them I found, to the full, a very sympathetic understanding and my esteem grew as I became more intimately acquainted with the character of their work and their accomplishments. Both have done a most remarkable work in their respective lines. It will not be an exaggeration to say that their work, together with the work of the late H. L. Gantt and Charles P. Steinmetz, may be considered as the first—to my knowledge—corner-stones of the science and art of Human Engineering, and form the first few volumes and writings for the New Library of the Manhood of Humanity. These books and pamphlets are based on facts analysed scientifically, marking the parting of the way of engineering thought from the past subjection to speculative fetishes.

Of all the pure and applied sciences, engineering alone has the distinction of being the first to have the *correct* insight into the human problem. The task of engineers was to convert knowledge—brain work—"bound-up time"—into daily bread by means of conserving time and effort. This concept is naught else but the working out of the imperfect formulation of the time-binding principle. It was inevitable, therefore, that some engineers had already beaten the path in the right direction. How straight and how far this sense of dimensionality has led some of them in their practical work may be seen from the work of Walter N. Polakov, in his *Mastering Power Production,* Engineering Magazine, N. Y., 1921.

"It was not my intention to compile a text book on power engineering; it was rather my care to avoid the treatment of any technical subject which could be found elsewhere in engineering literature; but I could not avoid trespassing in the adjoining fields of psychology and economics, for without familiarity with these sciences the mastery of power production is a futile attempt.

"I do not hold that the principles upon which the method is laid out are subject to choice or opinions, for they are based on facts. Yet work of this character cannot be complete, or examples may be illy chosen, for it deals with living and constantly reshaping relations and applies to things in process of development.

" If this work and its underlying idea will facilitate the solving of some of the problems now in the course of rapid evolution in our industrial relations, I shall feel that my own and my readers' time have not been altogether lost."

Indeed the readers' time will not be lost. This book gives an engineering, scientific—in the meantime practical—analysis of all human problems. It is a deep and practical treatise on all great questions concerning modern industrialism and so-called economic problems and is a foundation for a new scientific industrial philosophy. Another very clear outline of the *Principles of Industrial Philosophy* was given by Mr. Polakov in his paper presented at the annual meeting of the American Society of Mechanical Engineers, December 7-10, 1920. Anyone who has anything to do with industrial or economic problems cannot afford to overlook the important and fundamental work in this book.

It is obvious that a scientific knowledge of facts, is of the greatest importance for anyone who cares to approach any problem in a serious way. Statistics which are up-to-date are therefore of primary importance. I had the privilege of reading the manuscript of *Quo Vadis America,* the forthcoming book of Mr. Polakov, where a most valuable statistical picture of facts in modern America is given and the astonishing conclusions which are to be drawn therefrom. I can only regret that in Europe we have not such a knowledge written down concerning European conditions. If more such books had been written and *read* by the public, many crises and catastrophes would have been avoided.

The outstanding contribution of Mr. Robert B. Wolf to engineering was made in his study of physiology, biology, psychology and philosophy as applied to engineering.

"If anyone wishes to inquire into the forces which have led up to the individual development of mankind, he will find himself at once plunged into the realm of psychology and mental philosophy. I can heartily recommend such a course as immensely profitable and of practical value.

"The five important facts, however, that have to do with the subject in hand are:

"1st. That the human body is such a wonderful organization because it is the product of the forces of creation, acting through millions of years of evolution.

"2nd. That its capacity for progress depends upon the maintenance of the unity resulting from this creative evolution and upon a conscious recognition of this unity.

"3d. That this unity would not have been possible without the development of the nervous system.

"4th. That the conscious intelligent progress made by mankind could not have reached its present level until in the process of evolution a mechanism had been built up in the nervous system itself capable of recording the various impressions which the senses are constantly receiving.

"5th. That the recording of past events, with the power of consciously recalling them for the solution of problems immediately confronting it, is absolutely essential to its development.

"Now, what I want to point out is that inasmuch as man's progress depends upon the perfect co-ordination of his forces to produce unity of action, we have no right to expect an industrial organization to make progress which it must do as a unit without the establishment of a conscious co-ordinating mechanism similar to the nervous system in the human body." *Individuality in Industry.* By Robert B. Wolf.

Doctor Charles P. Steinmetz has given in his *America and the New Epoch* a most correct engineering picture of the political situation in the world, with a fine characterization of the psychological peculiarities of the different races. Although this book was written in 1916, that is, before the end of the World War, it will be of permanent value; because of its deep psychological analysis of the peoples and their institutions which ultimately shape the development of any nation and which do not change with victory or defeat.

"My tribute to the memory of Gantt will be, not only the homage of a friend and admirer, but the proof that his philosophy is scientifically true. A rigorous proof is necessary, because the word 'service' belongs to that category of words, the meaning of which can be completely reversed by the verb, be it 'give' or 'take.' Gantt took 'rendering service' as an axiom; my observation, shared with many others, is that our civilization had quite another axiom, 'we preach give, we practice take.' The problem which interested me, was how to find a way out of this contradiction that would be irrefutable. If one of them is true and natural law for humans, then the other is not; if our words are true, then our deeds are not true, or if our deeds are true then the words are camouflage. I found the solution, by applying mathematically rigorous thinking. Mathematics, with its exact concept of dimensions, gave me the method. The method we use in studying phenomena is analysis, or speaking mathematically, differentiation. I soon found, that the methods of differentiation are mostly correct, but our synthesis, or process of integration made by the use of metaphysics was faulty. The differentiation correctly lowered the dimensions, but our faulty integration did not restore the original dimensions. The investigation had to be made from the beginning, by defining the phenomena of life, in a specific way, which would not permit of any blunders in dimensions.

" I defined the classes of life by emphasizing their incontestable, dimensional characteristics: plants are 'Chemistry-binding,' animals are 'Space-binding,' Humans are 'Time-binding' classes of life.

"These definitions have the peculiarity that they make it obvious, that: 1 The classes of life have different dimensions, and that the intermixing of dimensions, as in mathematics it makes a correct solution impossible, so in life, the results of such elementary mistakes, produce tragic consequences.

"2 The old formula on which our civilization is built, HUMAN equal ANIMAL plus or multiplied by SPARK OF DIVINITY is basically and elementarily wrong, and is mathematical nonsense, which is identical to such an absurdity as x square inches equal y linear inches plus or multiplied by z cubic inches.

"3 This basically wrong formula on which our civilization rests, is the cause of all the periodical collapses, wars and revolutions.

"4 The old system was built on animal 'space-binding' standards, and human 'time-binding' impulses were, all the time, in rebellion.

"5 As the theory of gravitation and the calculus made engineers and mathematicians masters of inanimate nature, so these tangible and incontestable definitions give them a positive base which will enable them to approach and solve human living problems, by establishing the mathematical fact that man is man, not an animal.

"6 All of those who are blinded by traditions and refuse to investigate, or to know these mathematical truths, are a danger to humanity in directly helping to obscure issues, and in helping to maintain the faulty structure which, as in the past, is bound to collapse again and again in the future.

"7 The duty of mathematically thinking people is to throw such light on this problem as will stop the stupid, or willfully destructive, and show whether they are working for or against, mankind.

"8 For the 'time-binding' class of life, it is obvious then that in this dimension, 'time-binding' is the natural law, and, if understood and analysed, it is the highest human aim.

"9 Such 'natural laws' as 'survival of the fittest' for animals, which is the 'survival of the fittest in space,' result in fight, or the survival of the strongest; whereas such a law to be a NATURAL LAW FOR HUMANS, must be in the human dimension which obviously would be the 'Survival of the fittest in TIME,' resulting in the survival of the best.

"10 All known facts must be brought to the light, to be summed up, and correlated by mathematicians and engineers with the strictest attention to dimensionality.

"11 All of our ideas have to be revised; the animal 'space-binding' standards must be rejected as dangerous and destructive, must be replaced by 'time-binding' standards, which will correspond to the natural impulses and NATURAL LAWS for humans.

"12 The minds of mathematicians and engineers are by education the first to see the far reaching importance of the facts disclosed by these definitions, and just this realization will bring about the readjustment of values in life to a human dimension, wherein pending revolutions and wars could be turned into evolution, destruction into construction, discord into accord of a common aim.

"We are the masters of our own destinies, the responsibility is ours to correct the mistakes of our ancestors and to establish a scientific philosophy, scientifically true laws, scientifically true ethics, and a scientific sociology, which will form one unified science of man and his function in the universe, a science which I propose to call 'Human Engineering.' Gantt's methods would be the first practical application toward this end.

"Gantt's concept of rendering service is scientifically true because it is 'time-binding,' and therefore true for the human class of life and in human dimension. This is why Gantt's concepts have counted for so much and will survive 'IN TIME.'" . . . Discussion by Alfred Korzybski of Mr. W. N. Polakov's paper "Principles of Industrial Philosophy" presented at the Annual Meeting of The American Society of Mechanical Engineers, New York, December 7–10, 1920.

LITERATURE

GANTT, H. L.:

"Work, Wages, and Profits." The Engineering Magazine Co., 1913. N. Y.

"Industrial Leadership." Yale University Press. 1916.

"Organizing for Work." Harcourt, Brace & Howe, 1919. N. Y.

Selection from Contents: The Engineer as the Industrial Leader. Economics and Democracy. Democracy in Production. Democracy in the Shop. Democracy in Management. "The Religion of Democracy."

POLAKOV, WALTER N.:

"Mastering Power Production." The Engineering Magazine Co. 1921. N. Y.

Selection from Contents: The Descent of the Principle of Production for Use. The Power Industry as an Economic Factor. Mastering Labor Problems. (Conditions) Autonomous Co-operation. Aims of Labor. Right to be Lazy and the Right to a Job. Qualification of Men. The Working Day. Fatigue. *UNIVERSAL LABOR* (*Corresponding exactly to Time-binding—Author*). The Position of an Engineer. Mastering Labor Problems. Compensation. The Social Aspect. The Economic Aspect. The Basis of Wages. Incentive Payments. Profit Sharing. Premium Places. Rewarding Individual Efforts. Two-rate wages. Energy as a Commodity.

"Principles of Industrial Philosophy." Presented at the Annual Meeting of the A. S. of M. E., December, 1920.

"Equipment and Machinery." Y. M. C. A. Association Press. 1921. N. Y.

"Organization and Management." Y. M. C. A. Association Press. 1921. N. Y.

"Quo Vadis America?" In preparation.

Steinmetz, Charles P.:
"America and the New Epoch." Harper & Brothers. 1916. N. Y.
Selection from Contents: The Individualistic Era: From Competition to Co-operation. England in the Individualistic Era. Germany in the Individualistic Era. The Other European Nations in the Individualistic Era. America in the Individualistic Era. Evolution: Industrial Government.
"Incentive and Initiative." Y. M. C. A. Association Press. 1921. N. Y.

Wolf, Robert B.: Pamphlets.
"Individuality in Industry." Bulletin of the Society to promote the Science of Management. Vol. I. No. 4. August, 1915.
"The Creative Workman." Technical Association of the Pulp and Paper Industry. 1918. N. Y.
"Non-Financial Incentives." Presented at the Annual Meeting of the A. S. of M. E. December, 1918. N. Y.
"Modern Industry and the Individual." A. W. Shaw & Co. 1919. N. Y.
"Securing the Initiative of the Workman." American Economic Association. 1919. N. Y.
"Creative Spirit in Industry." Y. M. C. A. Association Press. 1921. N. Y.

MISCELLANEOUS LIST OF BOOKS

Von Bernhardi, General F.: "Germany and the Next War." E. Arnold, London. 1912.

Brandeis, Louis: Other People's Money and How the Bankers Use it." F. A. Stokes, N. Y. 1914.

Thomas Farrow and Walter Crotch: "The Coming Trade War." Chapman & Hall, London. 1916.

Hueffer, Ford Maddox: "When Blood is Their Argument." Hodder & Stoughton. 1915. N. Y.

Hauser, Henry: "Germany's Commercial Grip on the World, Her Business Methods Explained." E. Nash Co., London. 1917.

Laughlin, J. L.: "Credit of the Nations." Scribner's Sons, (N. Y. 1918.

MAETZU, RAMIRO DE: "Authority, Liberty and Function in the Light of War." Geo. Allen and Unwin.

DELAISI, FRANCIS: French Opinion, "The Inevitable War." Small, Maynard & Co., Boston. 1915.

NEILSON, FRANCIS: English Opinion, "How Diplomats Make War." B. W. Huebsch. 1916.

BY A GERMAN (German Opinion). "J'Accuse!" Hodder & Stoughton, London. 1915.

APPENDIX IV

SOME NON-ARISTOTELIAN DATA ON EFFICIENCY FOR HUMAN ADJUSTMENT*

by

ALFRED KORZYBSKI

The summary of Graicunas' work given at the end of this supplement, in a practically unchanged form, was a personal communication in 1934 from Walter N. Polakov, the outstanding engineer and industrial diagnostician in the United States. It was originally written for the Tennessee Valley Authority, which was then passing through acute managerial difficulties due to confusion of function and control. Mr. Polakov, writing about the T.V.A. project, evaluated the situation thus:

> The youthful T.V.A. inherited the language and metaphysics of a bygone age. It encounters unprecedented difficulties in expressing new relations in terms of vanished fancies. The night fear of ghosts remains. . . . The difficulties in building the T.V.A. without a language having correspondence to reality, are not difficulties peculiar to this project. They are signs of our time—a sort of dangerous epidemic, springing out of our slow adjustment to a profoundly changed environment.

In my work with students I have utilized Mr. Polakov's summary with his diagram adapted from the original data concerning the 'span of attention' or 'span of control', as well

*Reprinted from *Papers From the Second American Congress on General Semantics,* 1941. Published 1943 by the Institute of General Semantics, Lakeville, Conn.

as related foundations formulated in my own writings.[1] I have found empirically that these are invariably useful for the elimination of the individual's inability to handle *personal* life situations adequately.

At the root of the problem lies the significant fundamental difference in the *rate of growth* between arithmetical progression, which grows by addition, for example, 2,4,6,8,10, etc., and geometrical progression, which grows by multiplication, for example, 2,4,8,16,32, etc.

We must mention here permutations and combinations, and even combinations of higher order which also follow an exponential law. The different orders in which things can be arranged are called their *permutations*. The different collections which can be formed from things without regard to the order in which they are placed are called their *combinations*. For example, the four letters, *a,e,m,n* can form but one combination, but they occur in the English language in several permutations, as *name, amen, mean, mane.* The question may arise, 'How many changes can be rung with 10 bells, taking 7 at a time?' The answer is 604,800, quite a respectable number for a problem so seemingly simple on the surface.

The work of Graicunas, Urwick, etc., is based on empirical data from military and managerial experiences, where complications *dealing with human reactions* grow in a geometrical ratio. The disregard of the above considerations has led to many military and managerial disasters. I must stress that *the same principles apply also to our personal life difficulties.* For instance, in what psychiatrists call 'family attachment' (infantile clinging to 'papa' or 'mama'), in the notorious interference of mothers-in-law, or in the tragedies of marital tri-

---

[1] See in particular my *Manhood of Humanity: The Science and Art of Human Engineering* (New York: E. P. Dutton and Co., 1921), pp. 15–26, 63, 90–92, 112 ff., 126 ff., 134 ff., 161, 167 ff., 176 ff., 193 ff., 217 f., 232 ff., 245 ff., 255 ff.; and *Science and Sanity: An Introduction to Non-aristotelian Systems and General Semantics* (Second edition; Lancaster, Penn.: Science Press Printing Co., 1941), pp. 161, 264, 354, Chap. XXXIII. *Science and Sanity* will be referred to as *S & S.*

angles, it is not a question of just an 'added' factor, but the difficulties accumulate in some geometrical ratio. Similarly, a childless couple 'adds' a baby to the family, and the complications grow following some exponential law. Organismal responses to 'one more glass of whiskey' are certainly not additive. The followers of sick Schicklgruber-Hitler may have learned by now that the 'addition' of one more country introduces non-additive complexities not included in a naïve fool's paradise gained by brute force. And so it goes all through life in the more fundamental relationships.

If in personal life we undertake or have to carry too many responsibilities, interests, involvements, etc., the complexities often grow beyond the capacity of *one* human brain to manage them adequately, and human tragedies, disorganizations, etc., follow, very often culminating in maladjustment and even neurosis or psychosis.

Many times a single painful event in childhood or even later in life distorts the attitudes and colors the whole life. Thus, the 'addition' of a single factor results in unnecessary complexities which are certainly not additive, but spread all through life in some geometrical ratio.[2]

We hear remarks by some scientists that 'It is impossible to express the conduct of a whole animal as the algebraic sum of the reflexes of its isolated segments.' Yet later we find that same author saying, 'The individual represents heredity *plus* environment.' Another writes, 'Thus a clock-work is as little the mere *sum* of its little wheels as a human being is the *sum* of his cells and molecules'; and later on, 'to be exact the ego consists of the engrams of all our experiences *plus* the actual psychism.' These two examples, out of many, are given to show how even with those scientists who realize the fallacy of additivity, some 'plus' creeps in, which is obviously false to facts, demonstrating that ingrained additive tendency inherent in the aristotelian prescientific orientation.[3]

[2] *S & S,* p. xxiii ff.
[3] *S & S,* p. 605 ff.

On the other hand, a few modern psychiatrists familiar with the latest scientific developments by necessity realize those additive aberrations, and do not plant a falsifying 'plus'. We read, therefore: 'Before therapy can be discussed or put into practice, three fundamental concepts must be thoroughly understood: (1) the nature and characteristics of neurotic symptoms; (2) the formula, "Constitution *times* Environment *times* Stress"; and (3) the role that "attitudes" play in the creation of symptoms.'[4] Although Dr. Kraines has definitely a non-additive attitude, his 'times' does not represent the situation correctly. The correct representation would be functional, $N = f(x_1, x_2, x_3, \ldots x_n)$, where N represents neurosis, f represents function of, x_1, constitution, x_2, environment, x_3, stress, and the *etc.* ($\ldots x_n$) indicates special functional factors in a given case, all of which are interrelated. Such psychotherapeutic observations indicate why in a 'therapy of *attitudes*' it is so important to change from an aristotelian to a general non-aristotelian attitude, not only for psychiatry, but for prevention of misevaluations in life by everyone.[5]

As a matter of fact, most psychotherapy depends on efforts of the physician to eliminate, through reinterpretation in treatment, some of those original factors which produced worries, fears, anxieties, and other disorganizations. These factors were responsible for the introduction, because of exponential laws, of an enormous number of artificial complexities which made life adjustment difficult or impossible. In my personal experience and the experience of many of my students, who are physicians, educators, etc., it is found that the explanation of the above non-aristotelian principles is very useful, as the patients or students realize that with the old attitudes they are up against impossibilities. They become con-

---

[4] S. H. Kraines, 'Brief Psychotherapy,' *Mental Hygiene* XXVII (Jan., 1943), 70–79.

[5] *S & S*, pp. xx–xxii.

scious of the mechanisms of the difficulties, which is the only way to make a solution possible.

Mathematicians, in their often deliberate detachment from life, unfortunately have not forewarned us of these kinds of methodological traps, and in fact often repulse their students by the lifelessness of their teachings. Mathematicians quite glibly speak about their students being 'mathematical imbeciles'. Often I wonder whether this is true, or whether the responsibility has to be laid frankly on the mathematicians, who may be 'life imbeciles'. If before they begin to teach they would study in a 'mental' hospital and analyze the 'treatises' of the patients, they would become better teachers, better research workers, as they would understand what it means to be detached from living life.

The problem of additivity in life as well as in mathematics, where it is called 'linearity', is of great antiquity because it was the *simplest*. The mathematical formulation of additivity (linearity) is $f(x + y) = f(x) + f(y)$. One of the most striking consequences of additivity is the predictability from the characteristics of the elements to those of the results. In other words, no characteristic absent in the elements appears in the result. It is obvious that when we combine elements, and the results have *new* characteristics absent in the original elements, the new problems are structurally no more of an additive character, and the synthesis must be different.[6] If our attitudes are *limited* to the additive principle *alone* the results in the most fundamental issues of science and life are bound to be false to facts. For example, one pound *plus* one pound in weight results in two pounds, but one gallon of water 'added' to one gallon of alcohol results in less than two gallons of liquid because profound inter-molecular issues enter which are not additive, and so $1 + 1 \neq 2$. Similarly, one atom of mercury 'minus' one electron becomes one atom of gold. And so the results are not predictable by the principle of

[6] *S & S,* Chap. XXXII.

additivity. As Graicunas shows, the 'addition' of a sixth assistant by a supervisor may add 20 percent to his human resources, but adds approximately 100 percent to the complexity and difficulty of his task of co-ordination. And so it goes.

We have discovered by modern science that the world and life are not additive in their fundamental aspects. Even the epoch-making work of Einstein, the founder of a non-newtonian system, depends on the transformation of linear (additive) equations into non-linear (non-additive) more complicated equations.[7] But the structure of our ordinary subject-predicate language and corresponding attitudes is still aristotelian, and therefore in the main additive. Unfortunately extremely few of us, even among my readers and students, realize that fundamental gap between additive and non-additive relations and attitudes.[8]

My whole life work, and particularly since 1921, has been based on the *life implications* of this neglect to differentiate between the laws of growth of arithmetical and of geometrical progressions. Such neglect was partially responsible for most historical spasms of civilization such as wars and revolutions, and accounts for many disasters in private lives. This point must be stressed to the utmost. Because Graicunas, Urwick, etc., deal with *human relations* without disregarding mathematical issues, their work is based on the same principles, which automatically involve permutations and combinations. The interested reader is urged to consult his elementary algebra about the arithmetical and geometrical rates of growth, and the simple formulations of permutation and combination. It is sad to say that combinations of higher order are usually omitted in the textbooks and regarded as mathematical

[7] *S & S*, p. 612 ff.

[8] See 'Measures of Susceptibility to Nervous Breakdown' by W. Horsley Gantt, *American Journal of Psychiatry*, May 1943, in which Dr. Gantt shows that unconditional reflex reactions may be expressed by a linear (additive) equation, and conditional reactions, precursors of symbolic reactions, only by an exponential (non-additive) equation.

curiosities without application. Unfortunately life facts and complications, ultimately on the electronic and electro-colloidal levels, in principle follow these combinations of higher order. The computations as such are of little or no practical value; however, the methodological implications for life orientation, disregarded by mathematicians, are of primary importance. For further details the reader is referred to Jevons' and my own work.[9]

In human life one of our difficulties is that we are 'both the marble and the sculptor', as Carrel says, and so we are both the managed and the manager of our personal lives, the supervised and the supervisor, the co-ordinated and the co-ordinator. Perhaps one of the main sources of a great many maladjustments is exactly that self-reflexiveness and circularity which we do not know how to manage simply because we don't know that there are non-aristotelian methods to do so.[10]

In such a brief paper it is impossible to go into details short of writing a book. Plenty of books on modern science are available, but they have only very limited applications because the issues had not been formulated methodologically. It is generally not realized that with the advance of science the old aristotelian methodology, by which the majority of us still live, is thoroughly obsolete and unworkable today, and even harmful for the best of human adjustment.

This 'epilogue' was written to emphasize and partially explain the necessity of passing from the aristotelian orientation to a non-aristotelian, functional orientation, and to stress to what extent the issues have application in daily life. This non-aristotelian system is based frankly on physico-mathematical

[9] W. Stanley Jevons, *The Principles of Science* (London: Macmillan and Co., Ltd., 1920), Chap. IX. *S & S*, p. 340.

[10] Alfred Korzybski, 'General Semantics, Psychiatry, Psychotherapy and Prevention,' *Amer. Jour. of Psychiatry* XCVIII (Sept., 1941), 205-207. See particularly the unabridged paper (Institute of General Semantics, 1940), pp. 8-10; also *S & S*, p. 58 and Chap. XXVII.

methods, which, as this volume shows, have general human application, even on the level of nursery education. These are not problems for speculation or verbal arguments or debates; the issues are empirical and have to be tested by application. This paper is based on experience of how this non-aristotelian system *works* in practice, no matter whether the theoretical issues are formulated satisfactorily for everyone, or satisfy the author himself.

In the present unprecedented world crisis we are not facing a 'new order', we are witnessing the death-bed agonies of the inevitable dying of the old aristotelian system which has been applied to its deadly limit. I personally have no doubt that after this world crisis is over, and the dead are buried, the future of mankind will depend on some new non-aristotelian systems which would be frankly based on scientific extensional principles, and so ultimately on physico-mathematical methods. I emphasize that the title of my book 'Science and Sanity: An Introduction to Non-aristotelian Systems and General Semantics,' indicates that science and sanity are interrelated, which seems only natural. The reader should notice that I utilize 'non-aristotelian systems' in the plural, because the non-aristotelian system I have produced is not *the* system, but *a* system among many other possible ones.

Surveying the chain of historical world tragedies as they accumulate with accelerating acceleration and intensity, one naturally looks for the factors which are responsible for such cataclysms. This problem may be analyzed in many different ways, but here in this first non-aristotelian system we take frankly and explicitly an engineering point of view, in which there is no 'philosophy' for 'philosophy's' sake, nor science for science's sake, nor mathematics for mathematics' sake, but we consider all those activities as products of the human nervous system, to be *applied* for its optimum efficiency. When formulated methodologically, the interrelation between science and sanity becomes obvious, and the new child-like methods can be applied for more efficient management of our private as

well as public lives, and in particular for *prevention* of maladjustments, i.e. misevaluations in life.

From this, perhaps a new point of view, we must squarely
put the responsibility on 'philosophers', because of their innocence of science, their 'superiority', aloofness from non-
aristotelian issues, and so their *inability* to take into serious
consideration our *neuro*-semantic and *neuro*-linguistic *environment as environment*. The 'philosophers' somehow feel 'above'
experimental methods; they will argue endlessly on the verbal
level, but they will not experiment with the new extensional
methods. I must repeat that the new methods are not a problem for arguments or debates, but simply for empirical investigation of how they work. 'Philosophers' should have discovered long ago that maximum teachability is found in
method, and in our case ultimately physico-mathematical
method, even on the nursery level. Through their errors of
omission, 'philosophers' are largely responsible for the sterility
of education, be it on the primary or the university level, and
for the naïve 'isolationists' in science, and/or in life. For example, it is pathetic to watch university faculty members at
meetings, where many have nothing in common, because they
are not united by a general method. Under such conditions
the effectiveness of scientists as human beings is lowered and
often does not even command the respect of the layman, who
does not realize the handicaps of specialization without a
general method. In my experience with classes we have students who belong to widely separated fields such as medicine,
mathematical physics, education, social work, linguistics, law,
etc., and in a few days they become a more and more closely
knit unit because they get a *general method* which applies to
all their professions, as well as daily life. The present day
isolationism paralyzes the isolationists themselves, preventing
them from taking a general extensional attitude. We must
become and remain conscious that scientific work as well as
our private reactions in life are the end product of the electro-
colloidal processes going on in our nervous system. As ex-

perience shows, these processes are deeply affected, in different ways, depending on whether we use intensional or extensional *methods*. This correspondence and close interrelationship between neurological processes and the *method* used is the key problem in passing from one system to another, in this case from an aristotelian to a non-aristotelian system. The empirical demonstration of the above facts through actual application of the extensional method is, I believe, entirely new, and amounts to a 'therapy of attitudes'.

Is the blame to be put entirely on the shoulders of scientists or laymen? The answer is 'no'. With the old, aristotelian, two-valued orientation it is humanly impossible to have the modern, infinite-valued, non-aristotelian process orientation, and therefore it is impossible to 'think' about ourselves in electro-colloidal neurological terms. So once again the responsibility is the 'philosophers'', who have neglected this most important *neuro*-methodological field, and so have not given educators, scientists, etc., and laymen a foundation for mutual co-operation. This reflection is rather heavy in consequences, because the failure of 'philosophers', which is a matter of historical record, has actually prevented the co-ordination of diverse efforts for optimum human adjustment. 'Philosophers' of course will try to talk their way out of this dilemma, but this will not help because this work has not been done by them, and the only way for them is to investigate, *experiment,* and find out. A great many 'philosophers' will be shocked and consider sacrilegious a mere suggestion that 'philosophy' should become experimental, like any scientific theory is.

As to politicians, diplomats, rulers, etc., the situation seems hopeless because of their ignorance, lack of preparation for their human responsibilities, and in fact refusal to accept professional guidance when help is offered them. I will not go into details, as many hundreds of volumes have been written exhibiting the utter stupidity and incompetence of those who are supposed to guide our destinies, with the result that we are bled white in blood as well as in taxes, becoming more and more disorganized for years to come.

In the history of science and civilization we discover that living emergencies forced us to find some solutions to make adjustment to life more efficient, in spite of 'philosophers'. So far it has been done by men like Graicunas, Urwick, Polakov, etc., who based their work on the application of mathematical methods to empirical data about the limitations of what the human nervous system can stand. Their work dealt particularly with industrial and military fields, where lack of efficiency brings obvious disasters. In my own work I felt that mathematical methods should have broader applications, and apply to daily life, as even the smallest managerial unit, which we call the 'family', also must have some method for optimum human efficiency based on the understanding of human nature and the limitations of what one human brain can stand. Otherwise disasters, in different degrees, are bound to follow, which may even end in maladjustment, neurosis, or psychosis.

I admit that I can not see how anyone who has to deal with human affairs, be he the responsible member of a family, a teacher, a physician, or a politician, etc., can be competent at all to deal with the problems confronting him if he is entirely innocent of the problems raised in this paper, including the summary by Polakov taken from the work of Graicunas and Urwick, which follows. Original sources were published abroad in 1933. In 1937 the Institute of Public Administration, Columbia University, New York, reprinted the two fundamental papers referred to, with some new material, under the title *Papers on the Science of Administration*, edited by Luther Gulick and L. Urwick. I suggest that all my readers study this book.

SUMMARY OF SPAN OF ATTENTION BY WALTER N. POLAKOV

For a full exposition of Mr. V. A. Graicunas' theory, see *Bulletin of International Management Institute*, Vol. VII, No. 3, March, 1933, article entitled: 'Relationship in Or-

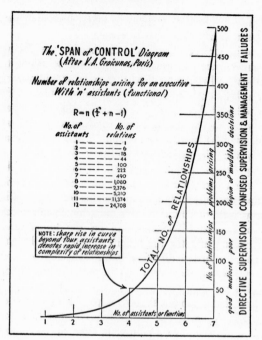

ganization.' Reference to this theory is also made in a paper read to the Department of Industrial Cooperation of the British Association for the Advancement of Science, Leicester, September 7, 1933, by Major L. Urwick, O.B.E., M.C., M.A., entitled: 'Organization as a Technical Problem.' Quoting from the last reference:

Students of administration have long recognized that, in practice, no human brain should attempt to supervise directly more than five, or at the most, six other individuals whose work is interrelated. Mr. V. A. Graicunas of Paris has recently shown why this is so. [His work is the second of the contributions of importance to the technique of organization since 1930.] An individual who is coordinating the work of others whose duties interconnect must take into account in his decisions, not only the reactions of each person concerned as an individual, but also his reactions as a member of any possible grouping of persons which may arise during the course of the work.

The psychological conception of 'the span of attention' places strict limits on the number of separate factors which the human mind can grasp simultaneously. It has its administrative counterpart in what may be described as *'the span of control'*. A supervisor with five subordinates reporting directly to him, who adds a sixth, increases his available human resources by 20 percent. But he adds approximately 100 percent to the complexity and difficulty of his task of co-ordination. The number of relationships which he must consider increases not by arithmetical but by geometrical progression. . . . Neglect of the limitations imposed by 'the span of control' creates insoluble problems in coordination.

The proposed formula for the number of direct group relationships is:

$$R = n \left(\frac{2^n}{2} + n - 1 \right)$$

where $R = a + b + c$ represents total direct and cross relationships; $n =$ number of persons supervised; $a =$ number of direct single relationships; $b =$ number of cross relationships; $c =$ number of direct group relationships. Thus computed on the *maximum* basis direct and cross relationships arising for the given number of subordinates is:

Number of assistants or functions	Number of relationships or problems arising	
1	1	(1)*
2	6	(4)
3	18	(10)
4	44	(21)
5	100	(41)
6	222	(78)
7	490	(148)
8	1080	(283)
9	2376	(547)
10	5210	(1068)
11	11374	(2102)
12	24708	(4161)

* Figures in parentheses are computed on the *minimum basis*.

APPENDIX V

SELECTIONS

from

SCIENCE AND SANITY*

by

ALFRED KORZYBSKI

AUTHOR'S NOTE

These selections from *Science and Sanity: An Introduction to Non-aristotelian Systems and General Semantics* were produced on the request of a number of teachers of General Semantics and study group leaders. They found that for some students the full text was too bulky or too expensive; yet they needed some fundamental textbook preserving the physico-mathematical approach.

Originally I wrote *Science and Sanity* for scientists, teachers, and other leaders in our civilization. In my judgment all the material presented was necessary for them, but not as necessary for beginning students.

Personally I would be biased in making any 'selections' from *Science and Sanity* and so had to rely on some teacher experienced with college and university students.

One such teacher, Guthrie E. Janssen, undertook the difficult task of making these selections. Following graduation from the University of Illinois in 1938 Mr. Janssen spent six

* The International Non-aristotelian Library Publishing Company, Lakeville, Connecticut, 1948.

years as instructor of English and history in American schools
in Egypt, particularly the American University at Cairo
where he used *Science and Sanity* as a textbook with university students on the third year level. The following two
years Mr. Janssen was war correspondent and broadcaster
for the National Broadcasting Company, attached for a period
to the United States Strategic Air Forces (B-29's). After
travelling in some twenty-seven countries and broadcasting
into the NBC network from Cairo, Athens, London, Manila,
Tokyo, Shanghai, and from an airplane over Nagasaki, etc.,
and seeing results of the atomic bomb as one of the first ten
Americans to enter Hiroshima, Mr. Janssen returned to this
country and was granted a fellowship (donated by Robert K.
Straus) for a year's study at the Institute of General Semantics. He produced these *Selections* as part of his working
fellowship during 1946–1947.

I personally am most grateful to Guthrie Janssen for his
considerable painstaking work, and to the Institute staff and
others for their valuable suggestions and help in production.
I wish to express my particular appreciation to M. Kendig,
the Educational Director of the Institute; she urged for many
years that such selections should be published, and gave valuable aid in bringing about its realization.

For teachers and students who will use this book I wish to
include a forewarning concerning the fundamental confusion
existing today about what the terms 'semantics' and *General
Semantics* represent.[1]

---

[1] For example in the *Dictionary of World Literature,* 'General
Semantics' appears under the term Semantics. The two disciplines
are confused, and even my 'extensional devices' are called 'semantic
devices', wheras such a thing does not exist. In Vol. III, No. 4 of
ETC., there appears a five-page glossary of terms used in General
Semantics, all of them fully explained in *Science and Sanity.* Practically every 'definition' misses the main point and trend of my
work. For instance, what is said in the glossary about the use of
the term 'semantic' in my '*General* Semantics', i.e., in a new theory
of *values,* is entirely misleading. Such initial errors lead automatically to further more aggravated misinterpretations. It would not

The original French *sémantique* was introduced into the
literature by Bréal in 1897 in his *Essai de sémantique; science
des significations,* which was translated into English in 1900
under the title, *Semantics: Studies in the Science of Meaning.*
Unfortunately the terms are not exactly equivalent in the
different languages, and thus caused a confusion among the
English-speaking people about the use of the term 'semantic'
and 'semantics' which persists up to today. *Sémantique* deals
with a branch of philology and the historical change of significance ('meaning'). Lady Welby somehow felt that difference in implication and formulated a more organismal
theory under the name of 'Significs'. The Significs International Movement in the Netherlands is still carrying on this
work, under the leadership of mathematicians such as Brou-
wer (the founder of the Intuitional School in Mathematics) and logicians, epistemologists, psycho-logicians, etc.

Both disciplines labelled by those terms were not non-elementalistic enough, and so different researchers attempted
further elaborations and amplifications under various old or
new terms such as 'semasiology', 'semiosis', 'semiotic', etc.

As to the relationship between those disciplines, Lady
Welby wrote in the eleventh edition of the *Encyclopaedia
Britannica,* 'Semantics may . . . be described as the applica-
tion of Significs within strictly philological limits.'

In his *Introduction to Semantics* (p. 9) Rudolf Carnap
says, 'If in an investigation explicit reference is made to the
. . . user of a language [from a businesslike, practical point

---

be an overstatement to say that definitions of 'semantics' and
'General Semantics' and other terms printed in this glossary must
be considered as seriously misinforming the public.

The most recent example is an article on 'Semantics, General
Semantics' in *Ten Eventful Years,* an *Encyclopaedia Britannica* publication, which considerably increased the confusion. It is not even
mentioned that 'semantics' is a branch of philology, nor is there any
clarifying discrimination made between the noun 'semantics' and
the adjective 'semantic'. Moreover, it has many misstatements and
even falsifications of my work and the work of others, and some
statements make no sense.

of view] then we assign it to the field of pragmatics [from the Greek *pragmatikos,* deed, business, act, etc.] . . . If we abstract from the user of the language [i.e., disregard the person] and analyze only the expressions and their designata [referents?] we are in the field of semantics. And if, finally, we abstract from the designata also and analyze only the relations between the expressions, we are in (logical) syntax. The whole science of language, consisting of the three parts mentioned, is called semiotic.'[2]

Obviously such a 'whole science of language' consisting of 'pragmatics', 'semantics', and 'logic', which is called 'semiotic', disregards the inner reactions of the individual person, and so eliminates the *possibility of evaluation* as a living issue with a living individual, which is the main aim of *General Semantics.*

Charles Morris says explicitly that 'Semiotic is not then a "theory of value".' Of 'Semantics' he writes, 'That branch of semiotic which studies the signification of signs.' (*Signs, Language and Behavior,* pp. 80 and 353). Of my work he says, 'The work of A. Korzybski and his followers is psycho-biological in orientation . . . aiming to protect the individual against exploitation by others and by himself,' (p. 283), in other words, dealing with the inner life of the individual, on the silent (non-verbal) levels.

---

[2] Carnap is an important constructive worker in the field of 'logic', representative of the Viennese school. However, even he adds to the confusion between 'semantics' and 'General Semantics'. Carnap was eventually entitled to use the term 'semantics', as he may be considered to deal with the philology of logical and mathematical languages. He seems acquainted with my *Science and Sanity: An Introduction to Non-aristotelian Systems and General Semantics,* which was published in 1933. Yet in his book published in 1942 he uses the term 'General Semantics' when he actually wants to say 'generalized semantics', and so adds to the linguistic chaos. Further dangers are still ahead, as Carnap announces on page ix a series of books, 'Studies in Semantics', where this misuse of language and terms may be propagated. The term 'General Semantics' was introduced in 1933 as a technical term in an empirical natural science of evaluation which deals with living human reactions and has nothing to do with 'logic' or mathematics as such.

From what was said here it is obvious that my work in General Semantics has nothing to do with the above-mentioned disciplines, although I know and respect the works of the corresponding investigators in those fields, with their stated limitations.

Even in the index of *Science and Sanity* the word 'semantics' does not appear except as 'Semantics, General'. I use 'semantic' there only as an adjective with other words, in the sense of 'evaluational', such as 'semantic aphasia', 'semantic blockage', 'semantic reactions', etc. I selected the term 'General Semantics' for an empirical natural science of non-elementalistic *evaluation,* a theory of *values.*

If I had not known of the work done in *Sémantique,* Significs, etc., I would have labelled my work by another name, but my system would have remained fundamentally unaltered. Thus, my papers before the International Mathematical Congress in Toronto in 1924, before the Washington Society for Nervous and Mental Diseases in 1925, and before the Washington Psychopathic Society in 1926 outlined practically my whole system *before* I became familiar with the works of Bréal, Lady Welby, et al. The word 'semantic' does not appear in those papers at all, and my work is called 'Time-binding, the General Theory', which remains as important as ever today. I also coined, I believe originally, the term 'human engineering', but since the publication of my *Manhood of Humanity: The Science and Art of Human Engineering* in 1921 that term has become so abused that I had to abandon it, and actually had to hunt for another term. 'Semantics', 'significs', etc., were unusable, as they did not even touch my field. From a time-binding point of view, and in fairness to the efforts of others, I coined the term '*General* Semantics', on the assumption that intelligent laymen will be able to discriminate between 'semantics' and 'General Semantics', as mathematicians are able to discriminate between the cartesian system and the vector, tensor, etc., calculuses as different disciplines, in the process of mathematical evolution.[3]

I selected it also for historical continuity, as the problems on the non-verbal levels outside or inside our skins are present with us and real, no matter whether their relations to the verbal levels were solved by my predecessors and contemporaries or not. The term 'General Semantics' seemed most appropriate to me because of the derivation from the Greek *semainein,* 'to mean', 'to signify'. A theory of evaluation seemed to follow naturally in an evolutionary sense from 1) 'meaning' to 2) 'signification' to 3) *evaluation, if we take into account the individual,* not divorcing him from his reactions, nor from his *neuro*-linguistic and *neuro*-semantic environments. Thus we allocate him in a *plenum* of some values, no matter what, and a *plenum* of language, which may be used to inform, or misinform by *commission* and/or *omission,* deceiving the individual himself and/or others. With such problems, without exception, the individual has to cope to be human at all. That's what I learned from the theory of time-binding and what I tried to convey to others through General Semantics and psycho-biological non-aristotelian considerations.

I showed several years ago that theories of 'meaning' are humanly impossible, as they do not take into consideration *undefined* terms, which label only the silent levels of non-verbal experiences, etc.[4] Confusion between non-verbal silent levels, and verbal levels, due to lack of consciousness of abstracting, leads inevitably to insidious identifications (misevaluations) of these different levels. Primitivism, infantilism, formalism, academic stupidites, un-sanity, and other types of pathological reactions, must then follow.

[3] Historically it is interesting to note that the original manuscript of *Science and Sanity* did not contain the word 'semantics' or 'semantic'.

[4] See Alfred Korzybski and M. Kendig, 'Foreword' to *A Theory of Meaning Analyzed,* General Semantics Monographs, No. III, Institute of General Semantics, 1942.

The words 'semantic' and 'semantics' are today commonly used even in newspapers and magazines mostly in the sense of 'meaning'. Important scientists, mathematicians and physicists included, also use these words, mostly in that sense. Many of them know something about General Semantics, and if they mention my work at all, they say explicitly that they use the term 'semantic' in an entirely different sense than I use the term 'General Semantics', and they are exactly correct.

The more my researches advanced, the more it became obvious that deeper studies in many branches of science were necessary. I had to investigate further hidden silent assumptions. Finally it became clear that nothing short of a *methodological synthesis* of mathematics and modern empirical sciences would suffice for a general theory of *values*. This synthesis turned out to be (although it was not planned as such) a non-aristotelian system, the first so far to be formulated. Today it becomes impossible to separate General Semantics and this Non-aristotelian System. One follows from the other, and *vice versa,* General Semantics being the *modus operandi* and foundation of the system.

As the center for training in these non-aristotelian methods, the Institute of General Semantics was incorporated in Chicago in 1938. In the summer of 1946 the Institute moved to Lakeville, Connecticut, where its original program is being carried on. The rapid spread of interest in our work, by now on all continents, has indicated the need for the new methods set forth here. I must stress that General Semantics gives no panaceas, but experience shows that when the methods of General Semantics are *applied,* the results are usually beneficial, whether in law, medicine, business, etc., education on all levels, or personal interrelationships, be they family, community, national, or international. If the methods are not applied, but merely talked about, no results can be expected. Perhaps the most telling applications were those on the battlefields of World War II, as reported by members of the armed forces, including psychiatrists on all fronts, and especially by Dr. Douglas M. Kelley, formerly Lieutenant Colonel in the Medical Corps,[5] who reports in part as follows:

'General semantics, as a modern scientific method, offers techniques which are of extreme value both in the prevention and cure of such [pathological] reactive patterns. In my experience with over seven thousand cases in the European Theater of Operations, these basic principles were daily employed as methods of group psychotherapy and as methods of psychiatric prevention. It is obvious that the earlier the case is treated the better the prognosis, and consequently hundreds of battalion-aid surgeons were trained in principles of general semantics. These principles were applied (as individual therapies and as group therapies) at every treatment level from the forward area to the rearmost echelon, in front-line aid stations, in exhaustion centers and in general hospitals. That they were employed with success is demonstrated by the fact that psychiatric evacuations from the European Theater were held to a minimum.'[6]

It is not generally realized that with human progress, the complexities and difficulties in the world increase following an exponential function of 'time', with indefinitely accelerating accelerations. I am deeply convinced that these problems cannot be solved at all unless we boldly search for and revise our antiquated notions about the 'nature of man' and apply modern extensional methods toward their solution. Let us also remember that the methods of exact sciences disregard national boundaries, and so the extensional methods and devices of General Semantics can be applied to all existing

[5]Chief Consultant in Clinical Psychology and Assistant Consultant in Psychiatry to the European Theater of Operations; also Chief Psychiatrist in charge of the prisoners at Nuremberg. Author of *22 Cells in Nuremberg*, Greenberg, New York, 1947.

[6]Korzybski, A. A Veteran's Re-Adjustment and Extensional Methods. *ETC.: A Review of General Semantics*, Vol. III, No. 4. See also
Saunders, Captain James, USN (Ret.). Memorandum. *Training of Officers for the Naval Service: Hearings Before the Committee on Naval Affairs, United States Senate,* June 12 and 13, 1946, pp. 55-57. U.S. Government Printing Office, Washington, D.C., 1946.

languages, with deep psycho-logical effects on tne users and through them on their countrymen. Thus the world *can* gain an international common denominator for inter-communication, mutual understanding, and eventual agreement.

Lakeville, Connecticut   A.K.
February, 1948

ADDITIONAL NOTE: As this was going to press a new paper by Allen Walker Read of New York, to be published soon, came to my attention. One paragraph in particular represents such an excellent, terse, historical statement of how I came to introduce the term 'General Semantics', that I asked for, and received, Mr. Read's kind permission to reproduce it here:

'The great popular vogue of the word *semantics* can be traced to the ferment caused by the works of Alfred Korzybski. In 1928, in the first draft of his *Science and Sanity*, he did not make use of *semantics, general semantics,* or *semantic reaction* at all. But . . . he was keeping in touch with the developments among Polish mathematicians, and he was particularly impressed with their work upon attending the "Congrès des mathématiciens des pays Slaves" in Warsaw in 1929. In 1931, in a paper given before the American Mathematical Society at New Orleans, Louisiana, he presented material on "the *restricted semantic* school represented by Chwistek and his pupils, which is characterized mostly by the semantic approach." ("A Non-aristotelian System and its Necessity for Rigour in Mathematics and Physics," printed in *Science and Sanity,* pp. 747–761; quotation, p. 748.) He announced that he was using the term "general semantics" for his own study (*Ibid.,* p. 749. Before this he has called his work "Time-binding, the general theory."), and that his researches had resulted "in the discovery of a general semantic mechanism underlying human behaviour, many new interrelations and formulations, culminating in a [Non-aristotelian]-system." (*Ibid.,* p. 750.) Thus the background of Korzybski's usage is found in the Polish logicians, though some of his followers have erroneously associated it with the antiquarianism of Bréal, Ernest Weekley, and popular writers on "the glamour of word study." '

                                                  A.K.

CASSIUS JACKSON KEYSER

LECTURE XX

from

MATHEMATICAL PHILOSOPHY*

1922

KORZYBSKI'S CONCEPT OF MAN

*Mathematical Philosophy is to be republished in the Collected Works of Cassius J. Keyser, by Scripta Mathematica, New York.

LECTURE XX

Korzybski's Concept of Man[1]

WHAT TIME-BINDING MEANS—DIMENSIONALITY AND
THE MATHEMATICAL THEORY OF LOGICAL TYPES—
THE NATURAL LAW OF CIVILIZATION AS AN INCREAS-
ING EXPONENTIAL FUNCTION OF TIME—HUMAN
ETHICS AS TIME-BINDING ETHICS, NOT THE SPACE-
BINDING ETHICS OF ANIMALS.

A FEW years ago our lives were lapt round with a
civilization so rich and comfortable in manifold ways,
so omnipresent, so interwoven with our whole environment, that we did not reflect upon it but habitually took it all for granted as we take for granted
the great gifts of Nature,—land and sea, light and
sky and the common air. We were hardly aware of
the fact that Civilization is literally a product of
human labor and *time;* we had not thought deeply
upon the principle of its genesis nor seriously sought
to discover the laws of its growth; we had not been
schooled to reflect that we who were enjoying it had
neither produced it nor earned its goods; we had not
been educated to perceive that we have it almost

[1] Part of this lecture is found in my Phi Beta Kappa address
on *The Nature of Man* (Science, Sept. 9, 1921) and some of it
in an article by me in The Pacific Review, Dec., 1921.

solely as a bounty from the time and toil of by-gone generations; we had not been disciplined to feel the mighty obligation which the great inheritance imposes upon us as at once the posterity of the dead and the ancestry of the yet unborn. We had been born in the midst of a great civilization, and, in accord with our breeding, we lived in it and upon it like butterflies in a garden of flowers, not to say as "maggots in a cheese."

Since then a change has come. The [First] World War awoke us. The awakening was rude but it was effectual. Everywhere men and women are now thinking as never before, and they are thinking about realities for they know that there is no other way to cope with the great problems of a troubled world. They have learned, too, that, of all the realities with which we humans have to deal, the supreme reality is Man; and so the questions that men and women are everywhere asking are questions regarding Man, for they are questions of ethics, of social institutions, of education, of economics, of philosophy, of industrial methods, of politics and government. The questions have led to some curious results,—to doctrines that alarm, to proposals that startle,—and we are wont to call them radical, revolutionary, red. Is it true that our thinking has been too radical? How the question would have made Plato smile—Plato who had seen his venerated teacher condemned to death for radical criticism. No, the trouble is that, in the proper sense of that much abused term, our thought has not been radical enough. Our questionings have been eager and wide-ranging but our thought has been shallow. It has been passionate and it has been daring but it has not been deep. For, if it had been deep, we could not have failed, as we have failed, to ask ourselves the fundamental question: What is that in virtue of which human beings are human? What is the distinctive place of our human kind in the hierarchy of the world's life? What *is* Man?

I have called the question "fundamental"—it *is* fundamental—the importance of a right answer is sovereign—for it is obvious, once the fact is pointed out, that the character of human history, the character of human conduct, and the character of all our human institutions depend both upon what man *is* and in equal or greater measure upon what we humans *think* man is.

Why, then, have we not asked the question? The reason doubtless is that we have consciously or unconsciously taken it for granted that we knew the answer. For why enquire when we are sure we know?

But *have* we known? Is our assumption of knowledge in this case just? Have we really known, do we know now, what is in fact the idiosyncrasy of the human class of life? Do we know critically what we, as representatives of man, really are? Here it is essential to distinguish; we are speaking of knowledge; there is a kind of knowledge that is instinctive,— instinctive knowledge,—immediate inner knowledge by instinct,—the kind of knowledge we mean when we say that we know how to move our arms or that a fish knows how to swim or that a bird knows how to fly. I do not doubt that, in this sense of knowing, we do know what human beings are; it is the kind of knowledge that a fish has of what fishes are or that a bird has of what birds are. But there is another kind of knowledge,—scientific knowledge,— knowledge of objects by analyzing them,—objective knowledge by concepts,—conceptual knowledge of objects; it is the kind of knowledge we mean when we say that we know or do not know what a plant is or what a number is. Now, we do not suppose fish to have this sort of knowledge of fish; we do not suppose a bird can have a just conception,—nor, properly speaking, any conception,—of what a bird is. We are speaking of concepts, and our question, you see, is this: Have we humans a just Concept of Man? If we have, it is reasonable to suppose that we inherited it, for so important a thing, had it originated in our time, would have made itself heard of as a grave discovery. So I say that, if we have a just concept of man, it must have come down to us entangled in the mesh of our inherited opinions and must have been taken in, as such opinions are usually taken in, from the common air, by a kind of "cerebral suction."

If we discover that we have never had a just concept of man, the fact should not greatly astonish us, for the difficulty is unique; man, you see, is to be both the knower and the object known; the difficulty is that of a knower having to objectify itself and having then to form a just concept of what the object is.

In saying that in the thought of our time the great question has not been asked, I have now to make one important exception and, so far as I know, only one.[2] I refer to Count Alfred Korzybski, the Polish engineer. In his momentous book (*The Manhood of Humanity: The Science and Art of Human Engineering*[3]), he has both propounded the question and submitted an answer that is worthy of the serious attention of every serious student, whatever his field of study. It is the aim of this lecture to present the answer and to examine it by help of the Theory of Logical Types, the Theory of Classes, and the author's closely allied notion of "Dimensions."

Let me say at the outset that one who would read

[2] Since writing the foregoing I have observed a learned discussion of the question by Professor Wm. E. Ritter in an article, *Science and Organized Civilization,* in the Scientific Monthly, Aug., 1917. Professor Ritter once more defines man as a *kind* of *animal* but the *distinctive* marks of the kind, as given by him, are so grave as to make one wonder why he did not altogether drop the "animal" element from the definition.

[3] E. P. Dutton & Company.

the book understandingly must come to it prepared to grapple with a central *concept,* a concept whose rôle among the other ideas in the work is like that of the sun in the solar system. It happens, therefore, that readers of the book, or of any other book built about a central concept, fall into three mutually exclusive classes:

(I) The class of those who *miss* the central concept—(I have known a learned historian to miss it)—not through any fault of their own,—they are often indeed well meaning and amiable people,—but simply because they are not qualified for conceptual thinking save that of the commonest type.

(II) The class of those who *seem* to grasp the central concept and then straightway show by their manner of talk that they have not really grasped it but have at most got hold of some of its words. Intellectually such readers are like the familiar type of undergraduate who "flunks" his mathematical examinations but may possibly "pull through" in a second attempt and so is permitted, after further study, to try again.

(III) The class of those who firmly seize the central concept and who by meditating upon it see more and more clearly the tremendous reach of its implications. If it were not for this class, there would be no science in the world nor genuine philosophy. But the other two classes are not aware of the fact for they are merely "verbalists." In respect of such folk, the "Behaviorist" school of psychology is right for in the psychology of classes (I) and (II) there is no need for a chapter on "Thought Processes"— it is sufficient to have one on "The Language Habit."

What is that central concept? What is Korzybski's Concept of Man? I wish to present it as clearly as I can. It is a concept defining man in terms of Time. "Humanity," says the author, "is the *time-binding* class of life." What do the words mean? What is meant by time-binding or the binding of time? The meaning, which is indeed momentous, will be clearer to us if we prepare for it by a little preliminary reflection.

Long ages ago there appeared upon this planet— no matter how—the first specimens of our human kind. What was their condition? It requires some meditation and some exercise of imagination to realize keenly what it must have been. Of knowledge, in the sense in which we humans now use the term, they had none—no science, no philosophy, no art, no religion; they did not know what they were nor where they were; they knew nothing of the past, for they had no history, not even tradition; they could not foretell the future, for they had no knowledge of natural law; they had no capital,—no material or spiritual wealth,—no inheritance, that is, from the time and toil of by-gone generations; they were without tools, without precedents, without guiding maxims, without speech, without any light of human experience; their ignorance, as we understand the term, was almost absolute. And yet, compared with the beasts, they were miracles of genius, for they contrived to do the most wonderful of all things that have happened on our globe—they *initiated,* I mean, the creative movement which their remote descendants call Civilization.

Why? What is the secret? Have you ever tried to find it? The secret is that those rude animal-resembling, animal-hunting, animal-hunted ancestors of ours were a *new kind* of creature in the world—a new kind because endowed with a strange new gift —a strange new capacity or power—a strange new *energy,* let us call it. And it is in the world today. What is it? We know it partly by its effects and partly by its stirring within us for as human beings, as representatives of Man, we all of us have it in some measure. It is the energy that invents—that produces instruments, ideas, institutions and doctrines; it is, moreover, the energy that, having invented, criticizes, then invents again and *better,* thus advancing in excellence from creation to creation endlessly. Be good enough to reflect and to reflect again upon the significance of those simple words: invents; having invented, criticizes; invents again and better; thus advancing, by creative activity, from stage to stage of excellence without end. Their sound is familiar; but what of their ultimate sense? We ought indeed to pause here, withdraw to the solitude of some cloister and there in the silence meditate upon their meaning; for they do not describe the life of beasts; they characterize Man.

We are speaking of a peculiar kind of energy— the energy that *civilizes*—that strange familiar energy that makes possible and makes actual the great creative movement which we call human *Progress,* of which we talk much and think but little. Let us scrutinize it more closely; let us, if we can, lay bare its characteristic relation to Time for its relation to Time is the relation of Time to the distinctive life of Man.

Compare some representative of the animal world, a bee, let us say, or a beaver, with a correspondingly representative man. Consider their achievements and the ways thereof. The beaver makes a dam; the man, a bridge or some discovery,—analytical geometry, for example, or the art of printing, or the Keplerian laws of planetary motion, or the atomic constitution of matter. The two achievements,—that of the beaver and that of the man,—are each of them a product of three factors: time, toil, and raw material, where the last signifies, in the case of purely scientific achievement, the data of sense, in which science has its roots. Both achievements *endure,* it

may be for a short while only,—as in the case of
the dam or the bridge,—or one of them may endure
endlessly,—as in that of a scientific discovery. What
happens in the next generation? The new beaver begins where its predecessor began and ends where it
ended—it makes a dam but the dam is like the old
one. Yet the old dam is there for the new beaver to
behold, to contemplate, and to improve upon. But
the presence of the old dam wakes in the beaver's
"mind" no inventive impulse, no creative stirring,
and so there is no improvement, no progress. Why
not? The answer is obvious: the beaver "mind" is
such that its power to achieve is *not reinforced* by
the presence of past achievement. The new beaver's
time is indeed overlapped, in part or wholly, by the
time of its predecessor for the latter time is present
as an essential factor of the old dam, but that old-
time factor, though present, *produces nothing*—it is
as dead capital, bearing no interest. Such is the relation of the beaver "mind,"—of the *animal* mind,—
to time.

Now, what of the new *man?* What does *he do?*
What he does depends, of course, upon his predecessor's achievement; if this was a bridge, he makes a
better bridge or invents a ship; if it was the discovery
of analytical geometry, he enlarges its scope or invents the calculus; if it was the art of printing, he
invents a printing press; if it was the discovery of

the laws of planetary motion, he finds the law of gravitation; if it was the discovery of the atomic constitution of matter, he discovers the electronic constitution of atoms. Such is the familiar record—*improvement* of old things, *invention* of new ones—*Progress*. Why? Again the answer is obvious: the mind of man, unlike animal "mind," is *such that* its power to achieve *is reinforced* by past achievement. As in the case of the beaver, so in that of man, the successor's time is overlapped by the predecessor's time for the latter time continues its presence as an essential factor in the old achievement, which endures; but,—and this is the point,—in man's case, unlike the beaver's, the old-*time* factor is not merely present, it *works;* it is not as dead capital, bearing no interest, and ultimately perishing—it is living capital bearing interest not only but interest perpetually compounded at an ever-increasing rate. And the interest is growing wealth,—material and spiritual wealth,—not merely physical conveniences but instruments of power, understanding, intelligence, knowledge and skill, beautiful arts, science, philosophy, wisdom, freedom—in a word, Civilization.

That great process,—involving some subtle alchemy that we do not understand,—by which the *time*-factor, embodied in things accomplished, perpetually reinforces more and more the achieving potency of the human mind,—the process by which

mysterious Time thus continually and increasingly
augments the civilizing energy of the world,—the
process by which the evolution of civilization involves the storing up or involution of time,—it is
that mighty process which Korzybski happily desig-
nates by the term, Time-binding. The term will recur
frequently in our discussion, and so I recommend that
you dwell upon its meaning as given until you have
seized it firmly. It is because time-binding power is
not only peculiar to man but is, among man's distinctive marks, beyond all comparison the most significant one—it is because of that two-fold consideration that the author *defines* humanity to be "the
time-binding class of life."

Such, then, is Korzybski's answer to the most
important of all questions: what is Man? Do not
lose sight of the fact that we have here a *concept*
and that it defines man in terms of a certain relation,
subtle indeed but undoubtedly characteristic, that
man has to time. By saying that the relation is "characteristic" of man I mean that, among known classes
of life, man and only man has it. Animals have it not
or, if they have it, if they have time-binding capacity,
they have it in a degree so small that it may be
neglected as mathematicians neglect infinitesimals of
higher order.

The answer in question is not one to which the
world has been or is now accustomed. If you apply

for an answer to the thought of the bygone centuries or to the regnant philosophies of our time, what answer will you get? It will be one or the other of two kinds: it will be a *zoological* answer—man is an animal, a kind or species of animal, the *bête humaine;* or it will be a *mythological* answer—man is a mysterious compound or *union* of animal (a natural thing) with something "supernatural." Such are the rival conceptions now current throughout the world. They have come to us as a part of our philosophical inheritance. Some of us hold one of them; some of us, the other; and no doubt many of us hold both of them for, though they are mutually incompatible, the mere incompatibility of two ideas does not necessarily prevent them from finding firm lodgment in the same brain.

That Korzybski's concept of man is just and important,—entirely just and immeasurably important,—I have no reason to doubt after having meditated much upon it. But the author does not content himself with presenting that concept; he goes much further; he denies outright the zoological conception and similarly denies the ages-old rival, the mythological conception, denouncing both of them as being at once false to fact and vicious in effect.

Why false? Wherein?

Let us deal first with the zoological or biological conception. Natural phenomena are to be conceived and defined in accord with facts revealed by observation and analysis. The phenomena the author is concerned with are the great life-classes of the world: plants, animals, and humans. What, he asks, are the significant facts about them, their patent cardinal relations, their distinctive marks, positive and negative? And his answer runs as follows: Of plants the most significant positive mark is their power to "bind" the basic energies of the world—to take in, transform and appropriate the energies of sun, soil, water and air; but they lack *autonomous* power to move about in space, and that lack is a highly significant negative mark of plants. The plants are said to constitute the "chemistry-binding" or basic-energy-binding class of life; the *name* suggests only the positive mark but it is essential to note that the *definition* of the class is effected by the positive and the negative marks conjoined. What of the animals? These, like the plants, take in, transform and appropriate the basic energies of sun, soil, water and air, taking them in large part as already transformed by the plants; but this power of animals to bind basic energies,—the positive one of the two defining marks of plants,—is not a *defining* mark of animals; the *positive* defining mark of animals is their autonomous power to move[4] about in space,—to crawl or

---

[4] Do sessile animals really constitute an exception? It can be shown, I think, that such animals are space-binders in Korzybski's sense.

run or fly or swim,—enabling them to abandon one place and occupy another and so to harvest the natural fruits of many localities; this positive mark, you observe, is a relation of animals to *space;* but they have, we have seen, a negative mark, a relation to *time*—animals lack capacity for binding time. Because of the positive mark, animals are said to constitute the "space-binding" class of life, but it is to be carefully noted that the definition (as distinguished from the name) of the class is effected by the positive mark conjoined with the negative one. Finally, what of humans? We have already seen the answer and the ground thereof—humanity is the time-binding class of life. For the sake of clarity let us summarize the conceptions, or definitions, as follows: a plant is a living creature having the capacity to bind basic energies and lacking the autonomous ability to move in space; an animal is a living creature having the autonomous ability to move about in space and lacking the capacity for binding time; a man, or a human, is a living creature having time-binding power.

It is to be noted that, as thus conceived, the great life-classes of the world constitute a hierarchy arranged according to a principle which Korzybski calls life-dimensions or dimensionality, as follows:

The plants, or basic-energy-binders, belong to the lowest level or type of life and constitute the life-dimension *I*.

The animals, or space-binders, belong to the next higher level or type of life and constitute the life-dimension *II*.

Human beings, or time-binders, belong to a still higher level or type of life and constitute the life-dimension *III*.

Whether there be a yet higher class of life we do not know and that is why in the conception of man no negative mark is present.

Now, it is, of course, perfectly clear that, according to the foregoing conceptions or definitions, the old zoological conception of man as a species of animal is false, as the author contends. But may we not say that he is here merely playing with words? Is it not entirely a matter of arbitrary definition? Has he not, merely to please his fancy, quite willfully defined the term "animal" in such a way as to exclude humans from the class so defined? The answer is undoubtedly, *No*. Of course, it goes without saying that we could, if we *chose,* define the mere word "animal" or any other noun so as to make it stand for the "class" of plants, elephants, humans, jabberwocks and newspapers. But we do not so choose. Why not? Because we desire our definitions to be *expedient,* to be helpful, to serve the purpose of rational thinking. We want them, in other words, to correspond to facts. Let us, then, forget the word for a little while and look at the facts. It is a fact that there is a class of creatures having space-binding capacity but not time-binding capacity; it is a fact that there is another class of creatures having both kinds of capacity; it is a fact that the difference between the two,—namely, the capacity for binding time,—is not only beyond all comparison the most significant of the marks peculiar to man, but is indeed the most significant and precious thing in the world; it is, therefore, a fact that not only the interests of sound ethics, but the interests of science, demand that the two classes, thus distinct by an infinite difference of *kind* of endowment, be not intermixed in thought and discourse; it is a fact that use of the same term "animal" to denote the members of both classes,—men and beasts alike,—constantly, subtly, powerfully tends to produce both intellectual and moral obfuscation; it is, therefore, a fact that the author's condemnation of the zoological conception as false to fact is amply justified on the best of grounds.

It is indeed true that humans have certain animal organs, animal functions, and animal propensities, but to say that, therefore, humans *are* animals is precisely the same kind of logical blunder as we should commit if we said that animals or humans are plants because they have certain organs, functions and properties in common with plants; and the blunder is of a kind that is fundamental—it is the kind which mathematicians call the confusion of types or of classes and which Korzybski calls the "mixing of dimensions." To say that humans are animals because they have certain animal propensities is logically on a par with saying that geometric solids are surfaces because they have certain surface properties or with saying that fractions are whole numbers because they have certain properties that whole numbers have.

Why is it that people are shocked on encountering for the first time a categorical denial of their belief that man is a species of animal? Do they feel that their proper dignity as human beings is thus assailed? Is it because the animal basis of their space-binding ethics is being thus attacked? Is it that a well-reasoned scientific conviction is suddenly contradicted? I do not think the shock is due to any of these things. It is, I believe, due simply to the fact that an old unquestioned, uncriticized creed of that great dullard,—Common Sense,—has been unexpectedly challenged. For it is evident to common sense,—it is obtrusively evident to sense-perception, —that humans have certain animal organs and animal experience—they are begotten and born, they feed and grow, have legs and hair, and die, all just like animals; on the other hand, their time-binding faculty is not thus evident; it is not, I mean, a tangible *organ;* it is an intangible *function,* subtle as spirit;

and so common sense, guided according to its wont
by the uncriticized evidence of sense, and thought-
lessly taking for major premise the false proposition
that whatever has animal organs and propensities is
an animal, concludes that our human kind is a kind of
animal. But in this matter, as in so many others, the
old dullard is wrong. The proper life of animals is
life-in-space; the distinctive life of humans is life-
in-time.

But why are mere concepts so important? Our
lives, we are told, are not controlled by concepts but
by impulses, instincts, desires, passions, appetites.
The answer is: Because concepts are never "mere"
concepts but are, in humans, vitally connected with
impulses, instincts, desires, passions, and appetites;
concepts are the means by which Reason does its
work, leading to prosperity or disaster according as
the concepts be true or false.

I have said that the ancient and modern rival of
the zoological conception of man is the mythological
conception according to which man is a mysterious
compound or hybrid of natural (animal) and supernatural. This conception might well be treated today
as it was treated yesterday by Plato (in the Timaeus,
for example). "We must accept," said he, "the
traditions of the men of old time who affirm themselves to be the offspring of the gods—that is what
they say—and they must surely have known their

own ancestors. How can we doubt the word of the children of the gods? Although they give no probable or certain proofs, still, as they declare that they are speaking of what took place in their own family, we must conform to custom and believe them."[5] But this gentle irony,—the way of the Greek philosopher, —is not the way of the Polish engineer. The latter is not indeed without a blithesome sense of humor but in this matter he is tremendously in earnest, and he bluntly affirms, boldly and confidently, that the mythological conception of man is both false and vicious. As to its validity or invalidity, it involves, he says, the same kind of logical blunder as the zoological conception—it involves, that is, a fatal confusion of types, or mixing of dimensions. To say that man is a being so inscrutably constituted that he must be regarded as partly natural (partly animal) and partly supernatural (partly divine) is *logically* like saying that a geometrical solid is a thing so wonderful that it must certainly be a surface miraculously touched by some mysterious influence from outside the universe of space. Among the life-classes of the world, our humankind is the time-binding class; and Korzybski stresses again and again the importance of recognizing that time-binding energy and all the phenomena thereof are perfectly *natural*—that Newton, for example, or Confucius, was as thoroughly natural as an eagle or an oak.

[5] Jowett's translation.

What does he mean by "natural"? He has not told us,—at all events, not explicitly,—and that omission is doubtless a defect which ought to be remedied in a future edition of the book.

You are aware that the terms "nature" and "natural" are currently employed in a large variety of senses—most of them so vague as to be fit only for the use of "literary" men, not for the serious use of scientific men. What ought we to mean by the term "natural" in such a discussion as we are now engaged in? The question admits, I believe, of a brief answer that is fairly satisfactory. Everyone knows that the things encountered by a normal human in the course of his experience differ widely in respect of vagueness and certitude; some of them are facts so regular, so well ascertained, so indubitable that they guide in all the affairs of practical life; they are *known* facts, we say, and to disregard them would be to perish like unprotected idiots or imbeciles; such facts are of two kinds: facts of sense-perception, or of this and memory, and facts of pure thought; the former are familiar in the moving pageant of the world—birth, growth, death, day, night, land, water, sky, change of seasons, and so on; facts of pure thought are not so obtrusively obvious but there are such facts; one of them is—"If something S has the property P and whatever has P has the property P', then S has P'." Now, all such facts are *compatible*—

each of them fits in, as we say, with all the others. I take it that what we ought to mean by natural is, therefore, this: *Nature (or the natural) consists of all and only such things as are compatible (consistent) with the best-ascertained facts of sense and of thought.*

If that be what Korzybski means by "natural,"— and I think it very probably is,—then I fully agree with him that humans are thoroughly natural beings, that time-binding energy is a natural kind of energy, and that his strenuous objection to the mythological conception of man is, like his objection to the zoological conception, well taken. If it were a question of biological data, mere mathematicians would, of course, like other sensible folk, defer to the opinion of biologists; it is not, however, a question of biological data, these are not in dispute; it is a question of the logical significance of such data; and respecting a question of logic, even biologists,—for they, too, are sensible folk,—will probably admit that engineers and mere mathematicians are entitled to be heard.

In this connection I desire to say that, for straight and significant thinking, the importance of avoiding what Korzybski calls "mixing dimensions" cannot be overstressed. The meaning of the term "dimensions" as he uses it is unmistakable; he has not, however, elaborated an abstract theory of the idea; such an elaboration would, I believe, show that the idea is reducible or nearly reducible to that of the Theory of Logical Types, briefly dealt with in a previous lecture and fully outlined in the *Principia Mathematica* of Whitehead and Russell; it is, moreover, very closely allied to, if it be not essentially identical with, Professor J. S. Haldane's doctrine of "categories" as set forth in his very stimulating and suggestive book *Mechanism, Life, and Personality* (E. P. Dutton and Co.) wherein the eminent physiologist maintains that mechanism, life, and personality belong to different categories constituting a genuine hierarchy such that the higher is not reducible to the lower, that life, for example, cannot be understood fully in terms of mechanism, nor personality in terms of life. It is, you observe, an order of ideas similar to that of Korzybski's thesis that humans can be no more explained in terms of animals than animals in terms of plants or plants in terms of minerals. And it is an order of ideas that recommends itself, to me at all events, because it is fortified by the analogous consideration that geometry cannot be reduced to arithmetic, nor dynamics to geometry, nor physics to dynamics, nor psychology to physics. It will, I believe, be a great advantage to science and to philosophy to recognize that there exists, whether we will or no, a hierarchy of categories and to recognize that, to an understanding of the higher categories, the lower ones, though necessary, are not sufficient.

Is there not, indeed, a highly important sense in which the phenomena of a higher category throw as much light upon those of a lower as the latter throw upon the former? Who can deny that, for example, dynamics illuminates geometry quite as much as geometry illuminates dynamics?

In Korzybski's indictment of the zoological and mythological conceptions of man there are, we have seen, *two* counts: he denies that the conceptions are true; and he denounces them as vicious in their effects, contending that they are mainly responsible for the dismal things of human history and for what is woeful in the present plight of the world. Of the former count I have already spoken; respecting the latter one, my convictions are as follows: (1) if humanity be not a thoroughly natural class of life, the term "natural" having the sense above defined, it is perfectly evident that there never has been and never can be a system of human ethics having the understandability, the authority, and the sanction of natural law, and this means that, under the hypothesis, there never has been and never can be an ethical system "compatible with the best-ascertained facts of sense and of thought"; (2) if, although our human kind be in fact a thoroughly natural class, we continue to *think* that such is *not* the case, the result will be much the same—our ethics will continue to carry the confusion and darkness due to the presence in it of mythological elements; (3) on the other hand, so long as we continue to regard man as a species of animal, the social life of the world in all its aspects will continue to reflect the tragic misconception, and our ethics will remain,—what it always has been in large measure,—an animal ethics, space-binding ethics, an ethics of might, of brutal competition, of violence, combat, and war.

Why so much stress upon ethics? Because ethics is not a thing apart; it is not an interest that is merely coordinate with other interests; it penetrates them all. Ethics is a kind of social ether which, whether it be good or bad, sound or unsound, true or false, pervades life, private and public, in all its dimensions and forms; and so, if ethics be vitiated by fundamentally false conceptions of human nature, the virus is not localized but spreads throughout the body politic, affecting the character of all activities and institutions,—education, science, art, philosophy, economics, industrial method, politics, government, —the whole conduct and life of a tribe or a state or a nation or a world. I hardly need remind you that only yesterday the most precious institutions of civilization were in great danger of destruction by a powerful state impelled, guided and controlled by animalistic ethics, the space-binding ethics of beasts. This is indeed an unforgettable illustration of the mighty fact, before pointed out, that the character of human history, human conduct and human institutions depends, not merely upon what man distinctively is, but also in large measure, even decisively, upon what we humans *think* man is. If a man or a state habitually regards humanity as a species of animal, then that man or state may be expected to act betimes like a beast and to seek justification in a zoological philosophy of human nature.

In view of such considerations it is a great pleasure to turn to Korzybski's concept of man, for it is not only a noble conception, as none can fail to perceive, but it is also, as we have seen, undoubtedly just. Nothing can be more important. What are its implications? And what are its bearings? You cannot take them in at a glance—meditation is essential; but, if you will meditate upon the concept, you will find that the body of its implications looms larger and larger and that the range of its bearings grows ever clearer and wider. Indeed we may say of it what Carlyle said of *Wilhelm Meister:* "It significantly tends towards infinity in all directions." Let us reflect upon it a little. We shall see that human history, the philosophy thereof, the present status of the world, the future welfare of mankind, are all of them involved.

The central concept or thesis is that our human kind is the time-binding class of life; it is, in other words, that there is in our world a peculiar kind of energy, time-binding energy, and that man is its organ—its sole instrument or agency. What are its implicates and bearings?

One of them we have already noted. It is that, though we humans are not a species of animal, we are *natural* beings: it is as natural for humans to bind time as it is natural for fishes to swim, for birds to fly, for plants to live after the manner of plants. It is as natural for man to make things achieved the means to greater achievements as it is natural for animals *not* to do so.

That fact is fundamental. Another one, also fundamental, is this: time-binding faculty,—the characteristic of humanity,—is not an effect of civilization but is its cause; it is not civilized energy, it is the energy that *civilizes;* it is not a product of wealth, whether material or spiritual wealth, but is the creator of wealth, both material and spiritual.

I come now to a most grave consideration. Inasmuch as time-binding capacity is the characterizing mark,—the idiosyncrasy,—of our human kind, it follows that to study and understand man is to study and understand the nature of man's time-binding energies; the laws of human nature are the laws,— natural laws,—of these energies; to study time-binding phenomena,—the phenomena of civilization,— and to discover their laws and teach them to the

world, is the supreme obligation of scientific men, for
it is evident that upon the natural laws of time-
binding must be based the future science and art of
human life and human welfare.

One of the laws we know now,—not indeed precisely,—but fairly well,—we know roughly, I mean,
its general type,—and it merits our best attention. It
is the natural law of progress in time-binding—in
civilization-building. We have observed that each
generation of (say) beavers or bees begins where the
preceding one began and ends where it ended; that
is a law for animals, for mere space-binders—there
is no advancement, no time-binding—a beaver dam
is a beaver dam—a honey comb a honey comb. We
know that, in sharp contrast therewith, man invents,
discovers, creates; we know that inventions lead to
new inventions, discoveries to new discoveries, creations to new creations; we know that, by such progressive breeding, the children of knowledge and art
and wisdom not only produce their kind in larger and
larger families but engender new and higher kinds
endlessly; we know that this time-binding process, by
which *past time* embodied as cofactor of toil in enduring achievements thus survives the dead and
works as living capital for augmentation and transmission to posterity, is the secret and process of progressive civilization-building. The question is: What
is the Law thereof—the natural law? What its gen-

eral type is you apprehend at once; it is like that of a rapidly increasing *geometric* progression—if P be the progress made in a given generation, conveniently called the "first," and if R denote the ratio of improvement, then the progress made in the second generation is PR, that in the third is PR^2, and that made in the single Tth generation will be PR^{T-1}. Observe that R is a large number,—how large we do not know,—and that the time T enters as an exponent—and so the expression PR^{T-1} is called an *exponential function of Time*, and it makes evident, even to the physical eye, the involution of time in the life of man. This is an amazing function, as every student of the Calculus knows; as T increases, which it is always doing, the function not only increases but it does so at a rate which itself increases according to a similar law, and the rate of increase of the rate of increase again increases in like manner, and so on endlessly, thus sweeping on towards infinity in a way that baffles all imagination and all descriptive speech. Yet such is approximately the law,—the natural law, —for the advancement of Civilization, immortal offspring of the spiritual marriage of Time and human Toil. I have said "approximately," for it does not represent adequately the natural law for the progress of civilization; it does not, however, err by excess, it errs by defect; for, upon a little observation and reflection, it is evident that R, the ratio of improvement, is not a constant, as above contemplated, but it is a variable that grows larger and larger as time increases, so that the function PR^{T-1} increases not only because the exponent increases with the flux of time, but because R itself is an increasing function of time. It will be convenient, however, and we shall not be thus erring on the side of excess, to speak of the above-mentioned law, though it is inadequate, as the *natural* law for the progress of time-binding, or of civilization-making.

Hereupon, there supervenes a most important question: Has civilization always advanced in accord with the mentioned law? And, if not, why not? The time-binding energies of mankind have been in operation long—300,000 to 500,000 years, according to the estimates of those most competent to guess—anthropologists and paleontologists. Had progress conformed to the stated law throughout that vast period, our world would doubtless now own a civilization so rich and great that we cannot imagine it today nor conceive it nor even conjecture it in dreams. What has been the trouble? What have been the hindering causes? Here, as you see, Korzybski's concept of man must lead to a new interpretation of history—to a new philosophy of history. A fundamental principle of the new interpretation must be the fact which I have already twice stated,—namely, that what man has done and does has depended and depends both upon what man distinctively is and also, in very great measure, upon what the members of the race have *thought* and *think* man is. We have here two determining factors—what man *is* and what we humans *think* man is. It is their joint product which the sociologist or the philosophic historian must examine and explain. In view of the second factor, which has hardly ever been noticed and has never been given its due weight, Korzybski, in answer to our question, maintains that the *chief* causes which have kept civilization from advancing in accord with its natural law of increase are man's misconceptions of man. All that is precious in present civilization has been achieved, in spite of them, by the first factor— by what man is—the peculiar organ of the civilizing energies of the world. It is the second factor that has given trouble. Throughout the long period of our race's childhood, from which we have not yet emerged, the time-binding energies have been hampered by the false belief that man is a species of animal and hampered by the false belief that man is a miraculous mixture of natural and supernatural. These are cave-man conceptions. The glorious achievements of which they have *deprived* the world we cannot now know and may never know, but the subtle ramifications of their *positive* evils can be traced in a thousand ways. And it is not only the duty of professional historians to trace them, it is your duty and mine. Whoever performs the duty will be appalled, for he will discover that those evils—the evils of "magic and myth," of space-binding "ethics," of zoological "righteousness"—for centuries growing in volume and momentum—did but leap to a culmination in the World War, which is thus to be viewed as only a bloody demonstration of human ignorance of human nature.

We are here engaged in considering some of the major implicates and bearings of the new concept of man. The task demands a large volume dealing with the relations of time-binding to each of the cardinal concerns of individual and social life—ethics, education, economics, medicine, law, political science, government, industry, science, art, philosophy, religion. Perhaps you will write such a work or works. In the closing words of this lecture I can do no more than add to what I have said a few general questions and hints.

Korzybski believes that the great war marks the end of the long period of humanity's childhood and the beginning of humanity's manhood. This second period, he believes, is to be initiated, guided, and characterized by a right understanding of the distinctive nature of Man. Is he over-enthusiastic? I do not know. Time will tell. I hope he is not mistaken. If he is not, there will be many changes and many transfigurations.

I have spoken of ethics and must do so again, for ethics, good or bad, is the most powerful of influences, pervading, fashioning, coloring, controlling all the moods and ways and institutions of our human world. What is to be the ethics of humanity's manhood? It will not be an ethics based upon the *zoological* conception of man; it will not, that is, be animalistic ethics, space-binding ethics, the ethics of beasts fighting for "a place in the sun," the ethics of might, crowding, and combat; it will not be a "capitalistic" ethics lusting to *keep* for self, nor "proletarian" ethics lusting to *get* for self; it will not be an ethics having for its golden rule the law of brutes—survival of the *fittest* in the sense of the *strongest*. Neither will it be an ethics based upon a *mythological* conception of man; it will not, that is, be a lawless ethics cunningly contrived for traffic in magic and myth. It will be a natural ethics because based upon the distinctive nature of mankind as the time-binding, —civilization-producing,—class of life; it will be, that is, a scientific ethics having the understandability, the authority, and the sanction of natural law, for it will be the embodiment, the living expression, of the laws,—natural laws,—of the time-binding energies of man; human freedom will be freedom to live in accord with those laws and righteousness will be the quality of a life that does not contravene them. The ethics of humanity's manhood will thus be natural ethics, an ethics compatible with the best-ascertained facts of sense and of thought—it will be time-binding ethics—and it will grow in solidarity, clarity, and sway in proportion as science *discovers* the laws of time-binding,—the laws, that is, of civilization-growth,—and *teaches* them to the world.

And so I am brought to say a word respecting education. In humanity's manhood, education,—in home, in school, in church,—will have for its supreme obligation, and will keep the obligation, to teach the young the distinctive nature of man and what they, as members and representatives of the race of man, essentially are, so that everywhere throughout the world men and women will habitually understand, because bred to understand, what time-binding is, that their proper dignity as humans is the dignity of time-binding life, and that for humans to practice space-binding ethics is a monstrous thing, involving the loss of their human birthright by descent to the level of beasts.[6] It is often said that ethics is a thing which it is impossible to *teach*. Just the opposite is true—it is impossible *not* to teach ethics, for the teaching of it is subtly carried on in all our teaching, whether consciously or not, being essentially involved in the

[6] In a recent bulletin of the Cora L. Williams Institute for Creative Education, Miss Williams has said, with fine insight, that "time-binding should be made the basis of all instruction and *The Manhood of Humanity* a textbook in every college throughout the world."

teacher's "philosophy of human nature." Every home or school in which that philosophy is zoological is, consciously or unconsciously, a nursery of animalistic ethics; every home or school in which there prevails a mythological philosophy of human nature is, consciously or unconsciously, a nursery of a lawless ethics of myth and magic. From time immemorial, such teaching of ethics, for the most part unconscious, the whole world has had. And we have seen that when such teaching becomes conscious, deliberate, and organized, a whole people can be so imbued with both the space-binding animal ethics of might and the mythical ethics of *Gott mit uns* that their State will leap upon its neighbors like an infuriated beast. Why should we not learn the lesson which the great war has so painfully taught regarding the truly gigantic power of education? If the accumulated civilization of many centuries can be imperiled by ethical teaching based upon a false philosophy of human nature, who can set a limit to the good that may be expected from the conscious, deliberate, organized, unremitting joint effort of home and school and press to teach an ethics based upon the true conception of man as the agent and organ of the time-binding, civilizing energy of the world? I cannot here pursue the matter further; but in closing I should like to ask a few general questions—pretty obvious questions—indicating roughly the course which, I believe, further enquiry should take.

What are the bearings of the new concept of man upon the social so-called sciences of economics, politics, and government?

Can the new concept transform those ages-old pseudo-sciences into genuine sciences qualified to guide and guard human welfare because based upon scientific understanding of human nature?

In view of the radical difference between the distinctive nature of animals and the distinctive nature of man, what are likely to be the principal differences between

Government of Space-binders, by Space-binders, for Space-binders

and

Government of Time-binders, by Time-binders, for Time-binders?

Which of the two kinds of government best befits the social régime of autocrats, or plutocrats, and slaves? And which best befits the dream of political equality and democratic freedom?

Which of them most favors the prosperity of "Acquisitive Cunning"? And which the prosperity of Productive Skill?

Which of them is the most friendly to the *makers* of wealth? And which of them to the *takers* thereof?

Which of them most favors "boss" repression of others? And which makes the best provision for intelligent self-expression?

Which of them depends most upon might and war? And which upon right and peace?

Which of them is government by "politics," by politicians? And which of them by science, by honest men who know?

If man's time-binding energy, which has produced all the wealth of the world, both material and spiritual wealth, be *natural* energy, and if, as is the case, the wealth existing at a given moment be almost wholly a product of the time and toil of the by-gone generations, to whom does it of right belong? To *some* of the living? To *all* of the living? Or to all of the living and the yet unborn? Is the world's heritage of wealth, since it is a natural product of a natural energy and of time (which is natural), therefore a "natural resource" like sunshine, for example, or a newfound lake or land? If not, why not? What is the difference in principle?

Are the "right of conquest" and the "right of squatter sovereignty" time-binding rights? Or are they space-binding "rights" having their sanction in animalistic "ethics," in a zoological philosophy of human nature?

What are the bearings of the new concept of man upon the theory and practice of medicine? Man, though not an animal, has animal organs and animal functions. Are all the diseases of human beings animal diseases or are some of them *human* diseases, disorders, that is, affecting humans in their distinctive character as time-binders? Can Psycho-analysis or Psychiatry throw any light upon the question?

And what of the power that makes for righteousness? Religion, it would seem, has the seat of its authority in that time-binding double relationship in virtue of which the living are at once posterity of the dead and ancestry of the unborn,—in the former capacity inheriting as living capital the wealth of civilization from the time and toil of by-gone generations,—in the latter capacity holding the inheritance in trust for enlargement and transmission to future man.

A final reflection : under the doctrine outlined there lies an assumption—it is that, when men and women are everywhere bred to understand the distinctive nature of our human kind, the time-binding energies of man will be freed from their old bondage and civilization will advance, in accord with its natural law, in a warless world, swiftly and endlessly. If the assumption be not true, great Nature is at fault and the world will continue to flounder. Of its truth, there can be only one test—experimentation, trial. The assumption appears to be the only scientific basis of hope for the world. Must not all right-thinking men and women desire ardently that this noble assumption be tried?